Sketches by
Cyrus leRoy Baldridge

RICKSHAW BOY

BY LAU SHAW

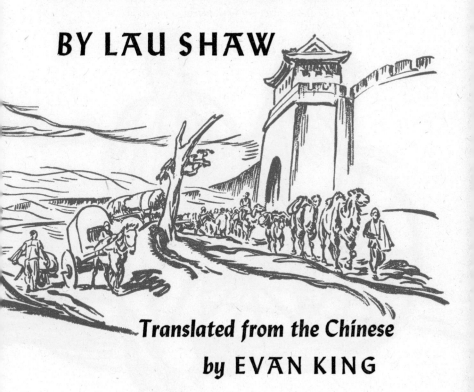

Translated from the Chinese

by EVAN KING

REYNAL & HITCHCOCK · NEW YORK

1945

Format by Richard Ellis

Composition, Electrotyping, Printing and Binding
by the Kingsport Press, Inc. Kingsport, Tennessee
United States of America

1

CHE person we want to introduce is Happy Boy and not Camel, because Camel is only his nickname. So we will first speak of Happy Boy, and when we have reached that point we will relate how he came to be connected with a camel, whereafter we will forget the sobriquet and call him by his proper name anyway, which should settle the matter.

We hope to describe Happy Boy's position with the same definiteness with which one would indicate the place of a certain bolt in a machine. Before he came to be connected with the nickname "Camel," he was one of those relatively independent rickshaw coolies, which is to say that he belonged to that group of strong young pullers who moreover own their own rickshaws; with their own rickshaws they have their own livelihood: they are the high-class rickshaw men.

But that certainly is no easy point to reach. A year, two years —three or four years at the very least; one drop of sweat, two drops of sweat: no one knows how many tens upon countless tens of thousands of drops of sweat it took to earn that rickshaw. It was reaped from many and many a time that he had gritted his teeth in the wind and the rain and from his long self-denial in the food he ate and the tea he drank. That one rickshaw was the end result and final reward of all his struggling and suffering, like the medal worn by the soldier who has survived a hundred battles. In the days when he had rented someone else's rickshaw he had been like a top that was perpetually whipped to keep it spinning. In a dizzy whirl from early till late, from east to west, from south to north, there had been nothing he could call himself. But in all this spinning around his sight had not become blurred, nor his heart confused: he had thought always of a far-away rickshaw that would free him, make him independent, and be as much a part of him as were his own hands and feet. With a rickshaw of his own he need no longer take the guff of the rickshaw owners, and there would be no need for lengthy explanations to any one else: with his own natural strength and his own rickshaw, he had only to keep his eyes open and he would have food to eat.

He was not afraid of hardship, nor did he have the bad habit that many rickshaw coolies had of condoning faults without making any effort to correct them: his mind and energy were both adequate to the task of turning his aspirations into facts. If his environment had been a little better, or if he had been given a little more education, he could certainly never have fallen into the rubber-tired corps, and in any case, whatever work he might have taken up, he would not have been insensible to his opportunities. Worse luck, he had no choice but to be a rickshaw coolie; all right, then, even in this trade he would prove his ability and his cleverness. It seemed as if even were he in hell he would still be a well-behaved devil.

He was born and raised in a village and had lost his mother and father and a few mou of ground, and when he was eighteen had come in to the city. He brought with him the country boy's robust health and guilelessness. At one time or another he worked at practically every one of the jobs in which one sells one's strength to get food to eat, but it was not long before he realized that pulling a rickshaw was an even easier way of earning money. In other kinds of manual labor there was a limit to your income; in rickshaw pulling there were more chances and better chances; you never knew at what time or in what place you might just happen to receive a greater reward than you had hoped for for your labors.

Naturally he also knew that this kind of chance was not altogether fortuitous; that it was necessary that both the man and his rickshaw be smart-looking and spirited, and that you had to have something of quality to sell before you could hope to meet with buyers who really knew quality.

Turning the matter over in his mind, Happy Boy felt sure he had the qualifications: he was strong, he was just in the prime of his youth; the only lack was that he had never pulled a rickshaw and did not dare try out his hand on a brand-new one. But this was not a difficulty over which it was impossible to triumph: with his physique and physical strength as a basis, he need only experiment for ten days or two weeks, in which time he would certainly be able to acquire a stride that had some style to it, and then he would go rent a new rickshaw. There would be no way of knowing how soon after that he might get into a job by the month, where by frugal eating and careful spending for one or two years, or even if it were so long as three or four years, he would surely be able to get his own rickshaw, as smart as they come. Looking at his own young muscles, he told himself that the question was only one of time, that this was something he could certainly do: that it was not just a dream.

His height and strength were both developed in advance of his age; he was under twenty and already very big and tall. Although the passing months and years had not yet molded the physical bearing of his body into any particular form, yet he already had the appearance of a full-grown man—an adult in whose face and manner was the suggestion of a child's unaffected naturalness and mischievousness. Watching the high-class rickshaw men, he laid his plans to gird his loins-among them, the better to show forth the iron strength of his own chest and the straight hardness of his back; he twisted his head to look at his own shoulders—they were broad enough. He would tighten his girdle and put on a pair of wide-legged white trousers which he would bind at the ankles with bands made from chickens' intestines, to show off his outsize feet. Right enough, there could be no doubt that he would become the best rickshaw man of them all! And like the simple country boy he was, he grinned largely at the prospect.

There was nothing special about his features—what made him likeable was the spirit in his expression. His head was small, his eyes round, his nose fleshy, his eyebrows very short and very coarse, and his head always shaved clean of hair. There was no surplus fat on his jowls, but his neck was almost as thick as his head, and his face was everlastingly as red as if it had just been slapped. A large scar between his right ear and cheek bone shone with special brightness—once during his childhood when he had fallen asleep under a tree a mule had taken a bite out of him. He didn't pay much attention to whether he was good-looking or not: the thing he liked about his own face was the same thing he liked about his physique—both had a firm hard strength. It was as if he regarded his face as being in the same category with his arms and legs—if there was enough strength in it, it was all right. Yes, even after he had come to the city to live he could still turn a handspring, or even stand on his hands, with his head down, for half a day. In that difficult stance he felt that he was very much like a tree—there wasn't a single part of him, either up or down, that wasn't straight and firm.

It was assuredly true that even when he was standing upright Happy Boy did have something tree-like about him. He was sturdy, silent, and alive. He had his own plans, and he was not unintelligent, but it was hard for him to talk to other people.

10

Among rickshaw men the wrongs which each has suffered and the difficulties with which each is confronted are proper subjects of public conversation. At the rickshaw stands at street intersections, in the little tea shops, or in the general market place, each man would report, describe, or just bawl out his personal affairs, and after that they would become a kind of capital of the whole group and would spread from one place to another like a new popular song.

Happy Boy was a countryman and his lips and tongue were not as quick and fast as those of fellows born and raised in the city. If quickness of the tongue is a matter of natural talent, it must be said that from the time he was a baby Happy Boy had never liked to talk very much, and on that account he was loath to imitate the spiteful lips and evil tongues of the city-dwellers. He knew about his own affairs himself and he wasn't happy to discuss them with other people. Because his lips were habitually unoccupied he had the leisure in which to think, and it seemed as if his eyes were always turned in on his own heart. It was only necessary that his mind should be made up, and he would follow the road opened up in it. If it happened that that road could not carry him to his objective, he was able to keep all words from his tongue for two or three days.

When he had decided to pull a rickshaw, he went directly to get a rickshaw to pull. He rented an old, broken-down one to try out his legs. The first day he earned no money; on the second his business was quite good, but for the next two days he was flat on his back, his ankles swollen up like two calabashes and hurting so that he couldn't lift up his feet. He bore it without complaint, no matter how great the pain was, because he knew that this was unavoidable, that it was an experience through which every rickshaw man must pass. Until he had suffered it he would not dare to really stretch his legs and run.

After his ankles got well again, he was no longer afraid. He was as happy as he could be, because there was nothing more to be scared of: he was thoroughly familiar with the names of streets and places, and even if occasionally he took a fare the long way round to the place he wanted to go it made no great difference. Fortunately Happy Boy had plenty of strength, and that was what it took. Nor did he find it difficult to pick up from his own experience the various methods of handling his rickshaw—of pushing it back, pulling it, lifting it up, and using his shoulders. Moreover, he had his axioms to guide him: if you spent more time in being careful, and less in wrangling for right-of-way, there certainly wouldn't be much chance of your committing a serious fault.

When it came to haggling about prices and competing for fares, his tongue was too slow, and for all the vigor of his appearance he was no match for the old oilies. Knowing his weakness, he simply did not go to the rickshaw stands at the big intersections, but wherever there were no other rickshaws, there he would put his own. In these out-of-the-way places he could talk price without embarrassment, and when sometimes he was unwilling to ask a definite fare, he would simply say, "Get in and pay me whatever you feel like." His manner was so sincere and his face so simple and likeable that it seemed as if people could only believe him and did not dare to think that this great big country bumpkin could possibly be trying to trick them. If they suspected him of anything, it was that he had just come to the city and not knowing his way about the streets or how long the haul would be, he did not know what the price should be. When it got to a point that the prospective passenger would ask him, "Do you know where that address is?" he would only smile, in a way that made him seem to be either pretending to be stupid or trying to be coy, leaving the would-be passenger bewildered.

In two or three weeks' time he had got his legs worked into it, and he realized that the style of running which he had developed was very good to look at. A rickshaw man's running style is the outward evidence of his ability and his qualifications. The fellow who throws his feet around, slapping them at the ground as if they were a pair of rush-leaf fans, is without any doubt a beginner who has just arrived in town from his village. Those whose heads are bowed very low, whose feet scrape along the ground, and who have all the appearance of running although their pace is actually not much faster than a walk, are the old ones, over fifty. There are also those whose experience is ten parts complete but who are without much strength—they have still another way. With their chests drawn in and their shoulders thrown forward, they lean far forward and lift their knees very high, ducking their heads with each step, so that they give the impression that they are running very hard, while as a matter of fact they are not moving a bit faster than any one else: they depend solely on appearances to maintain their "face."

Naturally Happy Boy would never choose such a carriage. His legs were long and his stride was big; with exceptionally sound thighs, he ran almost noiselessly, every step elastic, and the shafts of the rickshaw absolutely steady, so that the passenger would feel at ease and comfortable. When it came to stopping, he had only to scrape his big feet lightly along the ground for two or three paces, and no matter how fast he might have been running he could come to a standstill; it was as if his strength reached every part of the rickshaw he was pulling. With his back bent forward a little, his two hands loosely gripping the shafts of the rickshaw, he was alive, facile, sure; and though he showed no sign of haste, he was yet a very fast runner—fast and with no risk for his fare. Even among the pullers of private rickshaws this would be regarded as worthy of honor.

He changed his rickshaw for a new one. On the day that he made the change, he inquired carefully and discovered that a rickshaw like the new one he was renting, with soft springs, bright brass work, a rain cover for the top and a curtain for the front, two lamps, and a long-throated brass horn, was worth something over one hundred dollars. If the lacquering and the brass work were a little carelessly finished, then you could get it for a hundred dollars. Speaking generally, then, he need only have a hundred dollars to buy himself a rickshaw. Suddenly he thought to himself: if he could save ten cents every day, it would only take a thousand days to save a hundred dollars. A thousand days! When he thought of a thousand days all together, he could hardly figure out how far away the farthest was, but he made up his mind—a thousand days or ten thousand days, he had to buy his own rickshaw.

He thought the thing out to himself, and he could see that the first thing was for him to become the rickshaw man in a private family. If he ran into a master who had many friends, and went out often to dinner, there might be in an average month as many as ten dinners, and he would get two or three dollars extra in food tips from his master's hosts without any extra work. If he added to that the eighty cents or a dollar he could save from his wages, he might have three or four or even five dollars, and in a year he could save fifty or sixty. In this way his hope seemed much closer and more easily realizable. He did not smoke or drink or gamble, and he had no weakness of any kind. He was not tied down by a family, and if only he himself were willing to grit his teeth, there was nothing he could not do. He made an oath to himself: in a year and a half he would have his own rickshaw, whatever happened. It must be a new one, not an old one built over.

Happy Boy did in fact become the rickshaw man in a private family, but the actualities were not always an aid to his hopes. There was no mistake about it: he had gritted his teeth but by the end of a year and a half he had not made good his oath. It was true that he had become a private rickshaw puller and had been very careful not to do anything that would cost him his job, but unfortunately the affairs of this world are not simple. He thought only of doing his work carefully, but his masters were not prevented on that account from firing him. Sometimes it was two or three months, and sometimes perhaps only eight or ten days, and then his job would be gone as suddenly as a candle-light goes out when you blow on it, and he would have to hunt again for another employer. Naturally he had, on the one hand, to haul fares while, on the other, he was looking for a job; he was riding a horse in search of a horse, and he had no time for leisure.

In times like these he often made mistakes. He was forcing his energy because he could not make enough each day to fill his stomach for the day: he had to continue saving his money to buy himself his rickshaw. But forcing your energy is never a good thing to do. When he was pulling a rickshaw he could not keep his mind on the job and run straight along: it was as if he was always thinking of something, and the more he thought the more afraid and upset he became. Suppose things were always like this, when would he ever be able to buy his rickshaw? Why were things like this? Could anybody say that he wasn't trying to improve himself? Then his thoughts would become confused, he would forget his usual carefulness, and one of the rubber tires of the rickshaw would run over bits of twisted brass or broken crockery and when the tube blew out there would be a sound like a firecracker exploding. The only thing to do then would be to return the rickshaw to the shed from which he had rented it. Even more serious, he would sometimes run into people walking in the street, and there was one time when he was in such a hurry to get over a crossing that his rickshaw got run into and the whole covering was smashed. If he had been working as a rickshaw man in a private family these things could not have happened, but whenever he lost a job like that he was terribly unhappy and would go about in a kind of a daze. When he got into an accident and damaged a rented rickshaw he naturally had to pay for repairs: that made him more hot and burnt-up than ever, like a fire on which kerosene is poured. Because of his fear that he might get into even greater difficulties, he would sometimes, out of sheer vexation, sleep the whole day away. Then when he opened his eyes the hours would already be gone for nothing, and he would be filled with regret and hatred for himself.

There was another thing: in these periods of anxiety and fear, the more frightened he got, the more he subjected himself to hardship, and the less regularity there was in his eating and drinking. He thought that he was made of iron but actually he too could be sick. Once sick, he was unwilling to spend the money to buy medicine and would stubbornly hold out against his illness. The result would be that he would get sicker and sicker, and would finally not only have to buy medicine but also to rest for many days together. These difficulties only made him clench his teeth more grimly and work the harder, but the money with which to buy his rickshaw did not collect any more rapidly on that account.

Just exactly three years had passed by the time he had saved a hundred dollars.

He could wait no longer. The original plan had been to buy the most completely equipped, the most modern, the most desirable of rickshaws, but now the best he could do would be to speak within the one hundred dollars. By good fortune there was a rickshaw that had just been built, but the man who had ordered it now had no money with which to take delivery of it. It was not very different from the rickshaw of which Happy

Boy had dreamed, and originally it was worth more than a hundred but because the down-payment had been forfeited the rickshaw shop was willing to accept a little less than its value. Happy Boy's face was flushed red, and his hand shook. He brought out ninety-six dollars.

"I want this rickshaw." The master of the shop hoped to force him up to a round number and talked endlessly, pulling the rickshaw out and pushing it back again, putting the top of it up and letting it down again, sounding the horn, and with each motion producing the most beautiful adjectives to match the action; and finally he kicked the steel spokes of one of the wheels. "Listen to that sound! It's like a bell! Pull the rickshaw away with you—pull it until it falls apart, and if one spoke comes loose you can bring the cart back and throw it in my face! One hundred dollars! One penny less and we snuff out the deal."

Happy Boy counted his money once more. "I want this rickshaw. Ninety-six dollars." The shopkeeper knew he was up against a person with sense. He eyed the money and he eyed Happy Boy, and sighed. "For the sake of making a friend, the rickshaw is yours. I guarantee it for six months, and unless you smash up the frame of it I'll make repairs on it for you for nothing. Here's the guarantee—take it."

Happy Boy's hands trembled even more. He grasped the guarantee, and pulled the rickshaw out of the shop, feeling as if he wanted to cry. He drew it along to a secluded spot where he could go over it—his own rickshaw—with minute care, and could look at his own face in the bright polish of its lacquer, as if he were looking in a mirror. The more he looked at the rickshaw the more he loved it; even the things in which it did not quite come up to his expectations he could now overlook, because it was already his own rickshaw. He looked at it so long that he felt tired and sat down on the carpeted footrest, his eyes on the burnished yellow brass of the horn on the shaft.

17

Suddenly he remembered that this year he was twenty-two years old. Because his mother and father had both died early, he could not remember the date of his birth, and since he had come to the city he had not celebrated his birthday. Well, then, he would count today, the day on which he had bought his new rickshaw, as his birthday: both his and the rickshaw's. That would be easy to remember, and since he had bought the rickshaw with the sweat of his heart, there was actually no reason why he should not count it as part of himself.

How would he celebrate this double birthday? Happy Boy had his plan: his first fare must be a well-dressed person and must on no account be a woman. The best thing would be a passenger to be taken to the South Gate, or to the Market of Eastern Peace. When he got there, he should properly go to the best food stall he could find and buy himself a meal of hot rolls with roasted mutton—or something like that. When he had finished, if he chanced on another good fare or two he would take them, but if not he would put his rickshaw up for the night. That would be his birthday celebration.

From the day Happy Boy got his rickshaw life became more and more interesting. He could rent out his services by the month or he could pick up fares one by one: he need no longer worry about the rental money at the end of the day. All he earned in fares was all his own. Easy in his own heart, he was more than ever friendly to other people, and his business was because of that more than ever to his liking. When he had had his own rickshaw for six months, his hopes were even greater: if he could keep up at this rate, he need work only two years longer—not more than two—and he would be able to buy another rickshaw, and then another. In no time he would be opening a rickshaw shed!

But most bright hopes come to strange and bitter endings, and Happy Boy's were no exception to the rule.

2

BECAUSE of his high spirits, Happy Boy lost some of his temerity: after he had bought his own rickshaw he ran even faster than before. Naturally he was particularly careful with a rickshaw that was his own property, but when he looked at himself and then at it he felt that it wouldn't be quite right for him not to run as fast as he could.

He had grown over an inch in height since he had come to the city and he felt as if he would grow even taller. It was true that his features had settled a little, and that he had the beginnings of a mustache on his upper lip, but he still felt that he should grow a little more. When he walked through the door of some little room or some low gateway, and he had to duck his head way down to get through, he would be happy in his own heart, even though he said nothing. The fact that he was already so tall and big while he was still growing made it seem as if he was at once a full-grown man and still a child: it was a lot of fun to be that way.

A fellow as big as that, pulling a rickshaw as beautiful as his rickshaw was—his own rickshaw, with soft springs bouncing as he went along, so that even the shafts shook a little in his hands, with the back of the seat so brightly polished, the cushion so white, and the horn so loud—if he just dragged along and didn't run fast, how could he face himself? How could he face his rickshaw? This was not a false pride but rather a sense of responsibility. If he didn't fly along he would not be showing his own strength nor the excellence of his rickshaw. He could find no words to say these things, but they were in his heart and he could not do other than follow his feelings about them.

For this rickshaw of his was really lovable. By the time he had had it six months it was as if every part of it was alive and had feelings of its own. Whenever Happy Boy leaned to one side or the other, or bent his knees, or stood erect, his rickshaw would answer him at once, giving him the most suitable assistance that it could. There was not the least barrier between them, and no contrariness one to the other. When he came to places where the road was smooth and the people few, Happy Boy needed to use only one hand to hold the shafts, and the light sound of the rubber tires on the gravel behind him, like a favorable wind, would carry him along evenly and at a flying speed. When he had reached the address of his fare, his clothes would be dripping with sweat, as if they had just come out of the wash. He would feel tired but very happy—a kind of tiredness of which he could be proud, as if he had ridden a famous horse for several tens of li.

Granted that fearlessness and carelessness are different things, Happy Boy was anything but careless in the brave way he sped along with his rickshaw. If running slow would make him unable to face his fare, running fast and wrecking his rickshaw would leave him unable to face himself. His rickshaw was his life, and he knew how to be careful of it. With courage and care together, he became more and more self-confident: he was firmly convinced that both himself and his rickshaw were made of iron.

Thus he was not only not afraid to run fast, he no longer worried about the hours which he worked. He felt that to earn his rice by pulling a rickshaw was the most independent thing in the world. When he wanted to go out, no one could stop him. He did not take very much to heart the rumors that he heard outside; he could not be bothered with all the talk about soldiers coming back to the Western Gardens, or the fighting at Ch'ang Hsin Tien, or the conscripting of men outside the Western Gate of Forthrightness, or the Gate of Uniform Transformation's being already closed for half a day. Naturally the stores would have put up their shutters and closed their doors, and the streets would be full of armed police and members of the Peace Preservation Corps. He could not go hunting for trouble, and like everybody else he would put up his rickshaw as quickly as he could, but as for the rumors themselves he did not believe them. He knew how to be prudent, especially since his rickshaw was his own, but down underneath he was still a countryman, and not like the city people, who claimed it was raining whenever they heard the wind. Besides that, his size gave him confidence: if by some bad luck he should find himself "on the spot," he could certainly find some way out, so that he would not be likely to suffer too much loss. As tall as he was, and with such broad shoulders, it wouldn't be easy to take advantage of him.

News of war and rumors of conflict grew up each year in the springtime with the growing wheat, and for the Northerner the full ripe kernel was the symbol of his hopes, as the glistening bayonet the omen of his fears. Happy Boy's rickshaw was six months old just at that season when the new wheat needs the rains of spring. Spring rains are not sure to fall when the people hope for them, but war comes anyway, regardless of whether or not anyone wants it.

Whether the rumors were only rumors or actual facts, Happy Boy seemed to have forgotten that he had been a farmer; he did not think of how fighting ruins the farmlands, and paid no heed to whether the spring rains had come or not. He only thought of his rickshaw. It could produce hot rolls and steaming rice and all his other food for him. It was a plot of soil in which anything could be grown, and which very conveniently followed him around; a piece of precious, living farmland. Because there had been a scarcity of rain and also because of the reports of

21

fighting, all kinds of food went up in price: this much Happy
Boy knew. But he was like the city people—he could only complain about the price of food, without having any plan for doing
anything about it. Food was dear. Well, then, it was dear. Who
had the means of making it cheap? This attitude made him
think only of his own livelihood, putting all calamities and disasters out of his mind.

If the city people were without any means of helping themselves, they could at least invent wild rumors. Sometimes they
made them up out of nothing at all, and sometimes they started
with one part of truth and talked it into ten parts of fancy, all
to prove that they were neither stupid nor idle. They were like
a school of little fish that have nothing better to do than put
their mouths close to the surface of the water and amuse themselves mightily by blowing useless bubbles. Among false rumors
the most interesting are those about war: other false rumors
end up only as false rumors, like telling stories about devils and
fairy-foxes: no matter how much you tell about them, they
won't really appear. But as for rumors of war, the very lack of
reliable news makes it possible for the wildest of stories to turn
suddenly into fact. In small details there may be very great
discrepancies between rumor and truth, but when it comes to
the question as to whether fighting has broken out, rumor is
eight or nine parts reliable.

"There's going to be war!" Whenever this sentence is spoken,
you may be sure that sooner or later there will be war. As for
who is to fight whom and why, each man will have a different
answer. Happy Boy knew all this well enough. But although
rickshaw men cannot welcome war, still they may not lose by
its coming. Each time there has been war, it has been the rich
who were most frightened. When the wind of rumor rises, they
think at once of running for their lives; their money brings
them to a place quickly, but it makes them the first to run from
it when danger threatens. They can't run by themselves—their

feet and legs are laden down too heavily with their money. They must hire people to act as their legs; there must be people to carry their boxes; there must be rickshaws to haul men and women, old and young; at such a time the hands and feet of the brethren who sell their labor become more expensive. "The Gate Before"—"The East Station"—"Where?"—"The East Station"—"Oh—give me a dollar and forty cents—there's no use talking price—there'll be fighting here soon!"

It was in conditions like these that Happy Boy took a fare outside the city wall. Rumors had been current for over ten days and prices had all gone up, but the fighting seemed a long way off, and not likely to reach Peking in any very short while. Happy Boy was pulling his rickshaw as usual, unwilling to sneak two or three days of lazying around just because of a few rumors. One day, when he had run his rickshaw to the western part of the city, he saw there many signs of trouble. Neither at the mouth of the Road of the Temple for the Defense of the State nor at the New Road Gate was there a single rickshaw man calling for fares to the Western Gardens or Ch'ing Hua University. Near the New Road Gate he strolled about for a while. Someone told him that rickshaws no longer dared venture outside the city, that outside the Western Gate of Forthrightness everything on wheels was being seized—wagons, pushcarts, mule-carts, and rickshaws. He decided to take a cup of tea and then go back to the southern part of the city to put away his rickshaw. The emptiness of the street corners showed that there was real danger now. He had courage enough, but there was no use walking down a dead-end road.

Just at this juncture two rickshaws came up from the south carrying fares that looked like students. The rickshaw men were calling out as they ran, "Who will go to Ch'ing Hua? Hei— Ch'ing Hua!" Because the college by that name was so far beyond the safety of the city walls, none of the three or four rickshaw men at the corner answered: they simply looked at the two rickshaws and smiled a little without resentment. One of them was sitting smoking a long-stemmed pipe: he did not even lift his head. The two rickshaw men kept on calling, "Are you all dumb? Ch'ing Hua!"

"For two dollars I'll go," a shaved-head short little youngster answered, as if he were making a joke at the others who had said nothing.

"Come along then. We must find one more." The two rickshaws stopped. The short little fellow was silent for a moment, not knowing what it was best to do next. No one else moved. Happy Boy could see that it was certainly dangerous to go out of the city; otherwise, why, when ordinarily a haul to Ch'ing Hua was only a matter of twenty or thirty cents, was there nobody competing now when the price offered was two dollars? He didn't want to go either, but the youngster had made up his mind that if he could find someone to go with him, he would take a chance, whatever happened. He looked hard at Happy Boy. "Big fellow, how about you?"

The two words, "big fellow," made Happy Boy smile. It was a real compliment to him. He turned the thing over in his mind. For praise like that it looked as if he ought to help out the little shaved-head fellow with the big guts. And besides, two dollars are two dollars. It wasn't every day that you could run into a thing like that. Danger? Was it likely that he would just happen to run into it? Also he remembered having heard two days before that the Altar of Heaven was crowded with soldiers, when he had seen with his own eyes that there wasn't even the hair of a soldier there. With that he pulled his rickshaw over to the road.

When they reached the Western Gate of Forthrightness there was hardly anybody under the arches of the great gateway, and Happy Boy's heart grew chill. The little shaved-head youngster saw no good in the look of things either, but he still smiled, saying: "Take care, partner; 'if it's good luck it can't be bad; if it's bad luck we can't dodge it anyway'; and we won't have to wait until tomorrow to find out."

Happy Boy knew that things were going to turn out badly, but he'd been making his living on the streets for too many years to go back on his word or act like a nervous old woman.

Outside the Gate it was a fact that they didn't meet even one other rickshaw. Happy Boy kept his head down, not daring to look either to the left or the right of the road. His heart seemed to be knocking against his ribs. When they reached the Bridge of High Brightness he took a quick look around him without seeing a single soldier, and again felt a little easier at heart. Two dollars were after all two dollars, and he said to himself that if you didn't have a little backbone, how could you hope to run into a good thing like that? Ordinarily he very much disliked talking, but right now he felt like saying a few words to the little shaved-head. The road was so quiet that it frightened him.

"Let's follow the dirt path—this highway we're on . . ."

"You don't have to tell me that." The short fellow had guessed what he meant. "Once we get onto this path, we can figure that we've got a chance."

They hadn't yet turned off the road when Happy Boy, the short fellow, their rickshaws and the fares riding in them, were all seized by some ten soldiers.

Though it was already the season for the opening of the Temple on the Mountain of the Wonderful Peak, the night air was still too cold to be stopped by a single thin shirt. Happy Boy was not burdened down with either clothes or bedding, and had nothing to cover him but the thin gray coat of an army uniform and a pair of blue pants, both garments stinking with sweat. They were that way before he ever put them on. Looking at these tattered clothes, he thought of the small white jacket and the blue coat and trousers he had originally been wearing

—how clean and smart-looking they had been! Yes, there were plenty of things in the world that were smarter-looking than Happy Boy's clothes had been, but only he knew how hard it had been for him to reach the point in cleanliness and neatness which they had represented.

Smelling now the stench of his own body and of these filthy rags, his past struggles and accomplishments already seemed to him to be far away and more than ever praiseworthy. There was ten times more glory in them than there had originally been. The more he thought of what had already gone by, the more he hated the soldiers who had taken him. They had robbed him of his clothes, his shoes, his hat, his rickshaw, and even of the strip of cloth that he wound around his waist as a belt. They had left him with nothing but black and blue bruises all over his body and blisters covering the soles of his feet.

Well, the clothes didn't count for much and the bruises would disappear in a little while, but the rickshaw that he had earned from years of sweat and blood was gone! From the time they had reached the military barracks, he had not seen it again. He could forget all the hardship and difficulty in the batting of an eye, but he could not forget his rickshaw.

He was not afraid of suffering: it was simply that the business of getting himself another rickshaw was not one that could be brought about just by saying the words. At the least it would take several years' time. His past accomplishments were all now vain: he would have to start all over again from the very beginning. Happy Boy wept. He hated not only the soldiers but the whole world as well. Why had he been treated like this? Why? Suddenly his anguish found voice, and he could hear himself almost shouting: "Why?"

The sound of his voice startled him into a realization of the danger he was in. He had best forget all that for the present— the important thing was to get away alive.

Where was he? It was a question that he couldn't have answered properly himself. For the past days he had followed the troops, with the sweat pouring out of him from his head to his heels. When they were marching, he was either pulling or toting or pushing the property of the soldiers. When they halted, he had to carry water, make fires, and feed the animals. From morning to night he knew only how to use every last bit of the strength in his arms and legs—his mind was blank. When late at night he could at last lie down, it was as if he were dead. Nor was he certain that it would be such a bad thing if he never opened his eyes again.

In the beginning he seemed to remember that the troops were retreating into the Mountains of the Wonderful Peak. Once into them, he could pay no heed to anything but the climbing itself, and the thought was constantly with him that if once his foot should slip he would be hurled down some ravine and his bones picked clean by the wild eagles that circled above him. The troops tramped about in the mountains for many days, and then suddenly one day the road became less and less mountainous; when the sun was on his back, he could see the level plains away off in the distance. When the bugle for the evening meal had sounded to call back the soldiers who had been posted at some distance from the camp, several of them came back that evening leading three or four camels.

Camels! Happy Boy's heart jumped. All at once he could think, like a person who, having lost his way, suddenly stumbles upon a familiar landmark from which he can quickly figure out everything else. Camels cannot cross mountains: they were certainly back now to the plains. He knew that Whetstone Pass and others of the villages to the west of Peking raised camels: was he to believe that they had dragged back and forth for so many days only to come out at Whetstone Pass, to the west of Peking? He did not know what kind of strategy that was, or if this gang of troops, who could only march and steal, were capable of strategy. But one thing he did know: if this was really Whetstone Pass, then the soldiers had not been able to find their way across the mountains and had come back to the foot of them to get their bearings. The Pass was a good place; if you went northeast from it you could get back to the Western Hills; if you went south you would reach the Inn of Unending Bitterness or Luxuriant Terrace, where the railway was. There was also a road that went straight west from the Pass. He guessed that this was what the troops were probably thinking, but by the same token it was a road out for him too. The time for him to run away had come!

If it happened that the troops retreated again into the mountains, he would be in danger of starving to death even if he did escape. If he was going to run, he'd have to make the best of this opportunity. If he got away here, he could reach Seas' Domain in no time. In spite of the distance, he knew the way

perfectly. He was so excited that his heart seemed to be jumping out of his mouth. In the last few days his blood had all run
to his hands and feet, but now it was as if it had all returned
to his heart, making it very hot, while his limbs became cold.
He was trembling all over.

It was after midnight, and he still could not close his eyes.
His hope made him happy while he was at the same time almost
terrified with the fear that it wouldn't come true. He wanted to
sleep but couldn't. He had flung himself down on some dry
grass, his arms and legs thrown out as if they were no longer
parts of the same body. There wasn't the slightest sound, and
only the stars in the heavens kept company with his thumping
heart. The camels suddenly whinnied. They were not far away
from him. He liked the sound. It made him sad, like the crowing of a cock in the middle of the night, and yet was somehow
comforting.

There was the crack of cannon fire in the distance: it was a
long way off but was very distinctly cannon fire. He was afraid
to move, although around him the camp was immediately
thrown into confusion. He held his breath—the chance had
come! He knew for certain that the troops would have to retreat
again, and that they would be sure to go back into the mountains. His experiences in the past few days had taught him that
the way in which these soldiers fought was the same as that of
a fly locked in a room: they banged about wildly from one place
to another, without any direction. At the sound of cannon fire
they were sure to run. He'd have to be alert himself.

Slowly and without breathing, he crawled along the ground,
looking for the camels. He knew that the camels couldn't be of
any help to him, but he was almost as much a beast of burden
as they were, and it was as if he just had to feel a kind of fellow
sympathy for them on that account. The encampment was in
more confusion than ever. He found the camels, crouched down
in the darkness like mounds of earth, motionless except for

their heavy breathing. The whole world seemed at peace. The quiet gave him more courage. He crouched down beside the camels, like a soldier behind a barricade of sandbags. Quickly he reasoned to himself: the sound of the firing came from the south; even if it did not mean that there would really be fighting, it was at the very least a warning that that road was closed. At that rate these troops would have to flee back into the middle of the mountains. When it came to scrambling up the mountainside, they couldn't take the camels along with them. So the camels' fate and his own were one and the same: if the troops didn't let these animals go, he would be finished along with them. If they forgot the camels, he could get away himself. He glued his ear to the ground to listen for footsteps coming in his direction, his heart racing the while.

He didn't know how long he waited. No one came to take the camels along. He felt braver now and sat up looking out from between the humps of the camel at his side. He saw nothing at all. Everywhere there was only the blackest night. He would run. No matter—good luck or bad, he'd run.

3

WHEN he had already run twenty or thirty paces away, Happy Boy stopped, unwilling to leave the camels behind. The only thing he had left in the world was his own life. If he had seen only a hempen string in the roadway, he would have been happy to pick it up. Even were it useless, he would at least have felt that in holding it his hands were not altogether empty. To save himself was the important thing, but of what use was that when he had nothing else? He would have to take the camels along. He had not quite figured out what use the camels would be, but at least they were something and something pretty big, at that.

He pulled the camels to their feet. The right way to handle the animals was a thing he knew nothing about, but he was not afraid of them. They got up very slowly, and he couldn't be bothered with seeing whether were all tied together; when he felt that they could be led away, he simply started off, not caring whether he had the whole lot of them or only one.

He had taken only a few steps when he began to regret. Camels—ones that had become accustomed to carrying heavy loads—could not move fast. He must walk not only very slowly but very carefully as well. Camels were likely to slip: a puddle of water, a little mud, and they would be sprawled all over the road. Their value was all in their legs, and once their legs were done they were finished. And Happy Boy was trying to escape.

But he wasn't willing to let them go. He would leave the thing to heaven—how could he let go a flock of camels that he had got for nothing?

Accustomed as he was to pulling a rickshaw, Happy Boy had a very good sense of direction: for all that, he was a little confused now. When he found the camels, he had paid no attention to anything but them, so that with them in tow he didn't know which way was which. The night was so black, and he was so worried, that even if he had been able to get his bearings from the stars, he wouldn't have been able to go calmly about doing that. Just then, to his eyes, the stars, blinking so unsteadily in the middle of the heavens, seemed to be in an even greater panic than he was himself. Happy Boy didn't dare look twice at the sky, but kept his head down, wanting in his frightened heart to move much faster but unable to because of the camels.

He realized that, dragging them along with him, he would have to follow the main road and couldn't skirt along the foot

31

of the hills. From Whetstone Pass—if this was Whetstone Pass —there was a straight road to Yellow Village on which you could take camels, and which wasn't the least roundabout. For a rickshaw coolie, a road that goes straight from one point to another has a particular value. The trouble was that he would have no way of hiding on this road. What if, on the one chance in ten thousand, he should meet soldiers? Even if he didn't meet any soldiers, could he make anybody believe that these camels were his, dressed as he was in a tattered uniform and covered with dirt? He didn't look the part, not at all. If he wanted to escape, he'd have to let these animals go. But he couldn't finally make up his mind to let slip the rope in his hand that was tied to the ring in the lead-camel's nose, and he kept on walking. He'd keep walking as fast as he could, and when he couldn't go any farther he'd stop. He'd change his story according to whom he ran into—if he lived, he'd be the better by a couple of pack animals—if he died, he'd be dead, and there'd be nothing more to it.

He shed his uniform, ripping off the collar of the coat and throwing into the darkness the two brass buttons that had still clung to it. Then he threw the collarless, buttonless jacket over his shoulders like a cape, tying the sleeves into a knot over his chest. Thus he could reduce a little the suspicion that he was a defeated soldier; the legs of his trousers he rolled up halfway, to disguise them too. He knew that even so he didn't look altogether like a camel-boy; at the same time he no longer was the runaway trooper. Add the mud on his face and the sweat on his body, and probably he could pass as one of the coal-carting camel-men.

It occurred to him that he could save his strength and bear the hunger better if he rode one of the camels, but he didn't dare try to mount one: supposing he could stay on after he got on, he would still first have to make the beast kneel down. Time was worth too much—he couldn't be bothered. Besides, when

he got up that high it would be even harder to see the road before him, and if the camel slipped and fell he'd have to fall along with it. No, it would be better just to keep on walking.

He knew generally that he was on a main road; of the place where he was and the direction in which he was moving he was utterly ignorant. The depth of the night, the long days of fatigue, and the fright of running away, made his heart and body wretched. When he had walked a little while, the soft even sound of the padded hoofs on the roadway and the slowness with which he was moving, gradually lulled him into a kind of sleep. It was still very dark, and the air was heavy with a damp cold mist that made his heart feel even less sure. He looked as hard as he could at the road at his feet: with every step he took it seemed to rise up before him, but when his foot touched the ground it would be smooth and even. To be so careful and still to be fooled time after time, made him angry. He might as well not try to watch where he walked but just go on walking. He could see nothing around him, and he felt as if he were striding out of nothingness into nothingness again, with the silently moving camels trudging along at his back.

Gradually he became accustomed to the darkness; his heart stopped pounding, and his eyes closed without his wanting them to. He didn't know whether he was still going forward or had already come to a dead stop. All he could feel was one wave after another of motion, like the movement of a broad dark sea. His heart and the darkness around him had become one endless haze of indistinctness and confusion. He would have to think of something, have to keep awake. If he dropped down and slept, he knew that he wouldn't get up again for three days. What should he think of? His head was a little dizzy; his whole body was clammy with cold sweat; his head itched; his feet were heavy; his mouth was dry and rough. There was nothing else he could think of: he could only feel sorry for himself. His head was too empty and swollen: it was as if, just as he remembered himself, he forgot himself again. It was like a candle that is about to go out, and doesn't have enough light left to illuminate itself, much less anything around it.

Never before had he suffered from any such agony of uncertainty and gloom. He had not been much given to making friends in his ordinary life, but with the sun shining down on you, and everything around you clearly to be seen, you don't feel afraid of things.

If camels were as hard to handle as donkeys or mules, he probably would have had to keep alert to control them, but camels are particularly tame. These he was leading were so tame they got on his nerves. When he had been most frightened, he had suddenly suspected that they were no longer there at all. The thought had made him start: it was certainly possible that these beasts, moving so silently, could have slipped down some by-path without his knowing anything at all about it, as a cake

34

of ice that you dragged along after you might melt away before you knew it.

At some time or other—he couldn't remember when—he sat down. He sat there five minutes—or maybe it was an hour—he didn't know, any more than he knew whether he sat down and then went to sleep, or went to sleep and then sat down. Probably he went to sleep first, because he was so tired that even standing up he couldn't keep awake any longer.

Suddenly he woke up. It wasn't a natural awakening from sleep but a sharp jerk, as if in the time it took him to open his eyes he had jumped from one world to another. He could still see only the darkness, but he could hear very clearly the crowing of a cock. It was so clear it made the hard solid weight inside his head melt away, so that he could completely wake up.

The camels? He had no time to think of anything else. The rope was still in his hand, and the camels were still at his side. He felt relieved, and too lazy to get up. His body was weary, and he didn't want to move, but he didn't dare go to sleep again. He had to think out, and think out carefully, a good plan to follow. He thought of his rickshaw. Why had he had to lose it?

It did him no good at all to keep asking himself that question. He felt the camels: he didn't know how many there were of them, and now he was counting them. There were three. He didn't feel that that number was either too many or too few: he was simply going to think about the three of them. Although he didn't have any clear plan, he realized vaguely that from now on he must depend completely on these animals. Why shouldn't he sell them and buy himself another rickshaw? He was about to leap up to his feet but he didn't move. He felt ashamed of himself that he hadn't thought of such a simple thing earlier.

His mind was made up: hadn't he just heard a cock crowing? Granting that sometimes cocks crow as early as two in the morning, it was yet certain that it could not now be long before dawn. And where there were cocks, there must be a village.

35

Perhaps it was the town called Peace of Bitter Toil? There were camel breeders there. If he hurried he would be able to reach the village at daybreak, get rid of his camels, and as soon as he got into the city he would buy himself a rickshaw. With everything in a panic on account of the fighting, rickshaws would certainly be cheaper. He could only think of buying a rickshaw: it was as if the business of selling the camels was a very simple one.

Thinking of the relation between the camels and a new rickshaw gave him fresh energy, and all his discomfort disappeared. He wouldn't have been half as excited if someone had told him that he could buy a hundred mou of land with his three camels, or trade them for two or three real pearls. He jumped up quickly, pulled the camels to their feet, and started off. He didn't know what the current price of camels was, and could only remember having heard it said that in the old days, before railroads, a camel was worth fifty ounces of silver. Camels were strong, they ate less than horses or donkeys. He didn't hope to find a hundred and fifty ounces of silver, but only that he would be able to get eighty or a hundred dollars for them—just enough to buy a rickshaw.

The more he walked the lighter the skies became. There was no mistake: the lighted spot was on the horizon toward which he was walking—he was in fact going east. Even if he had got the wrong road, the direction was right. He knew that the mountains were to the west and the city to the east. From complete blackness it was gradually becoming possible to distinguish light and shade, although you couldn't yet make out one color from another. In the gray mist the forms of distant trees and farmlands had already taken shape. Gradually the stars were thinning out; the heavens were much higher than before, and blanketed now with a dull murkiness that could have been either cloud or mist. Happy Boy wasn't any longer afraid to lift his head, and he had begun to smell the fragrance from the fresh grass along the road and to hear the first faint cries of birds. Because now he could make out the forms of things, through the indistinctness, his other senses too seemed to come back to him. He could even see himself, and knew that however tattered and dirty he might look, he was still alive. It was like the feeling you have when you wake up from a bad dream: you realize how wonderful it is just to be alive. From himself he turned his eyes back to the camels. They were as dirty as he was, but he loved them too. It was at the season when animals shed their coats, and the grayish red skin of the camels showed through in great patches all over them, with only here and there a loose tuft of straggling hair hanging lifeless and ready to drop from their flanks. The saddest-looking part of them was their necks—they were so long and bare, bent and heavy, stretching so far that they looked like so many thin heart-broken dragons.

But Happy Boy didn't despise them: he didn't care how awkward they looked, the important thing was that they were living. He congratulated himself on being the luckiest man alive. Heaven had presented him with three precious camels in exchange for his rickshaw, and it wasn't every day that you ran into a thing like that. He couldn't help smiling about it.

The gray sky was beginning to show streaks of red, and the trees and landscapes were becoming clearer in outline. Gradually the red blended with the gray, turning almost purple in places, deep crimson in others, against a background of color that was like that of grapes that have not yet turned ripe. After another little while a bright orange showed through the red, and all the colors of the sky became brighter. Suddenly everything stood out distinctly; the morning mists in the eastern sky grew deep red, and the heavens above his head showed blue. Then the red mists scattered and the golden rays came down through them, weaving with the transverse clouds an immense and brilliant web. From a deep bluish green the fields, trees, and grass had changed to bright jade.

The trunks of ancient fir trees were brightly limned in the sunrise, and the wings of flying birds reflected the golden light. Everything around him seemed gay and smiling. Happy Boy wanted to call out in greeting to the sun: he felt as if he had not seen sunlight since the day the soldiers had siezed him. He had had a curse in his heart, and had kept his head down, forgetting that there was a sun or a moon, forgetting the heavens above him. Now he was free again, walking at liberty along a road that grew brighter as he walked. The glistening of the sun on the dewdrops in the grass warmed his heart and made him forget his wretchedness and his pain. He didn't care how shabby and filthy he was—the light and the warmth of the sun were not forbidden him. He lived in a world of warmth and light. He was so happy he wanted to shout for joy.

Looking at his tattered clothes and shaggy camels behind him, he had to smile. It was a miracle that four such funny-looking objects as himself and these camels could have escaped such danger and be able to walk again in the sunlight. There was no use trying to think any more about who was right and who wrong—the whole thing was as heaven had decreed it.

He was hungry for a sight of Peking. He had neither mother nor father there, nor anything that he could call his own, but still it was his home. The whole city was his home. Once he was there, he would find a way out of his difficulties.

In the distance there was a village, a large one. Before it stood a line of willow trees, like tall green soldiers standing guard. Looking down, he could see the squat houses with smoke floating up from their chimneys. The distant barking of the village dogs seemed a beautiful sound to him. He headed for the village, not thinking whether or not he might meet with good luck there.

The way the dogs barked at him didn't worry him, but the attention which he attracted among the women and children of the place made him ill at ease. He thought he must look like a very strange camel-boy: if not, why did everyone stare at him so open-mouthed? Suddenly he felt that it was all very hard to bear. The soldiers hadn't treated him as if he were a human being and now, among these villagers, everybody regarded him as some strange object! His size and strength had in the past given him a feeling of self-respect and pride, but in these last few days, without any reason or cause, he had been made to suffer the limit in wrong and misery. Over the ridge of one of the houses he caught sight again of the bright sunlit sky: somehow it was much less lovable than it had seemed just a little while before.

The single main road through the village was pitted with puddles of stinking filth, and Happy Boy was afraid his camels might lose their footing in one of them. He wanted very much to rest a while. To the north of the road there was a relatively well-to-do person's house. In the back was a tiled building, although the portal was only latticed wood, with no proper gate and no gatekeeper's house. Happy Boy's heart leapt: a tiled house meant a wealthy man; a latticed gate and no gatehouse meant that the owner kept camels, because with a gatehouse over the gateway the animals would be too big to pass in or out. Well then, he would rest a while, and maybe there'd be one chance in a thousand that he could get rid of his camels here.

"Sze, sze, sze"—Happy Boy called to his camels to kneel. That was the single call he knew in the language that camel-boys used to their charges. He was very pleased with himself to be able to use it, especially since it would make it seem to the villagers that he really knew his trade. The camels actually knelt down, and he himself sat down with a great flourish of elegance and dignity under a willow tree. People looked at him and he looked right back at the people. He knew that that was the only way to lessen the suspicions of the villagers.

When he had sat there for a while, an old man with a shiny face and a blue jacket open in front came out from the compound. You could tell with a glance that he was a wealthy villager. Happy Boy made up his mind. "Venerable Sir, is there some water at hand? I'd like to drink a cup."

"Ah." The old man rubbed his hand across his bare chest, rolling up a little ball of dirt between his fingers. He looked Happy Boy over carefully and studied the camels minutely. "Yes, there's water. Where'd you come from?"

"From west of here." Happy Boy didn't dare mention the name of the place whence he'd come, as he wasn't sure of it.

"There are soldiers to the west?" the old man asked, his eyes fixed on Happy Boy's soldier pants.

"I was nabbed by them and have just got away."

"Ah! You weren't in danger coming through the West Pass with those camels?"

"The soldiers all went into the mountains, and the roads are very peaceful."

"Uh." The old man nodded his head slowly. "You wait a while. I'll get you your water."

Happy Boy went in with him. In the compound he saw four camels. "Venerable Sir, why don't you take my camels? Putting them with yours, you could make up a train."

"Humph. If you were talking of thirty years ago, I had three trains. But times have changed. Who can afford to feed camels now?" The old man stood staring vacantly at the four animals. After a long time, he said: "A few days back I was thinking of going in with a neighbor and sending them out beyond the pass to graze. Then there were soldiers on the east and soldiers on the west—who would dare to go? It makes you miserable to see them here through the summer. Just to look at them makes you miserable. Look at the flies! And in a while, when the weather gets really hot, there'll be mosquitoes too. You just have to watch the poor beasts suffer under your eyes, it's the truth!" The old man kept nodding his head, as if he felt no end of sadness and chagrin.

"Venerable Sir, you take my three, make up a train of them, and take them out beyond the pass to graze. As lively and healthy as these animals are, if you keep them here over the summer, the flies and mosquitoes will surely eat them half alive." Happy Boy was almost pleading with him.

"But who has the money to buy them? These aren't times to be raising camels!"

"You keep them. Give me whatever you want to. I want to get them off my hands so I can get back to the city and make my living."

The old man looked Happy Boy over very carefully again. He felt sure he wasn't a thief. Then he turned around and looked at the camels outside the gate. He really liked them, but he knew he would get no good out of buying them. A man who loves books thinks of buying every book he sees, and a horse raiser can't leave horses alone. A man who has owned three trains of camels is just the same. The fellow had said that he would sell them cheap: when a man who understands a trade gets a chance to close a bargain, he can easily forget whether there is any real advantage to him in the purchase.

"Young fellow, if I had the money to spare, I really would keep them." The old man was telling the truth.

"Just keep them anyhow, and give me whatever you can." Happy Boy was so forthright that the old man was a little ashamed not to take them.

"To tell you the truth, thirty years ago those three camels would be worth a hundred and fifty liang of silver. In times like these, what with all the confusion and the fighting—no, you better go somewhere else to cry your wares."

"They'll cost you whatever you want to pay." Happy Boy couldn't think of anything else to say. He knew the old man was telling the truth, but he didn't want to wander all over the place selling camels. If he couldn't sell them, he might get into some trouble for having taken them.

"You look here," the old man said. "It's hard for me to offer you only twenty or thirty dollars, but it's not easy for me to pay that much in times like these—there's nothing to be done."

Happy Boy's heart grew cold. Twenty or thirty dollars! That was a long way from enough to buy a rickshaw with, but for one thing he wanted to sell the animals quickly and get it over with, and for another he didn't think he could easily find another person who wanted to buy them.

"Venerable Sir, give me whatever you can."

"What kind of work do you do, young fellow? I can see that this isn't your trade."

Happy Boy told him the truth.

"Oh. You risked your life for these animals." The old man felt very sympathetic toward Happy Boy, and relieved at the same time. These camels hadn't been stolen, though there wasn't much difference between stealing them and taking them the way Happy Boy had. After all, there was a troop of soldiers in between. Once the havoc of war had passed over a place, none of the old rules held.

"We'll do this, young fellow. I'll give you thirty-five dollars. And if I tell you that's not getting them cheap, I'm a dog. And if I could pay you one dollar more for them, I'd also be a dog. I'm over sixty years old. What else do you want me to say?"

Happy Boy did not know what to do. In the past he had been very tight with money. Now, after having been so many days with the soldiers, suddenly to hear anyone talking as honestly and sympathetically as this old man did made him ashamed to bargain any more. Moreover, actually to have thirty-five dollars in his hand was more dependable than ten thousand in his dreams, even though thirty-five dollars seemed a small amount for which to have risked his life. If you spoke of the camels—three big, live camels could never be worth only thirty-five dollars. But what could he do?

"The camels are yours, Venerable Sir. There's only one thing

He had hardly struggled to his feet when he thought of going out to look around. He wouldn't have believed it possible that his legs could become so weak. When he got to the door of the little inn he had to sit down on the ground, and he stayed squatting there stupidly for a long while, his forehead covered with cold sweat. When the dizziness had passed, he opened his eyes again. His stomach made a noise and he began to feel a little hungry. Slowly he raised himself up and dragged himself along to a little stand where a peddler was selling steamed cakes. He bought a bowl of them and sat down again on the ground. The first mouthful of the soup made him sick and he held it in his mouth a long while before he could force himself to swallow it. He didn't feel like taking any more, but in a moment the hot liquid made its way like a warm thread through his insides to the bottom of his stomach, and he belched a couple of times. He knew from that familiar sound that he had come back to life.

With a little food in his stomach, he had time to look himself over. His body was much thinner; the ragged old trousers he was wearing were already as dirty as they could ever become. He felt too lazy to move but he had to restore as quickly as he could his cleanliness and tidiness: he could not go into Peking looking like a shoddy old ghost. The only thing was that if he wanted to be clean and tidy he'd have to spend money. Getting his head shaved, changing his clothes, buying shoes and stockings—all these things would mean money. He shouldn't touch the thirty-five dollars he had in his pocket: even without spending a penny of it, it was still a long way from enough to buy a rickshaw with. But he felt sorry for himself. Although the soldiers had not held him for long, it all seemed like a nightmare now—a nightmare that had made him much older, as if he had suddenly and in one breath added many years to his age.

All told, it cost him two dollars and twenty cents to get fitted out again. A jacket and trousers of unbleached coarse cotton cloth cost one dollar; a pair of black cloth shoes were eighty cents; cheaply woven socks were fifty cents; and there was also the big-brimmed straw hat that cost twenty-five cents. In exchange for the rags that he had taken off, he got two packages of matches.

With the matches under his arm, he walked along the road toward the Western Gate of Forthrightness. He hadn't gone very far when he began to feel weak and tired, but he gritted his teeth. He couldn't take a rickshaw. However he looked at it, he just couldn't do it. If he couldn't walk to Peking, Happy Boy would be finished; the one thing he believed in was his own strength, no matter what kind of sickness he might be suffering from. His legs wobbling uncertainly, he stumbled on, walking faster as he went. In one stretch he walked to the entrance of the West Gate. Seeing there the rush of horses and men, hearing the medley of ear-piercing noises, smelling the stench of the dry dust of the road, treading that stinking dust himself, Happy Boy felt like getting down in the street and kissing the earth, the earth that he loved, the earth that sustained him! He had no mother or father, no relatives at all: the only friend he had was this ancient city. It gave him everything. If he had to starve in it, he would still love it more than the village from which he had come. Here there were things to see and things to hear; there were colors everywhere, sounds everywhere. If you had only your own strength to sell, there was still more money than you could count to be got for it here; here were ten thousand good things, more kinds of food than you could eat and more clothes than you could wear. If you begged for your food on the street, you could still get soup with meat in it, while the best that the village had was cornmeal bread.

When he got to the Bridge of High Brightness, he sat down on the river bank and wept.

In the slanting rays of the sun the movement of people and carts across the bridge seemed unusually hurried, as if they all felt disquieted by the imminence of evening, but Happy Boy was in no haste to go on. Everything about him was familiar to him and part of him: he would have been happy even to die here.

When he had rested for a long time, he went up to the head of the bridge and got himself a bowl of cooked bean curd. The vinegar, soybean sauce, pepper, and tips of leeks with which the hot white dish was seasoned gave off an order so fragrant that Happy Boy held the bowl cupped in his trembling hands, almost afraid to breathe, looking at the deep green of the leeks. He drank a mouthful from the bowl, the warm food opening a path down his gullet to his stomach. When he had finished the bowl he was perspiring, and with his eyes half closed he ordered another bowl.

Standing up, he felt like a man again. The sun was at its lowest in the west, tingeing the river water with crimson. Rubbing the scar on his face, the money in his belt, and looking again at the evening light slanting against the tall watchtower at the corner of the city wall, he forgot his illness and everything else. It was as if he had reached his heart's desire in returning to Peking.

The gateway was crowded with all kinds of vehicles and all sorts of people. No one dared push on too fast, but everyone was in a hurry to get through. The cries, the cracking of whips, the cursing, the honking of horns, the tinkling of bells, the laughter, all mingled together to form a single medley of sound that seemed as if it came from an immense amplifier. Happy Boy planted his big feet first in one place and then another, using both hands to ward off the mob around him, like a long thin fish leaping from wave to wave, finally working his way through the gate and into the city. Before him was the plaza of the New Street's Mouth. The road was so straight and broad it made his eyes shine like the tile roofs of the houses in the twilight. He bowed his head.

His bedding was still in the Human Harmony Rickshaw Shed on West Gate Road, so he headed in that direction. Be-

46

cause he didn't have a wife, he lived in the rickshaw shed, although he hadn't always pulled rented rickshaws. The manager of the Human Harmony, the Fourth Master Liu, was nearly seventy years of age. The man himself was old, but in his heart he was still full of tricks. In his youth he had been a treasury guard, had run a gambling house, had bought and sold women, and had lent out money at the devil's own rates. Fourth Master Liu had all of the endowments and qualifications necessary to these occupations—the strength, the shrewdness, the trickiness, the social knack, and the name. Before the fall of the Ch'ing Dynasty he had taken part in mob fighting, had stolen the daughters of good families, had knelt on chains before the magistrate. On chains he had not even knitted his brows, nor once called for mercy. The officer was taken in by his fortitude, and accepted his innocence: from this he had gained his name.

As it happened, the republic had been established by the time he got out of jail; the power of the police was getting stronger all the while, and Fourth Master Liu could see that the time of the local heroes had passed. So he had opened a rickshaw shed. A local bully by profession, he knew how to deal with poor people—when to be hard, when to let up a little. And he had a flair for using people. The rickshaw pullers were afraid to talk back to him: all he had to do was to glare at them and laugh, and they could only stand stupid before him. It was as if he had one foot in heaven and the other in hell—it was best to do what he told you to.

He now had sixty-odd rickshaws, the oldest of them at least seven parts new. He wouldn't keep broken-down carts around. The rent he charged was higher than other sheds but at each of the three yearly festivals he allowed two more days rent-free than did the others. There was a place to live in the Human Harmony Yard, and unmarried rickshaw boys could stay there rent-free. But you had to pay your rickshaw rent: if you couldn't settle your accounts and tried to hang on anyway, he would keep your bedding and throw you out of the door like a broken teapot. But if any of the men had some pressing trouble, or some sudden illness, they had only to tell him: he would not hesitate but would go through fire or water to help them. Such was his name and fame.

Fourth Master Liu looked like a tiger. Nearly seventy, his back was unbent and he could still lift up his feet and walk ten or twenty li. With big round eyes, heavy lips and prominent teeth, he had only to open his mouth to look like a beast of prey ready to spring. He was as tall as Happy Boy, shaved his head till it shone, and had neither beard nor mustache. He accepted the role of tiger, regretting simply that he had no son but only one daughter, of thirty-seven or eight. Everyone who knew Fourth Master Liu was certain to know Tiger Girl. She had the head and face of a tigress and on that account frightened the men away. She was a good hand at helping her father in his business, but nobody dared marry her. She was the same as a man in everything: even when it came to cursing a person, she was just as fluent and sometimes had more ways of expressing herself.

48

Fourth Master Liu took care of outside matters, and Tiger Girl looked after things inside the house. Between father and daughter, the Human Harmony Rickshaw Shed was so well managed that it was as firm and tidy as a steel box, and came to be the most influential of its kind. The methods of Liu and his daughter were frequently on the tongues of rickshaw owners and pullers alike, as scholars quote the classics to prove their point.

Before he had bought his own rickshaw Happy Boy had rented one from Human Harmony, and the money he saved he had given to Fourth Master Liu to keep for him. When he had collected enough, he had asked for it back and had bought his new rickshaw.

He pulled it right back to Human Harmony. "Fourth Master Liu, look at my new rickshaw!" Happy Boy said. The old man looked at it and nodded his head. "It's good enough."

"But I've still got to live here. When I get a job by the month, I'll go to live in the house where I'm hired," Happy Boy proudly added.

"All right." Fourth Master Liu nodded his head again.

Thereafter, when Happy Boy was hired by the month he lived at the house of his master, and when he lost the job and had to pick up fares on the streets he lived at Human Harmony.

In the eyes of the other rickshaw men, it was a rare thing to be able to live in Human Harmony without renting one of its rickshaws. Because of this, some people guessed that Happy Boy was a relative of Old Man Liu; other people went so far as to say that the old man liked Happy Boy and planned to provide his daughter with a bridegroom who could move into the house of his father-in-law. Although this kind of guessing was a little envious, still if by chance it turned out to be true, then when Fourth Master Liu died Human Harmony would certainly be Happy Boy's. As to this they could only make wild guesses, but they didn't dare say anything nasty in Happy Boy's hearing.

As a matter of fact, Old Man Liu's good treatment of Happy

Boy was on another account. Happy Boy was this kind of a person—in a new environment he could still maintain his old habits. If for instance he had become a soldier, it would have been impossible for him, as soon as he had put on his uniform, to go about pretending to be stupid when he wasn't stupid, and to cheat the populace. In the rickshaw shed he was never idle. As soon as he had stopped sweating from his day's work, he would find something to do. He would go polish up his rickshaw, put air in the tires, put the canvas rain cover out in the sun to dry—it wasn't necessary for anyone to tell him to do these things: he did them because he wanted to do them himself, and was absorbed in the task, as if it were the greatest pleasure for him. There were usually on an average about twenty rickshaw men living in the shed at any one time. When they had put their rickshaws up, they either sat around talking or went sound asleep. Only Happy Boy's hands were not idle.

In the beginning everybody thought he was trying to show Fourth Master Liu how diligent he was, and was running back and forth like a trained dog just to curry favor; after a few days they could see that he had no idea at all of attempting to make a good impression. He was so forthright and natural there was nothing they could say.

Old Man Liu never said a word in praise of him, and never wasted a glance on him, but in his heart he kept a clear account. He knew that Happy Boy was a good worker, and he was glad to have him live in the shed even if he didn't rent one of its rickshaws. Not to mention anything else, while he stayed there, the yard would always be swept as clean as could be.

And Tiger Girl liked this big gawky boy even more than her father did. When she said anything, Happy Boy listened very carefully and did not talk back; the other rickshaw men, because they had suffered as much bitterness as they could endure, were always irritable and unreasonable in their speech. She wasn't in the least afraid of them, but at the same time she didn't like to pay much attention to them, and so she saved most of what she wanted to say for Happy Boy's ears. Whenever he got a job in a private household it was as if the Liu family, father and daughter, had lost a friend, and when he would come back again it would always appear that even in the old man's cursing he was happier and kinder.

Happy Boy, his two packages of matches in his hands, went into the Human Harmony Shed. It was still not dark, and the Lius were just eating dinner. When Tiger Girl saw him come in, she put down her chopsticks.

"Happy Boy! Did a wolf run off with you or did you go to Africa to work in the gold mines?"

"Hm." Happy Boy only grunted.

Old Man Liu's large round eyes looked him over in silence.

With his new straw hat still on his head, Happy Boy sat down facing them.

"If you haven't eaten yet, have dinner with us," Tiger Girl said, as if she were welcoming a close friend. Happy Boy didn't move. He suddenly felt an intimacy with them in his heart that he could not express. For a long time he had taken the Human Harmony Rickshaw Shed to be his home. When he worked for private families he was always changing employers; when he was picking up fares on the streets he had a different person in his rickshaw every few minutes: this was the only place where he had always been permitted to stay on, where there was always someone to talk to. Now, when he had just escaped with his life and had come back to the people he knew, they even asked him to have dinner with them. He was almost suspicious that they meant to cheat him, but at the same time he was almost in tears.

"I just ate two bowls of bean curd," he answered, refusing politely.

Fourth Master Liu's large eyes were still on Happy Boy. "What have you been doing? Where's your rickshaw?"

51

"Rickshaw?" Happy Boy spat on the ground.

"First come over here and eat a bowl of rice! It can't poison you! What use are two bowls of beancurd?" Tiger Girl pulled him over to the table, with all the solicitude that the elder brother's wife might have for her young brother-in-law.

Before he touched his rice bowl Happy Boy took out his money. "Fourth Master, you keep this for me—thirty dollars." The change he put back in his pocket.

The lift of Fourth Master's eyebrows asked more plainly than words, "Where did it come from?"

While Happy Boy ate he told the story of his capture by the soldiers.

Fourth Master heard him out, shaking his head the while. "Hm. You're a foolish young fellow. You could have brought the camels into the city and sold them to a slaughter house and got more than ten dollars apiece for them. If it was winter time and their hair was full, the three of them would be worth sixty dollars."

Happy Boy had early regretted his bargain, and when he heard this he felt worse than ever. But when he thought about taking those three living animals to be slaughtered, it seemed wrong. He and the camels had escaped together, and they all had an equal right to live. Although he said nothing, his heart became easier again.

Tiger Girl cleared away the dishes, while Fourth Master sat with his head back, as if he were thinking of something. Suddenly he laughed, showing his two big front teeth. "Foolish One! You say you were sick at Seas' Domain. Why didn't you come straight back by the Yellow Village road?"

"I went the long way round by the Western Hills. I didn't take the main road for fear of getting caught. And suppose by some chance the villagers had figured the thing out and taken me for an army deserter?"

Fourth Master Liu smiled, the pupils of his eyes turning

52

inward to his heart. He had been afraid that Happy Boy's words hid some evil act: suppose that, on the one chance in ten thousand, this money was stolen? It would not do for him to keep stolen goods for another. In his own youth he had done every lawless thing there was to do, and now that he was holding himself out as having reformed he could not be too careful. And he knew how to be careful. Happy Boy's story had had only this one hole in it, and now that he had explained it without turning a hair the old man was easier in his heart.

"What do you want done with it?" he asked, pointing to the money.

"Whatever you say."

"Do you want to buy another rickshaw?" The old man's teeth showed again as if to ask, "You buy your own rickshaw, and still want to live here free!"

"It's not enough. If I buy one I want a new one." Happy Boy hadn't noticed Fourth Master's teeth—he was looking only into his own heart.

"I'll lend you money—at one per cent interest. For other people, it's two per cent."

Happy Boy shook his head.

"Buying on installments from a rickshaw store wouldn't be as good as paying me one per cent."

"I'm not going to buy by the month either," Happy Boy said absent-mindedly. "I'll save up gradually and when I've got enough I'll pay cash for what I want."

The old man stared at Happy Boy as if he were looking at some strange hieroglyph—a thing you disliked but couldn't get angry at. After a while he picked up the money. "Thirty dollars —don't get mixed up about that!"

"Right." Happy Boy got up. "I'm going to bed. I'll make you a present of a package of matches." He put one of the packages on the table, and stood silent for a while, staring out at nothing. "Don't tell anyone else about the camels."

IN real truth, Liu did not spread the story of the camels abroad for Happy Boy, but it very quickly reached the city from Seas' Domain. Formerly, although they could not name his short-coming, Happy Boy's diffidence had made the others feel that he was not very friendly, not one of the crowd, and of a difficult nature. After this story got around, they began to take a different view of him for all the fact that he was still not cordial and kept on grimly at his job. Some said he had picked up a gold watch; some said he had got hold of three hundred dollars; but those who were confident that they had the most detailed and reliable information nodded their heads and said he had brought back thirty camels from the Western Hills.

The stories were different but they all amounted to the same thing: Happy Boy had come into easy money. And no matter how queer a fellow might be, when he came into easy money everybody treated him with respect. Since making money by the sale of your strength was so hard, everybody dreamed of coming by a little easy money. Because it was a thing that one could hardly hope to meet with in a thousand years, it was certain that a person who had that kind of luck was not like other people but was possessed of great good fortune and a great destiny. It was thus that Happy Boy's silence and his solitary habits came in a single change of view to be the quiet manner which characterizes great personages. It was proper that he should be that way, and by rights they should seek him out instead of his coming to them.

"All right now, Happy Boy. Won't you tell us how you got

rich?" He heard things like that every day. He would say nothing at all until he was pressed to the limit and then, with the scar on his face showing a livid red, he would reply, "Get rich? Your mother's! Where did my rickshaw go to?"

Yes, that was true. Where was his rickshaw? Everybody began to wonder. But to worry about another's misfortune is never as pleasant as to be happy about his good fortune, and they therefore soon forgot about the rickshaw and thought about his good luck. After a few days, when they saw that Happy Boy was still pulling a rickshaw, and had neither changed his trade nor bought himself a house or a piece of land, the crowd grew cooler toward him, and when his name was mentioned no one any longer asked why he should so particularly be called "Camel"; it was as if that were originally his name.

Happy Boy himself, though, had not lightly forgotten the affair. He wished with all his heart that he might buy a new rickshaw right away. The more anxious he became, the more he thought of his first rickshaw. From dawn until dark every day he bore with his weariness and his wrongs to carry on his work. But even while he was working he would think of his experience; as soon as it came to his mind he would feel as if the orifices of his heart had been stopped up, and, without wanting to, he would be asking himself what good it did him to be trying to improve himself. The world did not deal any more fairly with you because you worked hard and tried to get ahead: if it did, on what grounds would his rickshaw have been taken away from him? Suppose he could make enough right away to buy another one, how was he to know that he might not again meet with the same experience?

He felt that the past was like a nightmare that left him afraid to think what hope the future might hold for him. Sometimes when he saw the others drinking, smoking, or running about to whorehouses, he almost admired them. Since trying to get ahead was useless, why not have a good time now? They

55

were right. Even if he didn't go to whorehouses, he ought to drink a cup or so of wine occasionally to make himself feel easier. Cigarettes and wine had now for him a special attraction. They didn't cost much money and they would certainly be a consolation to him and make it possible for him to carry on along his bitter road. At the same time he would be able to forget the pain of his past.

For all that, he still didn't dare take up either cigarettes or wine. If he could save an extra copper, he absolutely had to save it: he had to do that or he would never be able to buy himself another rickshaw. Granted that if he bought it today he might lose it tomorrow, he would still go out and buy it. This was his will, his hope, even his religion. There was no doubt about it: if he could not pull his own rickshaw he might as well be dead. He did not think of becoming an official, or of becoming rich, or of buying property. The only thing he was able to do was to pull a rickshaw; his most dependable hope was to buy a rickshaw; if he could not buy one, he would not be able to face himself. All day, every day, he turned this thing over in his mind, counting and re-counting his money. He felt that if he were to get up one morning forgetful of this purpose, he would then have forgotten himself and would have become only an animal able to run about the streets, without any hope of becoming anything else or anything like a human being.

No matter how good the rickshaw, if it was rented, he could not put his heart into pulling it. It was as unnatural as if he were carrying a big stone on his back. Even with a rented rickshaw he didn't lie down on the job; he kept it always perfectly clean and was always careful to avoid recklessly running into things on the street. But this was only being careful and cautious; it was not out of joy that he did it.

Yes. To keep your own rickshaw in order was like counting your own money—it was a real pleasure. He would have to keep on without smoking or drinking wine; he might as well not

56

even drink good tea. Rickshaw pullers of his respectability were accustomed after a fast run to go into a teahouse and drink a cup of tea made from leaves that cost ten coppers a packet, with two lumps of white sugar to it, in order to catch their breath and lessen the heat within them. When Happy Boy had run until the sweat was dripping even from the lobes of his ears, and there was an acrid feeling in his breast, he would want very much to do the same thing. This certainly was not from habit, or from a desire to put up a front, but rather because one or two such cups of tea were truly necessary to press down the bitterness inside him. But he would only think about it, and would still drink tea made from the sweepings of tea leaves that cost only a copper a packet.

There were times when he wanted to curse himself. Why should he treat himself so badly? But how could a rickshaw man expect to save money if he didn't do it this way? He made up his mind grimly: he would buy the rickshaw first, then see about the rest. When he had his rickshaw it would make up for every-thing else.

So deadly tight about spending money, Happy Boy was even more grasping about earning it. When he was not hired by a private family by the month, he worked the whole day, taking his rickshaw out early and bringing it in late. If he had not made a certain sum of money he would not stop for the day, no matter what time it was or how tired his legs were. Sometimes he went right on working a whole day and night together.

In the old days he had been unwilling to try to take cus-tomers from other pullers, especially if they were old men or young boys, soldiers who were already beaten. He had always felt that, with his height and strength and his well-kept rick-shaw, if he condescended to take their fares away from them, they wouldn't have a chance. Now he didn't pay much attention to all that. He thought only of money: each copper more was another copper, and he didn't care whether the business was bitter or sweet, nor with whom he contested for it. He cared only to get fares, and thought of nothing else, like a wild animal mad with hunger. When he got a fare he raced away, his heart easier, as though the only hope he had of buying his rickshaw was to keep his feet constantly in motion.

On one count or another, Happy Boy Camel's reputation was a long way from being what it had been before the "Camel" was added to his name. Many a time when he stole someone else's fare and started off, the other man's curses would follow; he would not reply but would keep his head down and fly on, thinking in his heart, "If it weren't that I wanted to buy a rickshaw, I could never be so shameless!" It was as if he sought to beg the forgiveness of the others with this sentence but was unwilling to say it to them.

It made him feel even worse to remember with what respect they had treated him when he first returned from the mountains, and to compare that with their present contempt of him. In the teahouses he was left alone with his pot of tea, and at the rickshaw stands he was left alone to count his coppers. He used all his strength to keep down his rage: although he was not afraid of a fight, he didn't want one. Nor was the crowd afraid to fight, but to fight with Happy Boy was something to think carefully about. No one of them was his equal, and it wouldn't be very honorable for them all to fight one man. He had to force himself not to lose his temper: he could think of no other plan but to bear it for the while and wait until he could buy his rickshaw, when it would be easier to handle things. He would not then have to worry every day about the rent of his rickshaw and could act more largely and would not be offending people by taking their fares away from them. With this thought in mind he would look the others in the eye, as if to say to them, "We'll see how it turns out."

From the standpoint of his own health, he should not have gone so desperately about his work. After he had escaped and got back to the city, he had not waited to recover completely from his illness but had begun pulling a rickshaw at once. Although he would not admit weakness, he frequently felt completely exhausted. Exhausted, he yet did not dare to rest and thought always that to work up a sweat by running would lessen his feeling of weariness. As for food, he didn't dare go hungry but at the same time he didn't dare eat well. He could see that he was much thinner, although he was as tall as ever and his muscles just as hard. This latter made him easier in his heart. He always thought that because he was taller and bigger than other people he could certainly stand more than other people. It seemed that he had never thought that the bigger he was the more nourishment he would require.

Tiger Girl had already remonstrated with him several times. "You there, fellow! If you keep on like this, it'll be your own affair if you begin spitting blood."

He knew very clearly that this was well-meant, but because things were not going as he wished, and he was undernourished, his temper had become brittle. He would glare at her a little and ask: "If I don't do this, when will I be able to buy a rickshaw?"

If anyone else had looked at her like that Tiger Girl would at the very least have cursed him for half a day, but toward Happy Boy she was truly one hundred and one points polite and solicitous. With only a suggestion of a sneer on her lips, she would say:

"Buying a rickshaw is something that you go about more slowly. You think you're made of steel. You ought to take a good rest for two or three days!" Seeing that Happy Boy paid no attention to this, she would add: "All right, you've got your same old idea. If you die at it, you can't blame me."

Fourth Master Liu also disapproved a little of Happy Boy. Naturally Happy Boy's reckless determination to be out on the streets as early as possible and come back as late as he could was hard on the rickshaw he hired. Although the arrangement was to rent the rickshaws for the whole day, and the pullers could take them out at whatever time they wished, if everybody stuck so doggedly at the task as did Happy Boy, the rickshaws would be all worn out at least six months before their time. No matter how strong and firm a thing is, it can't stand constant use like that. Besides that, with Happy Boy thinking only of making more money by hauling more fares, he didn't have time to help out by cleaning rickshaws and so forth, which was another item of loss. The old man wasn't very happy about that, but he didn't say anything. It was a general custom to rent rickshaws by the day, without any limit on their hours of use, while helping to keep the rickshaws clean and in repair was a matter of friendship rather than of obligation. With his name and reputation, he couldn't involve himself by speaking to Happy Boy about it. All he could do was to show a little of his dissatisfaction in the corners of his eyes and keep his lip shut tight.

Sometimes he thought a good deal of throwing Happy Boy out, but he'd look at his daughter and wouldn't dare. He didn't have the slightest idea of making Happy Boy an expectant for the post of son-in-law, but since his daughter was fond of this pig-headed youngster it wasn't easy for him to meddle in the matter. He had only this one daughter, and it was evident that there was no hope of her finding a husband; he could not, then, chase away even this friend of hers.

To tell the truth, Tiger Girl was so useful that he really didn't want her to get married. For this selfish idea of his he felt a little apologetic toward her and on that account was just a little afraid of her. Throughout his life the old man had feared nothing in heaven or on earth, only to come in his old age to fear his own daughter. In his chagrin he thought of a reason for this: as long as he feared some one person, that fact was proof that he was not altogether without respect for God or man. Perhaps on this account he would not suffer the retribution which overtakes the evil when they are about to die. All right, he himself admitted that he should fear his daughter and that it was for that reason he was unwilling to run Happy Boy out. This, naturally, was not to say that he would let his daughter make a fool of herself and go so far as to marry Happy Boy. No. He could see that his daughter was not without ideas of doing just that, but Happy Boy hadn't dared try to curry favor with one of his betters.

Well then, he would have to be a little careful, but it was not worth making his daughter unhappy about now.

Happy Boy had not even noticed the old man's attitude. He didn't have time for such idle monkey-business. If he thought of leaving the Human Harmony Shed, it was not at all because of any ill-feeling but simply because he hoped to get a job by the month. He was a little fed up with hauling individual fares; first, because the others had come to despise him for trying to take their fares away from them and, second, because there was no certainty as to the amount of his daily income. Today it might be a lot, tomorrow only a little: he had no way of telling ahead of time how long it would be before he had saved enough to buy himself his rickshaw. He wanted to have a sure aim in his heart; he wouldn't be afraid if the sum he could save were small, just so he could depend on saving a certain amount each month. Only then would he really have a chance and his mind be at ease.

Finally he found work by the month. Huh! It was no more to his liking than hauling individual fares on the streets had been. This time it was with the Yang family. Mr. Yang was a Shanghai man, his principal wife was from Tientsin and his second wife from Soochow. With these two wives, and the mixture of southern singsong and northern shrillness, there were more children than anyone cared to count.

The first day he went to work Happy Boy missed fainting

only by a little. Very early in the morning the principal wife went to the market to buy provisions. When he had hauled her back, he took the young masters and their little sisters to their various schools. Some went to middle school, some to primary school, and some to kindergarten. The schools they went to were all different, their ages were all different, they didn't look alike, but they were all equally disgusting. This was especially true when they were riding in his rickshaw: the best behaved of the lot had two more hands than any monkey. When he had got all the children delivered to their schools, he would have to take Mr. Yang to his government office, whence he'd hurry back to haul the No. 2 wife to the Market of Eastern Peace or to see relatives or friends. By the time he got back he would have to go after the little scholars to bring them home to eat lunch. When they were finished he'd take them back to school. He thought he could get something to eat himself when he'd done with that, but the No. 1 wife yelled at him in loud Tientsinese to go draw some water from the well. The sweet water for drinking was brought to the Yang household but the bitter water for washing had to be carried in from the well by the rickshaw boy. This work was outside the terms of his contract, but in order to make out with his work Happy Boy didn't dare to argue, and filled the cistern without a word. Just as he finished drawing water and was about to go get his rice bowl, the No. 2 wife sent him out to buy something.

The No. 1 and No. 2 wives had never agreed about anything, but in the management of the home they followed the same policy, one article of that policy being never to let the servants be idle and another was their unwillingness to see the servants eat. Happy Boy didn't know that, and thought it was only by accident that his first day with the family should be such a busy one. So he didn't say anything about that either, and spent his own money to buy a couple of fried cakes. He loved money as his own life, but to keep his job he had to make sacrifices.

62

THE
TERRIBLE
TRUTH ABOUT
LAWYERS

How Lawyers Really Work
and How to Deal
with Them Successfully

MARK H. McCORMACK

BEECH TREE BOOKS
WILLIAM MORROW
New York

Library of Congress Cataloging-in-Publication Data

McCormack, Mark H.
　　The terrible truth about lawyers.
　　1. Attorney and client—United States—Popular works.
2. Businessmen—United States.　I. Title.
KF311.Z9M39　1987　　　　174'.3'0973　　　87-11491
ISBN 0-688-06621-6

Printed in the United States of America

First Edition

1 2 3 4 5 6 7 8 9 10

BOOK DESIGN BY RICHARD ORIOLO

The word "book" is said to derive from *boka,* or beech.
The beech tree has been the patron tree of writers since ancient times and
represents the flowering of literature and knowledge.

To my father, Ned Hume McCormack, who urged me to go to law school, correctly assessing that, if nothing else, it would help me to think more logically and to be more aware of the importance of the written and spoken word.

To the three most important legacies that I have in the world:

My son Breck, a lawyer with IMG, who is struggling valiantly and effectively to move within "the wall of molasses";

My son Todd, an educator and executive, who is becoming ever more aware of the necessity to teach the values and workings of the "real" world;

My daughter, Leslie, a student at William and Mary, who is learning so graciously and well that there is much more to our lives than can be taught or learned in the academic milieu; and

To my wife, Betsy, who helps keep my feet squarely on the ground, keeps reminding me to stop and "smell the roses," and, quite simply, makes it all worthwhile.

Acknowledgments

It would be impossible to write a book like this without acknowledgments and thanks to a lot of very special people:

To the professors at Yale Law School, who gave me my first exposure to the "Law";

To the partners at Arter, Hadden, Wykoff & Van Duzer—especially Clyde Comstock, Clint Horn, Jim Stewart, and Tom Koykka—who taught me how the "Law" worked in the real world and gave me the chance to try to make it in the sports management business;

To Bob Burton, Jay Lafave, and Bill Carpenter, who taught me and are still teaching me what conscience and the "Law" really mean;

To Laurie Roggenburk, Leah Detwiller, Sarah Wooldridge, and Judy Stott, who tirelessly helped me and/or put up with me during the preparation of this book;

To Larry Shames a brilliant and responsive collaborator, without whom this book could never have been completed; and

To Arnold Palmer, who in the last analysis made everything possible.

CONTENTS

PREFACE

George Bernard Shaw once quipped, "All professions are conspiracies against the laity."

Now, I don't know how seriously Shaw intended this remark. I do know, however, that it comes pretty close to summarizing the feeling that many people—maybe most people—have about the men and women who make up the profession of law.

In the general view, lawyers are a clubby group who, with the benefit of an arcane body of knowledge and under the smokescreen of an elaborate system of professional courtesies and rituals, look out for their own—at the expense of the rest of us.

Successful lawyers wield more power than most people. They make more money than most people. Typically, they are called in after ordinary reason has failed, when people are already angry, disillusioned, and ready for a fight. For all these and other reasons, lawyers are the targets of an enormous amount of resentment.

Much of that resentment is well deserved. The terrible truth is that lawyers—to be blunt—tend to be a real pain in the neck.

In a world where time is money, lawyers are masters at stalling.

In business contexts, where clear communication is crucial, lawyers hide behind mumbo jumbo that nobody else understands.

In a society where justice, in theory at least, is held up as the highest ideal, lawyers are always looking for technical and sometimes dubious means of bending the law to their advantage.

We all know it shouldn't be that way.

All but the most cynical among us believe it doesn't *have* to be that way.

But in the meantime that's the way it is.

I know. I'm a lawyer myself—albeit a nonpracticing one. But back before I took a lucky $500 and launched the company that became International Management Group, I *did* practice law, and the experience has proved invaluable both to my understanding of human nature and to my career in business.

By now, IMG has grown into a worldwide company with annual revenues approaching half a billion dollars. A global industry of sports management and sports marketing has sprouted up around us. I'm proud to say we are still the leaders in our original business: representing celebrity athletes such as Arnold Palmer, Muhammad Ali, Bjorn Borg, Billie Jean King, Martina Navratilova, Herschel Walker, Jean-Claude Killy, and many others.

But IMG has expanded far beyond its original mission. We produce and/or sell television programming for Wimbledon, the NFL, the U.S. Tennis and U.S. Golf associations, and the NCAA. More than fifty major corporations use our marketing consulting services all over the world. We have been advisers to the organizing committees of both the Winter and Summer Olympics of 1988, and we have represented entities as far removed from sports as the Nobel Foundation, the Vatican, and the Van Cliburn International Piano Competition.

In all our far-flung enterprises, we deal in situations where the stakes are high, the personalities often volatile, and litigation an all too frequent ending to a story that started off happy. In my role as chairman and CEO, I have found that being a trained attorney as well as a practicing businessman has given me a dual perspective that has proved enormously useful.

I have sat on both sides of the lawyer-client relationship, so I know how both sides feel when legal fees start escalating.

I am acquainted with the use of legalese as a dodge and as a weapon, as an intimidator and as a stalling device.

I understand the deep temperamental differences that often make lawyers and businessmen drive each other crazy, and I have learned ways to deal with those differences so that businessmen and lawyers can work more smoothly as a team.

As a lawyer, I am aware of the things that attorneys don't want their clients to know. As a client, I am familiar with the questions and complaints that laymen have about lawyers, but are either too intimidated to ask or don't know how to bring up.

Most basically of all, I have come to realize that a legal education does not a lawyer make, and that, on the other hand, one doesn't *need* a legal education to think the way a lawyer thinks—or to protect oneself effectively against lawyers.

The education I received at Yale Law School was a fine one, and I am grateful to have had it. Yale takes the training of attorneys about as far as it can be taken in three classroom years—and if that sounds like a backhanded compliment, it is.

The fact is, a law school graduate, on the day he or she picks up the sheepskin, is like a rookie who has studied everything about the science of hitting but has never swung at a baseball. In both cases, the heart of the matter lies not in abstract knowledge but in the sharpening of innate talents by experience. The effective lawyer, like the .300 hitter, is one who, by a blend of common sense and a savvy grasp of human nature, knows when an adversary will try to overpower him and when he'll throw him a curveball.

And you can't pick up that kind of intuition at school—not at Yale, not anywhere.

The reason is that the study of law entails so many hundreds of hours of rote memorization and blind absorption that there simply isn't much time left over for the study of what makes people tick. The technical side of law is so complicated and abstruse that it takes up about 95 percent of most law students' time; that leaves about 5 percent for learning about *people*— and it's people, after all, who make the laws, interpret the laws, and have no choice but to be bound by the laws.

The irony is that not only is the technical aspect of law of little interest to nonlawyers, it's not even so compelling to most attorneys, once they have gotten through school and passed the bar. Practicing attorneys don't *remember* all that stuff; they look it up in a book when they have to—or, better yet, they have a clerk look it up *for* them. And of course it's the client who pays a fat hourly fee while the attorney has his memory refreshed.

In the real world, then, it's not the technical details that are most germane to the practice of law; it's the *human* side—the shrewd yet sympathetic understanding of human conflicts and human motivations, the honing of the powers of persuasion, the mastery of the nuances of logic and argument—that is the meat of what a lawyer needs to know. And in *those* areas, a savvy client can meet an attorney on even terms.

It is the human skills that get practical results. Those are the universal tools that a successful lawyer should have in common with a successful businessman, a successful scientist, a successful *anyone*.

They are skills that no law school can teach, and they are precisely what this book is about.

In this volume, I'll be speaking both as an attorney and as a client. If my sympathies generally fall on the client side, it's because as a businessman I have found that all too often it's the lawyers who:

1. gum up the works;

2. get people mad at each other;

3. make business procedures much more expensive than they need to be; and

4. now and then deep-six what had seemed a perfectly workable arrangement.

Accordingly, I would say that probably the best way to deal with lawyers is not to deal with them at all.

I think, quite frankly, that the best agreements I have ever made have been those with no contract or no written agreement attached to them—no legalese, no what-ifs, no fine print.

The first and most crucial of these agreements was a handshake deal I made with Arnold Palmer back in early 1960—a handshake that, more than any other single event, ushered in the era of mutual profit between professional athletes and professional managers. Basically, Arnold and I had an understanding. We were reasonable people. We trusted each other and had a common goal. Our arrangement was simplicity itself.

In the twenty-seven years since that handshake, a lot has happened that neither Arnold nor I could have anticipated. But for all that has changed, we have rarely had to take more than a minute or two to resolve any issue.

For example, when I first started representing Arnold, our arrangement called for a commission based on his gross income —and that included *all* his income, right on up to the interest on his savings account. In the beginning of our relationship, Arnold's savings account was the only investment he had, and the interest on it came to about $120 a year. Sometime later, Arnold's interest income alone was running into six figures annually, and we were still taking our commission.

One day Arnold said, "You know, Mark, we never really had

in mind that you'd be getting this kind of money from investment income, especially since you already commissioned most of the money before it went into the accounts." Now, sticking to the literal facts of our agreement, I could have argued. But the simple fact was, he was *right*. So I agreed, we shook hands on our revised understanding, and that was that.

If business deals could always be so amicably concluded, there would be little need for lawyers, right?

Wrong, unfortunately.

Because, even assuming the best faith and most congenial of circumstances, there is still the grim but real possibility that one party or the other will be hit by the proverbial truck.

People change. People forget. People die, but deals, especially when the stakes get high, live on and on. So the terrible truth is that the lawyers cannot be kept out of the picture forever. Even deals that start with a handclasp and a big smile eventually take on the baggage of signed documents and memos back and forth.

But here's the crucial point, which I think of as one of my axioms.

McCormack's Axiom of Good Contracts

If a lawyer is serving his client faithfully and well, and if a client is using his lawyer effectively and appropriately, then a legal contract should allow for the same flexibility and ongoing goodwill as a handshake deal.

Lew Wasserman, the chairman of MCA, once told me that he thought of a legal contract as no more than a piece of paper setting forth the foundation from which settlement discussions might commence. In other words, the contract—no matter how much the lawyers hem and haw over details and how shamelessly they murder the English language in the name of legal precision—can only be an *approximate* description of the understanding between the parties.

A *deal is a living thing,* a contract is static. And the purpose of a contract is to *support* the living, evolving deal, not supplant it.

To put it another way: Although law schools don't preach this, **lawyers are in a service business,** and what they service is other people's hard-won understandings. Since professional arrogance is one of lawyers' occupational hazards, they don't like to think of it that way. But it's really that simple: Lawyers, in typical business situations, are called in *after the fact,* to consolidate and safeguard the work done by someone else, namely the person who made the deal. If both the lawyer and the client would keep that in mind, things could run relatively smoothly.

The situation is more complicated, of course, when the attorneys are brought in not merely to formalize a good-faith deal, but to fight out a dispute. In those instances, the so-called adversary relationship can become a full-fledged war.

A client's sense of justice can all too easily become warped by a hunger for revenge.

An attorney's professional judgment can all too often be clouded by an ego-driven obsession with winning.

Time, money, peace of mind, and even self-respect are squandered in the name of . . . what? Getting even? Proving a point? Trying to get rich quick on the quirky largesse of a jury?

Lawsuits, by their very nature, are unpleasant proceedings, and nothing I might say could change that. But I happen to believe that the inherent unpleasantness and expense of litigation are made far worse by certain flaws in Western legal systems and by certain unconscionable elements in the standard operating procedures of attorneys.

What are those flaws and those inequities? Just to name a few:

the "time charge" method of billing, whereby lawyers charge clients up to $500 or even more per hour, *irrespective of whether their work produces any result whatsoever, or even if it was really necessary;*

the "contingent fee" system, which creates a no-lose scenario for plaintiffs and thereby encourages frivolous suits with shoot-the-moon requests for damages;

the "deep pockets" psychology of juries, which leads to verdicts based not on culpability or reasonable redress for harms, but on jurors' perceptions of how much the defendant—typically a corporation—can afford.

Those things make me mad—and part of my reason for writing this book is that I want them to make *you* mad, too.

I don't intend to get up on a soapbox and hold forth about how things ought to be. But I can read you chapter and verse —through real-life stories that involve IMG and the people we deal with—on the ways in which bad laws and bad lawyering cost us money, as business people and as taxpayers.

I can show how the "fine-print mentality" hamstrings us as executives.

I can demonstrate how the fear of liability cripples innovation.

I can illustrate the ways in which competing in the courtroom hampers and perverts the principle of competing in the marketplace.

If this book contributes at all to the kind of indignation that brings about constructive change, then I will feel I have done something worthwhile.

Our main subject, though, is not law and lawyers as they should be, but as they are—imperfect, infuriating, human. And the issues we will deal with are mainly practical ones. For the layman: How to get the most bang for the legal buck. How to judge when you can avoid lawyers altogether. How to get around the *other* person's attorney. How to make sure your own lawyer remains responsive and accountable. How to integrate lawyers into an effective business team.

For attorneys, I hope to provide some useful feedback from the world beyond their paneled offices: **What simple, common-sense steps can lawyers take to maintain their client's loyalty? When should an attorney yield to a client's business savvy and** set aside his own, more technical, and often more belligerent expertise? When does an eager-beaver businessman desperately *need* an attorney to save him from himself?

Beyond these specific issues for clients and practitioners, there's another, more subtle kind of advice that I hope the reader will carry away from these pages. People are funny. They gripe about lawyers, they make snide jokes about lawyers, yet secretly they wish they could be more *like* lawyers.

They wish they could be more effective in argument, more coolheaded and dispassionate in the midst of confrontations. They wish they could remain suavely logical even when angry, and they wish they had the knack of using that logic like a fist, a sledgehammer, or a scalpel.

People wish, in short, that they could win more arguments, prevail in more conflicts, and enjoy the confidence of knowing they can stand up for their point of view.

I like to think this book will help people—and even attorneys—accomplish those things a little more effectively.

*Discourage litigation. Persuade your neighbors
to compromise whenever you can. Point out to
them how the nominal winner is often a real
loser—in fees, expenses, and waste of time. As
a peacemaker, the lawyer has a superior opportunity of being a good man. There will be business
enough.*

—ABRAHAM LINCOLN

The first thing we do, let's kill all the lawyers.

—WILLIAM SHAKESPEARE

THE TERRIBLE TRUTH ABOUT LAWYERS

PART ONE

THE WAR
BETWEEN
LAWYERS AND
CLIENTS

1

WHAT WE'RE UP AGAINST

LIFE INSIDE THE "WALL OF MOLASSES"

I didn't write this book to win friends, and over the course of the next couple of hundred pages, I'll have some very uncomplimentary things to say about attorneys.

I have laid in more than a quarter century's worth of war stories showing lawyers at their most stubborn, adversarial, and obstructive.

I have formulated some advice that will put clients on a more equal footing with their attorneys, and that will probably cost attorneys money.

But I would like to make it clear that, while I may be critical of certain features of our legal system and of the general run of legal practitioners, I'm not fundamentally unsympathetic to attorneys. If most of us, as laymen, are up against ridiculously high legal costs and ridiculously slow legal actions, lawyers have troubles of their own.

Lawyers, like dentists, are well aware that no one wants to have any more to do with them than he or she absolutely has to. They go through life knowing that they are complained about and mistrusted by most of the general populace. Toughest of all, they spend their arduous careers laboring inside a "wall of molasses."

Just what is this wall of molasses?

It is probably the most apt metaphor I have ever heard for describing the American system of jurisprudence. Like Justice American-style, molasses is gummy, slow, and more or less opaque.

Once you make contact with the wall of molasses, you can't move up, you can't move down, and you can't move from side to side.

Most horrifying of all, you usually find you can't even get back out again.

Anyone who has ever been involved in even the most routine legal procedure can testify how exhausting it is to make any progress whatsoever through that wall. Well, that's what lawyers are up against every day of their working lives—and I would argue that even those who pull princely livings out of the wall of molasses are not immune to its frustrations.

The poignant part is that no attorney-to-be starts off thinking of the law that way. Future lawyers are taught in terms of elegant abstractions and nifty-sounding Latin phrases. Law schools excel in highfalutin rhetoric.

Only after graduation do young attorneys come to the depressing realization that 90 percent of what they were taught in academia will never be used in practice; and, conversely, 90 percent of what they need to know in practice was never taught to them at school.

NOTES FROM UNDERGROUND

Let me tell you about the incident which, more than any other, brought that hard truth home to me.

I was an eager young associate at the large and highly reputed Cleveland firm known then as Arter, Hadden, Wykoff, and Van Duzer—the oldest law firm, by the way, west of the Appalachian Mountains. Like any serious-minded fledgling fresh out of Yale, I was perfectly willing to put in sixteen-hour days, reading until my eyes went bleary, doing research and writing memos until, quite literally, language simply stopped making sense because of my utter exhaustion.

But I liked to think that there was some logical connection between the amount of time a given procedure took, and the intrinsic value of that procedure.

Then the *Geffine* v. *Doyle* case came along.

A man named Victor Geffine had brought a suit against a Canadian promoter named John Doyle and a number of co-defendants, one of whom—the Steel Company of Canada—was a client of ours. The entire basis of what went on to become a multimillion-dollar action was this: Geffine alleged that at some point Doyle had said to him, in essence: "If you will go along with me and together we are able to interest steel companies in the development of iron ore properties on which I hold the leases, I will make you a rich man."

Geffine claimed that this statement constituted a contract and that Doyle had reneged. Doyle claimed that he had never made the statement or even implied such a promise.

In preparing to defend the suit, it was my task to go through all the files pertaining to any business that Doyle and Geffine had ever done together, *or* that Doyle had done with the Steel Company of Canada in which Geffine might possibly have been mentioned, *or* that Geffine had done with any of the co-defendants in which *Doyle* had possibly been mentioned.

Now, how long would you expect such a process to take? A week? A month?

Well, it took a year and a half—a year and a half of my young life.

As it happened, some of the files, years old, were stored in the sub-subbasement of a garage in the Dominion Square Building in Montreal. Others were stashed away in a cellar in St. John's, Newfoundland. For eighteen months I lived like a mole, like Dostoevski's "underground man."

Our client spent tens of thousands of dollars keeping me in airplane tickets and hotel rooms so that I could sit in Canadian cellars, read in terrible light with my coat on, and eat expense-account dinners alone.

To make matters worse, I was painfully aware that the whole grand noble sweep of my law school education was now focused on one tiny question of the sort that is routinely argued among six-year-olds: *Did someone promise something to so-and-so, or did he not?*

The capper was that the whole object of this eighteen-month scavenger hunt was *not* to find anything!

It wasn't my job, you understand, to prove that Doyle *hadn't* promised anything to Geffine, but only to confirm that no documents existed proving that he *had*. Sure enough, at the end of my research, when I confidently reported to the partners that no compromising papers could be found, it was decided to call the plaintiff's bluff. We told Geffine's attorneys that settlement was out of the question and we would see them in court. The suit gently vanished.

And I was left to ask myself the incredibly simple but too often overlooked question that *every* lawyer and *every* client should ask himself with regard to *every* legal process: Was it worth it?

That depends, of course, on how you reckon. Measured against the millions of dollars that would have been at risk had the case been tried, yes, my time and the client's money were well spent.

But considering that the action was without merit to begin with, and that 99+ percent of what I had learned in law school was going unused as I slogged through hundreds of hours of mechanical chores, well, I'm not so sure.

In another sense, however, the experience of that solitary confinement in northern basements was enormously valuable because it helped convince me that the pure practice of law was not for me, that I craved the more freewheeling eventfulness of business.

I believed then—and I believe now—that a good legal education provides an incomparable background in mental discipline and logical thinking.

But *Geffine* v. *Doyle* taught me that, in the real world, lawyerly discipline and logic are usually applied to issues of stupefying pettiness! That realization, in turn, led me to formulate another axiom.

McCormack's Axiom of Demystification

Once you get past the mumbo jumbo, the overwhelming majority of what lawyers do is basically high-level research and make-work paper-shuffling that takes too damn long and costs too damn much for what you get.

So I sympathize with my brothers and sisters of the working bar, whose professional lives will consist of *Geffine* v. *Doyle* many times over. I say to them, sincerely, Good luck—but don't try to kid me about the deep mysteries of your expertise!

THE OTHER SIDE OF THE FENCE

These days, of course, I play a very different role when complex and protracted lawsuits like *Geffine* v. *Doyle* come along. Now I'm either the one who's suing or the one who's being sued. Either way, I'm the one who's footing the bill as the legal fees mount up.

I have thought long and hard about ways to minimize legal bills, not to mention disruption of business. And I have evolved a policy of asking myself a series of questions—questions that are all variations on one crucial query: Is it worth it?—*before* spending dollar one on lawyers or initiating any sort of legal action.

Going through the following questions calmly and openmindedly is the best way I've come across to decide when I do or do not need a lawyer, or when a dispute should or should not be legally pursued:

1. Does this problem *necessarily* call for a *legal* resolution, or can it be handled in some other way—e.g., by a business maneuver or negotiation?

2. If IMG is thinking of suing, is there a reasonable chance of collecting a judgment? Is the other side broke? Can the other side *present itself* as broke? Is the principle at stake so crucial that I can't afford *not* to sue?

3. If IMG is being sued, is there an affordable and honorable way to settle or, better still, to persuade the other side to drop the action?

4. When one has the choice of initiating a legal action, is the net result—figuring in time, money, anger, anxiety, and ruined relationships—likely to be more advantageous than *doing nothing at all*?

Let's look briefly at the implications of each of these questions.

1. Legal Gambit, Business Parry   Back in 1984, Trans World International, the IMG entity that produces television sports programming, was sued by the U.S. Ski Team for allegedly using some film footage without permission.

This was a bizarre suit, for several reasons. First of all, the footage was used as part of our *Sarajevo '84* coverage, in a preview series for the 1984 Sarajevo Winter Olympics, and it constituted some of the most advantageous exposure the ski team had ever enjoyed. It was a boon to the ski team's fund-raising efforts.

Second, TWI *had* gotten releases from the individual skiers involved.

Third, TWI and the USST had, up to that point, shared a friendly and mutually profitable relationship, and until the day the complaint landed on our general counsel's desk, there was no hint of any sort of trouble in the air.

So what was going on?

What was going on was that the ski team was having internal political problems, and had broken into warring factions, one of which was hostile to TWI.

But here's the point: **If our company had responded to the complaint only in strict legal terms, we would never have known that, and so would have been unable to defend ourselves effectively.**

Legal language is so highly stylized that *it conceals as much as it reveals.* To get to the crux of the ski team's grievance against us, I had to resist the panicky, knee-jerk temptation to call in *our* lawyers to deal with *their* lawyers.

Instead, I elected to talk to decision makers within the ski team organization *as a businessman.*

One on one, without the tension of courtroom drama and the implied threats of legal documents, I was able to learn of the internal power struggle that was the real reason for the conflict. I was advised just to sit tight and wait for the good guys to win—at which point the suit would disappear.

And it did.

So consider the advantages, in this case, of seeking a *business* solution to a problem that seemed at first glance legal.

1. We saved many thousands of dollars in lawyer's fees.

2. We spared ourselves the negative publicity of being portrayed —inaccurately—as exploiters of our beloved Olympic athletes.

3. Perhaps most important, we avoided the ill will of a full-blown
legal fight and cemented our relationship with the more reasonable elements within the ski team hierarchy.

For all those reasons, and others that may apply in various
cases, one should *always* consider informal, one-to-one solutions
before tackling a problem on a formal, legal footing.

2. Avoiding Pyrrhic Victories   If it takes considerable re-
straint not to call in the lawyers immediately when you are
attacked legally, it sometimes takes even greater forbearance not
to sue when you know you have been abused.

In those instances, moral indignation combines with an eye
for the main chance. You have a tendency to assume that the
whole world will sympathize with the wrongs you have suffered,
and that society will compensate you in a big way.

To prevent feelings like those from getting the best of my
better judgment, I make it a point to take a deep breath and a
walk around the block before deciding to sue someone. And I
also make it a point to ask myself **not only if law and justice are
on my side, but also if I'll be able to collect the money I'll
presumably be awarded.**

Now, there *are* times when one should sue, irrespective of
the likelihood of collecting a judgment. There are times when
a bulldog stance must be struck on behalf of a client, or when
a strong signal must be sent to a business partner who isn't
playing fair.

But frankly those times are relatively rare. Making points for
the sake of making points is the role of essayists and philosophers;
the business of business is to get things done.

And I must say there are few things in my business life that
frustrate me more than going to all the trouble and expense of
bringing a suit and winning a suit, and then walking away empty-
handed.

To gain an idea of just how futile and irritating this can be, consider a case we pursued a few years back on behalf of golfer Donna Caponi.

Donna had an endorsement contract with a club manufacturer called Swinging Promotions. Suffice it to say that Swinging Promotions was not the most successful sporting goods company in history, and it eventually found itself with a warehouse full of Donna Caponi autographed sticks and a commitment it didn't feel like honoring. We tried reasoning; we tried threatening; we sued.

As so often happens, Swinging Promotions' first tactic was to stall. The company's lawyers concocted all sorts of pretrial motions, argued over jurisdiction, and pulled all the standard delaying stunts.

After costing us some six months and $20,000 or so, the company suddenly did an about face: It agreed to move the case out of full-scale litigation and submit it to an arbitrator.

This was the first reasonable thing Swinging Productions had done, and we should have realized there was more to the move than met the eye. But we went ahead with the arbitration. We flew witnesses from California to Buffalo, New York, where the proceeding was being held. We juggled Donna Caponi's tournament schedule so she could testify on her own behalf.

And sure enough, we were awarded everything we asked for in the arbitration.

Whereupon we were informed that Swinging Promotions had filed for bankruptcy in the meantime.

There was no money to collect. And we weren't particularly interested in taking our judgment in the form of golf clubs.

So why had we bothered? We knew all along that Swinging Promotions was a shaky company at best. There was no great principle at stake, and we were not likely to do repeat business with this outfit anyway. About the only positive result of our action was that we had demonstrated to a client that we would go to the wall on her behalf.

As a business gesture, an important point was made. But was

it worth all the trouble and expense, and was pursuing a pyrrhic lawsuit the best way to assure our client we were with her?

Frankly, I don't think so. Chalk that one up as a learning experience. If I had it to do over again, I wouldn't do it.

3. Pay the Two Dollars   Nobody likes to be shaken down, and nothing is more in keeping with human nature than to adopt a defensive posture when someone is assailing you. In the great majority of civil lawsuits, therefore, people will vigorously defend themselves even when they know they're flat, dead wrong.

But let's not be naïve. **Justice is only one factor in a lawsuit, and often not the most compelling.** Being right doesn't necessarily mean you'll win, and there are times when it's easier, cheaper, and more dignified to settle. Sometimes, as much as it hurts, the rational decision is to swallow your losses and get on with your life.

A number of years ago, IMG hired an "expert" to serve as a consultant on a sports event we were staging for TV. This "expert" did less than nothing for us. He promised us contacts who, it turned out, barely knew who he was. He had no ideas. He slowed us down by inserting himself in the middle of certain decisions and then being unresponsive.

We canceled his contract for nonperformance, and he sued us.

Here was a case where we were morally in the right but legally exposed. It is incredibly difficult to prove that someone didn't perform a service, when that service is as loosely defined as "consulting." We knew that if we went to trial, this individual could produce a log of phone calls answered, meetings attended, and so forth; that he *accomplished* nothing would be nearly impossible to demonstrate. Additionally, the psychology of juries would almost certainly favor the poor defenseless individual against the big monolithic corporation.

So we bought this person off for several thousand dollars. I realize that's not a phrase in official use in law schools, but there's no prettier way to put it. They don't teach you in law school that *often the choice comes down to paying the plaintiff or paying the lawyers.* We made what I believe was a sound business decision.

By settling, we put a cap on our losses. By *not* settling, we would have remained vulnerable both to the running up of huge legal fees and to the possibility of an off-the-wall judgment.

For those reasons I urge everyone to put aside ego and moral indignation, and to be open to the possibility of settling and settling early.

4. The Passive Option   Everyone knows that a defendant in a criminal trial can plead either innocent or guilty.

Not everyone knows that there is a third option: nolo contendere, or "no contest." A plea of nolo contendere means basically that one neither admits blame nor claims innocence, but simply lets the matter rest with the wisdom and mercy of the court.

In other words, one chooses to do nothing.

Now, given that our whole system of law is based on *argument,* the concept of nolo contendere is intriguing and a little bit subversive: The whole adversarial process is short-circuited if one side refuses to fight!

Nolo contendere is a concept from criminal law, not civil law. Still, I would argue that in *figurative* terms, the concept of "no contest" has valuable applications.

There's an old Zen maxim that goes, "Never to argue is never to be wrong." In business situations, that bromide can be stated even more strongly: Not arguing can often make you something of a hero.

For that reason, I would urge anyone who's deciding whether to pursue a lawsuit to consider what I call **The Passive Option.**

Let's say, for argument's sake, that our client Chris Evert is hired—some months in advance, of course—to play an exhibition at the grand opening of a new tennis resort. By no bad faith on management's part, the opening is delayed because of construction difficulties, labor problems, or whatever. The company makes a bona fide effort to reschedule Chris for another time, but there are simply no free dates on her calendar. So the tennis resort reneges on its contract.

The resort's management realizes, of course, that they are opening themselves to a lawsuit. Chances are they are braced to have us sue, whereupon they will try to settle for *part* of what they had intended to pay Chris to do the exhibition.

But what if we don't sue?

What if, after getting Chris's approval, I call the CEO and say, "I'm sorry your project got off schedule, and we're going to let you walk away from the contract you have with us"?

First of all, the CEO would probably be shocked: *And it is always an advantage in business to be able to surprise someone.*

Second, he would be grateful that we were making his life easier rather than harder, and he would probably feel that he "owed us one." Assuming that his company will be around awhile, we would almost certainly come out ahead in the long run.

Third, since people like to talk about unusual happenings, chances are this CEO would tell other members of his circle about how we let him off the hook, and since *every business is a word-of-mouth business,* this would enhance our reputation for being a good bunch of people to deal with.

Aren't all those advantages better than the expense, uncertainty, and ill will of one more acrimonious and drawn-out lawsuit?

WHERE *NOT* TO GO FOR LEGAL ADVICE

Whenever possible, you should think about the above considerations *before* plunging into the "wall of molasses."

Further, whenever possible, you should at least begin to think about them **before even *talking* to a lawyer.**

Why?

Let me answer by analogy. How many times have you asked a car mechanic if you need a tune-up, and had him tell you no?

Lawyers are educated and programmed to resolve differences by way of the judicial process. This is not simply the way they make their livings, it's the lens through which they look at the world.

So you can't expect an attorney to look at a legal problem and see an intuitive, business-based solution.

You can't expect an attorney to look at a case he could probably win and see a battle not worth fighting.

You can't expect an attorney to be overly enthusiastic about The Passive Option when the benefits of doing nothing will accrue only to you and not put a nickel in his pocket.

The terrible truth is that you can't expect an attorney *not* to be an attorney.

And everything that follows in this book will be clearer and more useful if we take a few minutes now to explore what being an attorney really means.

2

HOW LAWYERS GOT
THAT WAY

IS IT TRUE ALL LAWYERS
LOOK ALIKE?

Think about the business people you know.

They probably run the gamut of personality types. Some are quiet, some are boisterous, some are worriers, some are bold. In their business styles they probably cover the range from conservative-executive to visionary-entrepreneur.

Now think about the lawyers you are acquainted with. Unless I miss my guess, they probably all resemble each other quite a bit.

Chances are they have in common a certain solemnity of aspect and formality of expression, a "lawyerliness" that shows even in their smallest gestures.

An attorney friend of mine once told me that wherever he goes—even to the hardware store, dressed in jeans and a sweat-shirt on a Saturday morning—people say to him, apropos of nothing: "You're a lawyer, aren't you?"

What accounts for this strong family resemblance shared by the great majority of practicing attorneys?

The answer can only be that *there are powerful forces shaping these people on their way to becoming lawyers.*

These forces operate first of all in law schools, and second, at the associate level in which young attorneys do what amounts to a medieval-style apprenticeship.

WHAT THEY *DO* TEACH YOU AT YALE LAW SCHOOL

By an interesting coincidence, one of the most stinging indictments ever written about American legal education was written by a professor from Yale Law School.

His name is Charles A. Reich, and in 1970 he published a very popular and influential book called *The Greening of America.* In assessing what he felt was right and wrong about our culture, he started with the part of that culture he knew most intimately, and this is what he had to say:

Finding themselves in law school . . . [students] discover that they are expected to become "argumentative" personalities who listen to what someone else is saying only for the purpose of disagreeing; "analytic" rather than receptive people, who dominate information rather than respond to it; and intensely competitive and self-assertive as well. Since many of them are not this sort of personality before they start law school, they react initially with anger and despair, and later with resignation. . . . In a very real sense, they "become stupider" during law school, as the range of their imagination is limited, their ability to respond with sensitivity and to receive impressions is reduced, and the scope of their reading and thinking is progressively narrowed.

SAY IT AIN'T SO, JOE

It would be nice if I could refute Reich's observations. But I can't. Let's look at a few of his assertions individually.

Are law students expected and in fact pressured to become "argumentative" personalities? You bet they are.

The whole thrust of their classroom training is geared toward the inculcation of what is known as "the adversarial turn of mind."

A case is introduced in class. By their nature, law cases have two sides. It's always Us against Them, Me against You. Whatever the other side says, you *have* to disagree.

Not only that, but if the professor tells you, halfway through a case, to shift your allegiance to the other side of the question, you have to argue *that* side just as deftly and with as much *semblance* of commitment as you argued the other.

In real life, this would be called hypocrisy; among law students, it's known as survival. And it gets to be an intellectual habit.

But law students aren't trained to do battle only against other law students; they're constantly put on the spot to argue against professors as well.

This creates just one problem: Since law cases can be argued in any number of ways, no matter *what* the student says, the teacher can show him to be wrong—in front of a hundred or so of his peers.

This way of teaching is known as the Socratic method. It can also be thought of as **The Professor Always Wins, and the Student Lives in Terror.**

Make no mistake, *terror is an integral part of the law school experience, and the long-term consequence of that terror is to make it very difficult for lawyers to admit when they've made an error or when they simply don't know something. The ultimate sin is being at a loss for words.*

Law school has taught them to hide uncertainty at any cost.

It has also taught them what a powerful weapon intimidation can be.

Finally, law school *does* tend to make people narrower in their interests, just because it's so damn difficult and so relentlessly competitive.

People who go to law school are accustomed to being academic stars. Chances are they were at the top of the heap all through high school and college. Suddenly, for the first time ever, they find themselves in the middle of the pack. There's always someone smarter, someone willing to study an hour longer.

Maybe Professor Reich is a shade harsh in saying that people "become stupider" in law school. But there's no denying that they leave parts of themselves behind.

You can't read novels or practice the cello when you're fighting for your life.

And in dealing with lawyers, here's something important to keep in mind.

McCormack's Axiom of Delayed Rewards

People who have sacrificed large amounts of time and money to get a professional credential—doctors, lawyers, MBAs—come away ferociously determined to get their investment back with interest—from the system and from you!

OOPS, WE FORGOT TO TEACH YOU LAWYERING!

The irony is that this three-year stint in purgatory doesn't have a lot to do with turning someone into an attorney. It has to do only with getting a *degree* so that *in later life one may perhaps develop into a competent practitioner.*

Back around 1960, as you may recall, there was a major brouhaha in the American press when then President John F. Kennedy nominated his brother Bobby to be attorney general. The president's detractors claimed that the appointment was sheer nepotism, and that the younger Kennedy's background in no way justified such a lofty post.

No one questioned that Bobby Kennedy was brilliant or that his University of Virginia legal education was top-notch. The only problem was that he had never in his life tried a case!

Was the position of chief lawyer for the United States government to be held by someone who had never argued to a jury, never jockeyed for advantage with a judge?

In actual fact, however, *the job of attorney general was the one lawyering position in the country that RFK's education was* perfectly *suited to!*

As attorney general, he wouldn't have to do most of the work that practicing lawyers actually spend their time on:

He wouldn't have to go through the sticky business of soliciting and dealing with clients.

He wouldn't have to keep a billing chart or worry about a payroll.

He wouldn't have to fret over courtroom tactics because he'd have a staff that would actually try the cases.

What Bobby Kennedy *would* have to do is exactly *the one and only thing* he had been taught to do at school: think legally.

It would be his job to analyze the cogent points of law and justice in a given appellate or legislative process, and to make judgments about the meaning and implications of legal theory and precedent. *That,* RFK could do as well as anybody.

So the moral of the story is this: **A good legal education prepares you to pass the bar and to be attorney general. For anything in between, you're basically on your own, so lots of luck!**

WHAT'S LEFT OUT

The rest of this book is essentially devoted to the things you *don't* learn in law school—the intuitive skills of reading people and devising solutions in order to enhance business or personal opportunities—so I won't belabor the point. However, consider briefly just a couple of the elements that the standard law school education either glosses over or omits entirely:

THE BASIC LAWYERING SKILLS

As usually defined, the four basic skills that every practicing attorney needs to have are: Interviewing, Counseling, Negotiating, and Drafting.

> *Interviewing* has to do with early client contact, getting to know the client's needs and goals, being clear on what you can or cannot accomplish on the client's behalf; and of course with winning the business in the first place.
>
> *Counseling* is the giving of appropriate advice in an appropriate manner, based on a good working knowledge of the applicable laws and *also* on a sound reading of the client's particular situation.
>
> *Negotiating* entails a host of strategies, including decisions about when to be cooperative and when intransigent, when to settle and when to fight to the bitter end.
>
> *Drafting* refers to writing contracts and other legal documents.

As I have said, these are the bedrock lawyering skills. Amazingly enough, *they are not generally taught in law school.* If this strikes you as bizarre, it is. But any candid law school graduate will tell you it's the terrible truth.

How is it possible that the *absolutely basic skills* of a profession can be neglected in the course of three years' professional education?

Essentially, it's because most law school professors are brilliant men and women whose interest is in the twists, turns, and nuances of what is known as Black Letter Law—law as it is written in the statute books, not as it is bent and sometimes mangled by the exigencies of real life.

Law school professors are admirably equipped to teach reasoning and theory. But it is the rare academic who has the foggiest notion of what really goes on in the trenches. So the fact remains that **law school doesn't teach people the things they'll be doing day in, day out, as lawyers.**

THE REALITIES OF LAW FIRM MANAGEMENT AND ECONOMICS

Though lawyers seem to chafe at having it put this way, *a law firm is essentially a store, a retail operation.*

Like any business, a law firm offers a product, the sale of which, it is hoped, will cover the payroll and the overhead, with some profit left over for the owners—in this case, the partners.

In recent years, the running of law firms has become so complicated that there are people who specialize in it—nonlawyers who come in to manage the store. Law firm economics are complex enough to be the subject of surveys by Big Eight accounting firms and other independent auditing concerns.

For all that, *law schools teach virtually nothing about how law firms really work.* Perhaps they don't want to deal with such squalid subjects as paying the rent and covering the utilities, vying for business and dealing with clients who stiff you.

But there is a thin line between idealism and hypocrisy, and let's face it, Yale Law, Harvard Law, and all the rest are essentially top-level trade schools. So why not teach what really makes the trade go round? As of now, the subject is anathema.

PILGRIM'S PROGRESS—THE ASSOCIATE YEARS

One of the more humane developments in the history of education was the introduction of the use of cadavers in medical schools. Future doctors could slice-and-dice to their heart's content, and no one would get hurt.

They could work by trial and error, and keep going till they got it right. By the time the doctors touched a living patient, they knew which was the liver and which was the spleen.

There are no cadavers in law school, and, in the typical instance, a law graduate receives a diploma without ever having had real responsibility for a flesh-and-blood client. Not till signing on as an associate with a firm does a young attorney stick a toe in the waters of actual practice.

But "sticking in a toe" is not really what fledgling attorneys do; it's more apt to say they are suddenly thrown in way over their heads, and left to sink or swim.

THE CASES NO ONE WANTS

In my own experience at Arter, Hadden, the immersion consisted of being handed nearly a hundred "subrogation cases," and being told to take care of them—with a minimum of supervision.

Subrogation cases have to do with insurance matters; essentially, they are property-damage defense suits in which the insurance companies pay a settlement but the insured is responsible for the deductible. Since the "subrogation" part only concerns the deductible, these suits are small potatoes, and law firms take them on basically as an accommodation to their insurance company clients.

What better way to break in new associates than to bury them in actions where the firm's exposure is minimal, and none of the partners want the business anyway?

These subrogation actions taught me plenty. They dragged me down from the ivory tower of Yale, and cast me into the pit of sheriff's auctions in and around Cleveland, where repossessed furniture was routinely sold off to cover a judgment.

Far from the academic milieu, where arguments were won on the basis of elegant logic and diligent preparation, I now found myself in rough-and-tumble settings where battles were fought by needling, bluffing, intimidation—and sometimes just seeing who could scream the loudest.

I was confronted with the sort of gritty dilemmas that no law school professor had ever lectured about:

What did you do if your client didn't show up for a trial?

How did you respond if the other side out-and-out lied, it was obvious as hell, everybody knew it, and it couldn't be proved?

How did you handle it when a jury returned a decision that was utterly inscrutable except in terms of prejudice?

How did you get to sleep at night when you *lost*?

THE RUDE AWAKENING

Being confronted with situations like those is part of the initiation and culture shock that every associate goes through on the way to becoming a full-fledged professional.

And every layman who wishes to understand what makes lawyers tick should understand the effect that that culture shock has on tenderhearted young attorneys:

Some lawyers never quite recover from the disillusionment that attends the first rude rush of actual practice, and they quickly take on a pragmatic cynicism that will help them flourish in our far-from-perfect system. I'm sure we've all met lawyers like that.

Others resolve to keep their ideals intact and to battle the status quo even while being embroiled in it. This is a rarer breed, but it does exist.

And still others begin quickly to wonder if they really want to be practicing attorneys after all.

I fall into that final category, though I have no regrets at all about the time, effort, and money that went into making me a lawyer in the first place. My legal background affords me certain pleasures, not the least of which is the privilege of being able to pass along to the nonlawyer some inside information that his or her own attorney might be just as happy not to share.

3

WHAT LAWYERS
DON'T WANT THEIR CLIENTS
TO KNOW

One of the great half-true maxims of all time is Knowledge is Power.

In fact, knowledge can *become* power, but *only if it is wedded to sufficient strength and practical savvy so that it can be put to use.*

This observation puts me in mind of a story about a client of ours, the great running back Herschel Walker. Back when Herschel was in college, he had a habit of glancing quickly, as he came out of the huddle, toward the spot he'd be hitting on his next carry.

A coach pointed out to the future Heisman Trophy winner that an opposing linebacker might pick up the glance, and so know where to position himself.

Walker shrugged. "Then he'd be the first guy to get knocked down," he said.

The moral of the story can be expressed this way:

McCormack's Axiom of Brains and Brawn
Knowledge alone is not sufficient protection against
getting steamrolled.

On the other hand, without pertinent knowledge, one is at a
serious disadvantage in every power-based transaction. And in
lawyer-client relationships this is what tips the balance in favor
of the lawyer.

THE ATTORNEYS' EDGE

Lawyers know two things that the rest of us do not:
One of them is the law. As any honest attorney will acknowl-
edge, however, they "know" far less law than you might imagine.
The rest they look up as they go along.

Still, attorneys have put in three long years of study, and what
their time and trouble has gotten them is a monopoly on a certain
high-priced commodity.

**Just as a law firm is basically a store, the knowledge of legal
principles and procedures is essentially a high-ticket product
that only lawyers can dispense.** That's what it comes down to,
once you get past the rhetoric.

The other thing that lawyers know—which can and should be
known by laymen, too, but which attorneys, for their own profit
and convenience, tend to be hush-hush about—is how lawyers
actually *operate:*

How do they behave toward each other, and why?

What do they say to each other that they wouldn't say to a
client?

How much of your legal dollar is used productively and how

much pays for oak paneling and handsome leatherbound books that no one but the cleaning lady ever touches?

What are the questions you should ask your lawyer—whether you're a business person involved in litigation, or an individual seeking counsel in a divorce, or simply an excited first-time buyer closing on a house—*before* you put your fate in his hands?

These are the sorts of things your lawyer would probably just as soon keep you in the dark about. They are the bread-and-butter issues that attorneys talk about among their own, but on which they maintain a staunch silence in the presence of strangers, as if trying to foster the myth that such venal concerns are beneath their notice.

They're not, believe me.

HONOR AMONG SHARKS

Let's start with how lawyers deal with each other—a dynamic nicely illustrated by an old joke.

Two lawyers and a priest are cast adrift in a tiny lifeboat in the aftermath of a shipwreck.

Day and night they float without direction on the limitless sea. Their fresh water runs out. They have no food. The sun beats down on them relentlessly.

Finally, on the third day, they drift within sight of an atoll. But as luck would have it, the currents are adverse and they can't get closer than 300 yards or so. To complicate matters, there is a convoy of sharks scudding back and forth between the atoll and the boat.

Still, one of the lawyers, half mad with thirst, gasps that he just can't take it anymore and leaps out of the boat. He starts swimming to shore while his two companions look on in horror, waiting for him to be torn to bits by the sharks.

Strangely, however, the sharks part ranks and let him swim right past.

"It's a miracle," says the priest.

"No," says the other lawyer, "just professional courtesy."

Professional Courtesy—not a subject you are likely to see offered in many law school catalogs but an absolutely central concept in the life of attorneys.

CODES AND PASSWORDS

What exactly *is* professional courtesy, and how exactly does it work?

If you don't know, you shouldn't feel that you've been remiss. The fact is, there's something of a tacit conspiracy among attorneys to *prevent* you from knowing.

Professional courtesy is learned not by precept but by osmosis, and its tenets are conveyed from lawyer to lawyer by way of codes and passwords.

Beyond the hocus-pocus, however, the bottom line on professional courtesy is this: **It is a system whereby lawyers make life easier for themselves and for each other, generally at the expense of their clients.**

"AT A MUTUALLY CONVENIENT TIME" . . . HA, HA

Let me give you an innocent little example of professional courtesy in action. It has to do with a phrase that anyone who has ever dealt with a lawyer has heard: "at a mutually convenient time."

Convenient to whom?

You guessed it.

Back when I was a young associate in Cleveland, I was put in charge of a case that frankly didn't interest me much and that I was ill prepared to present at the appointed time.

I *could* have been prepared to present it, but on the weekend before the action was to be tried, I had a member-guest golf tournament that I was very keen to play in. So I simply picked up the telephone, called the other side's attorney, and asked for a postponement as a professional courtesy. He accommodated me, no questions asked.

So I played my golf game, and prepared the case afterward.

Shortly before the *second* trial date, however, the other lawyer called *me* on the phone, asking for another delay. I gave it to him, of course. But by this time I felt we knew each other well enough so that a little collegial ribbing would not be out of line.

"Golf tournament?" I asked.

"No," he answered with a chuckle. "Tennis is my game."

So, between my golf and his tennis, a quite simple procedure took on a sort of Mediterranean tempo and dragged on far longer than it needed to. This sort of thing happens all the time.

Why is it *allowed* to happen?

It is allowed to happen because clients are generally too damn polite about demanding to know why a given procedure has been postponed.

This is another area in which lawyers typically have the upper hand over clients: **Lawyers are professionals at the art of confrontation; clients tend to be amateurs.**

Clients don't like to risk unpleasantness by asking their own attorney just why the hell this twenty-minute issue is taking six months to resolve.

But they *should* ask.

Every client should ask, at the outset of every legal procedure, how long the matter is likely to take to be resolved.

Typically, a lawyer will fudge on the answer, claiming—correctly—that it's impossible to say with any certainty. Still, asking the question sends the message that the client wants a timely resolution—and will take an active stance to get one.

I remember, some years ago, when we were negotiating a very complicated deal for a European exhibition tour on behalf of Muhammad Ali. The tour dates could not be set until a host of issues were resolved, and Ali was impatient. Ali said to us on more than one occasion: "I don't need to know the fine print and ins-and-outs. *Just tell me the dates.*"

"Ali," we had no choice but to answer, "we're doing the best we can. But it's out of our control."

"But you don't understand," he said to us. "I gotta start training. I gotta get psyched up. I gotta know when to *stop eating!*"

The conversation reminded me that, while the lawyer or the agent is usually more or less content to bide his time, it's the client who is most intimately affected by delays!

If there *are* delays, therefore, a client should *always* insist on knowing the reasons. Don't settle for mealy-mouthed excuses like "scheduling conflicts"; demand to know what those conflicts *are*.

And if the reasons given don't strike you as persuasive, say so.

Frankly, if a lawyer postponed *my* case because of a golf tournament, I would be inclined to get a different lawyer!

WHERE THE BREAD IS *REALLY* BUTTERED

Not that professional courtesy operates only in the realm of scheduling. In fact, it is a consideration that enters into every nook of legal practice—so much so that some quipsters claim Professional Courtesy is the real meaning of the letters P.C. that come at the end of many law firm names.

Now, it should be understood that lawyers are ethically bound to pursue their clients' interests with all due diligence, and to steer clear of any conflicting claims on their professional loyalties. All reputable attorneys treat that fiduciary responsibility with the highest respect; and of course clients have recourse to malpractice suits or complaints to local bar associations if they feel their lawyers have in any way breached their trust.

For all that, however, lawyers have a broad range of discretion as to how they can behave in a given situation.

A lawyer can be less aggressive or more aggressive, cooperative or belligerent.

In a contract negotiation, a lawyer can be flexible or intransigent; in a dispute, he can lean toward settlement or toward pitched battle.

A lawyer can make the other side's attorney look good or look bad, appear reasonable and fair or seem the soul of villainy.

And every client should be aware that those choices have to do, in part, with the sort of relationship that the lawyer has, or has had, or would like to have, with the other side's attorneys.

In every business, after all, one's colleagues and competitors are as important as one's customers.

THE DYNAMIC OF THE TWO-LAWYER TOWN

Let's say that you and I are the only two lawyers in a sleepy little town in Arkansas. Let's analyze the professional relationship between the two of us.

First and foremost, we are competitors. We compete for clients, we compete for reputation, we both want to be known as the smartest legal eagle in town.

On the other hand, we really can't afford to be enemies. Chances are we'll be on the phone with each other three, four times a week, every week of our working lives. We'll be trying to expedite settlements which, aside from benefiting our clients, will free us up to take on other business and make more money. Now and then you'll be booked solid and you'll send clients my way; now and then I'll do the same for you.

Clients will come and go, magistrates will come and go, but you and I will still be there, the only two entries in the local yellow pages under Lawyers.

So I don't want you mad at me.

If a prospective client comes to me and wants to know why he should hire me as opposed to you, I'll do my sell job, but I'll think twice before I say anything negative about you. (If I want the business bad enough, however, making you look terrible will probably be easy, as we shall shortly discuss.)

If we show up before a judge one day, and it turns out you haven't done your homework, I'll stop short of humiliating you because I don't want you waiting for an opportunity to embarrass me in return.

If we're due at a closing at 9:00 A.M. and you call me at eight to ask for a postponement, I'll give it to you because next time it might be *my* kid who has the flu and keeps me up all night.

Again, these courtesies that you and I extend to each other should not substantively affect the results of the services we provide. Still, *politesse* costs time and money—*clients'* time and money.

Your customers and my customers are picking up the tab for our mutual graciousness. And let's face it—it's easy to be gracious when someone else is paying.

THE HIDDEN COSTS

Everybody complains about legal fees. Not everybody thinks about the *hidden* costs that are incurred when lawyers, practicing professional courtesy, do not take the shortest path between points A and B.

Some years ago, a woman of my acquaintance had to bivouac at the Carlyle Hotel for three weeks, at around $200 a night, because *her estranged husband's lawyer* was on vacation and her own attorney felt it would be improper to file divorce papers till he was back.

Another time, our company was negotiating an endorsement deal for French skier Jean-Claude Killy. Killy was to be paid in dollars, but the number of dollars was pegged to the dollar's value relative to the franc.

Well, midway through the contract process, the other side's attorney had to fly to Milan to tend to another matter altogether. Our lawyers, rather than insisting that the Killy business be passed along to another attorney so that it could be resolved in a timely manner, agreed to wait until the first fellow returned from Italy. Meanwhile, the franc went on a short-term spree that lowered the value of Killy's deal by around 6 percent.

Now, they don't teach you about currency fluctuations at law school, and that 6 percent won't show up on anybody's legal bills—but what is it, if not part of the cost of dealing with lawyers?

MEANWHILE, BACK AT THE RANCH . . .

But coming back to the example of the two-lawyer town—I realize that situation is an extreme one, but I use it for a very simple reason: **In any location, within any legal specialty, and at any level of prestige and clout, the dynamics that obtain among attorneys are essentially the dynamics of the small town.**

Whether you're talking about sole practitioners who do criminal work in Brooklyn, or three-hundred-lawyer firms engaged in billion-dollar antitrust suits, the number of players in any given arena is finite.

"What goes 'round, comes 'round," as the saying goes, and if lawyers do business once, chances are they'll do business again. Unless they are saints or fools, protecting their ongoing relationships with fellow attorneys will be part of their agenda. No client should be so naïve as not to realize that.

Insofar as it's possible to do so, therefore, clients should always try to learn about the history of the relationship between the lawyer they themselves intend to hire, and the attorney or firm retained by the other side.

How can you do this? In the simplest way imaginable: ask.

Ask your lawyer if he or she has dealt with the other side before.

Ask if those dealings have been friendly or hostile.

Ask if there are grudges or outstanding scores to settle.

Ask if there is any factor that might prevent your lawyer from serving your interests wholeheartedly and without complications.

In this, as in other aspects of dealing with lawyers, I cannot urge you too strongly to keep these two simple precepts in mind:

It is always to the client's advantage to show sophistication by knowing the pertinent questions.

Showing awareness *up front* is a great deterrent to being taken advantage of later on.

If you're embarking upon a hostile procedure that will call for snarling, threats, and stonewalling, don't hire the other guy's brother-in-law or good old roommate from Dartmouth.

Conversely, for a matter that requires tact and cooperation, don't align yourself with an attorney who has a twenty-year grudge against his opposite number.

McCormack's Axiom of Showmanship
Lawyers, like vaudevillians, play as much to each other as to the audience.

HOW LAWYERS MAKE
OTHER LAWYERS LOOK BAD

Not so very long ago, professional tennis was a fledgling enterprise that consisted largely of barnstorming pros who put on exhibitions, not for fat purses put up by corporate sponsors, but for only a percentage of the gate.

The nonpareil among those barnstormers was the great Australian lefty Rod Laver, who happened to be one of our earliest tennis clients, and whose long career spanned the eras of barnstorming and big sponsorship.

One day I asked Laver how it was that in even-split exhibitions, he always made his opponents look so darn good and just barely edged them out; whereas in winner-take-all matches, it couldn't have been clearer that he had them all outclassed.

What Laver told me was that he truly wasn't conscious of hitting the ball any differently in either case. It was just that when there was money on the table, he mysteriously became a different sort of player.

I mention this story because it suggests an analogy to the behavior of many lawyers: As long as lawyers are in a situation where both sides will benefit from making each other look good, they'll bend over backward to do so.

When fees and clients are up for grabs, however, and one lawyer or firm is out to steal business from another, all bets are off so far as professional courtesy is concerned. The idea in these instances is to impugn the quality of the other lawyer's work—and no matter how solid that work really is, it can always be impugned.

"FOURSCORE AND SEVEN YEARS AGO . . ."

I can still recall my eighth-grade history teacher who made us memorize the Gettysburg Address. As far as this teacher was concerned, the Gettysburg Address was the greatest document of all time—stirring, elegant, heroic.

Years later, I read an article by a college English professor who approached the Gettysburg Address as he would a freshman composition, and gave it a C−! This article included references to Lincoln's mistakes in grammar and lapses in logic, and made a quite persuasive case that the speech was nothing special after all.

So if the Gettysburg Address can rate a C−, imagine what the run-of-the-mill contract or legal memo would rate in the hands of someone with a vested interest in being a hard marker!

LAWYER SMITH AND LAWYER JONES

Lawyers don't simply welcome the opportunity to review the work of a competing attorney, they wallow in it.

Let's say that I am a lawyer named Smith and you are a client currently being represented by a lawyer named Jones. On some pretext or other, you call me up and ask to talk with me.

Now, before a word has been said, I'm at a strategic advantage: obviously you're having some qualms about the service you're getting from Jones, or you wouldn't be consulting me.

You come up to my office (which is decorated in such a way as to inspire total confidence, of course), and I make it a point to be extra attentive and totally sympathetic. I go into what I think of as my "audition mode"—which is probably more impressive than Jones's usual behavior simply because it's more impressive than *my* usual behavior; it's our first date, after all

Now, if you are a typical client, you will probably avoid saying anything overtly bad about Jones, because ironically you'll be concerned about insulting *me* by insulting a member of my profession. So we'll do a delicate little dance around the subject of your not being happy with Jones. The dance will go something like this:

You say: I'm involved in a very important matter and I want to make sure I understand what's going on.

(You mean: I'm terrified that this procedure is going to

take me to the cleaners and I'm desperately in need of reassurance.)

I say: In any matter of this sort, it's very important that you have total faith in the person representing you.

(I mean: I know you're nervous about Jones and I want to make you so nervous that you won't be able to stand one more day with him as your attorney.)

You say: It's not that I don't have faith in Mr. Jones . . .

(You mean: It *is* that I don't have faith in Mr. Jones.)

I say: Sometimes these things are just a matter of personal chemistry.

(I mean: You don't have to feel guilty if you think this guy's a jerk.)

You say (meekly): Well, I wonder if I might just ask you a question or two.

(You mean: Save me!)

I say: I can't advise you while you're being represented by someone else, but if there's some specific document . . .

(I mean: Let me get my hands on something Jones has written, so I can gleefully tear it to shreds.)

WHAT, NO FRAMASTAM CLAUSE?!

Let's suppose that you have brought along a contract that Jones has drafted for you. You hand it to me across the desk, and now the real fun begins.

I peruse the document and, without looking up, I am perfectly aware that you are scrutinizing my expression, looking for any sign of disapproval. If I so much as raise an eyebrow, you will probably think, "Oh my God, what is this clown Jones doing to me?"

If I murmur something to the effect of, "Odd that he didn't put a choice of laws clause in here," you'll probably go through agonies wondering what *else* he didn't put in.

And if, after going through three or four pages, I say, "Now here's something I would have done differently," chances are you'll find yourself wishing that the whole thing had been in my hands to begin with.

Maybe I win you over as a client. At the very least, I've exacerbated the doubts you already have about Jones. But here's the thing that most clients would probably not realize:

In the whole mini-drama that you and I have just played out, there has been *not one solitary scrap of evidence that I, in fact, could represent you better than, or even necessarily as well as, Jones.*

Maybe I have made you *feel* I could—but that's an emotional response, not one based on anything that has actually been demonstrated.

Poor Jones hasn't been around to defend himself or state his case. If the situation had been reversed, and Jones was looking at a contract that *I* had drawn up, he could have nitpicked every bit as effectively as I did.

Not that my contract would have been flawed, any more than *his* was necessarily flawed; it's just that there are virtually infinite ways to draw up a document, and a lawyer can always say, or suggest, that his own way is superior.

SO WHAT'S A CLIENT TO DO?

This state of affairs, as should be clear, leaves clients with a dilemma. Given that any competent lawyer can call into question the quality of another lawyer's work, how *should* a client know which attorney to stay with—or, for that matter, to do business with in the first place?

The terrible truth is that there are no hard-and-fast rules about this. If there were, the best lawyers would get all the business, and the rest would get none at all—and anyone with eyes in his head knows that isn't the case. In general, however, I would suggest the following bits of practical advice:

Appraise a lawyer *not* by what he says about other lawyers' efforts, but on the basis of *positive* statements of what he himself would do for you.

Don't base the choice of attorney *solely* on the first impression he makes on you, but don't disregard that factor, either. If he impresses you, he'll probably impress colleagues, judges, and juries as well.

Whenever possible, ask around about a lawyer's reputation. Talk to other clients who have employed him. One of the few things a smart lawyer can't conveniently misrepresent is what other people think of him.

HOW LAWYERS MAKE OTHER LAWYERS LOOK *GOOD*

If competing attorneys sometimes have obvious motivations for denigrating each other's work, *opposing* attorneys sometimes have just slightly less apparent reasons for praising each other to the skies. Let me illustrate this by way of an example.

A few years ago, IMG was forced, on behalf of tennis star Mats Wilander, to sue a foreign clothing manufacturer for non-payment of royalties that were approaching the million-dollar mark. The case, unfortunately for us, had to be tried in a jurisdiction in which we had no previous litigation experience. We hired local counsel, of course—a firm we had not dealt with before, but which had come to us very highly recommended.

Very early on in the preparation of the case, we noticed a somewhat odd pattern emerging. In all their correspondence with us, the lawyers of the firm we had engaged seemed to be straining to say nice things about the *other side's* attorneys: They were so brilliant. They were so thorough. They were so well connected, so discreet, so resourceful.

Our lawyers made *their* lawyers sound so good, we kicked ourselves for not retaining them before our adversary did!

For a brief time, we tried to deny the truth of what was really going on. In multinational dealings, it is always a mistake to jump to conclusions; maybe this excessive collegial generosity was simply their version of such American conventions (almost always insincere!) as calling one's opposite number "my esteemed colleague."

After several months and some tens of thousands of dollars in legal fees had slipped away, however, the simple facts became clear: our lawyers didn't believe we could win the case, and they were already taking steps to avoid or minimize the blame for losing it.

The right was unquestionably on our side, but for technical reasons peculiar to this jurisdiction, the judgment was not likely to go our way, and collection would probably be impossible even if it did.

But our hired counsel, of course, hoped to do business with us again. So their idea in praising the opposition so highly was to make us believe that in this particular case they had labored heroically but tragically against incalculable odds, but that in any other battle they would surely prevail.

Since we take our battles one at a time, we were not unduly impressed.

THE DAVID-AND-GOLIATH TRICK

The ploy of building up the opposing lawyers is not used only to make a loss seem less embarrassing.

If anything, the tactic is even more appealing to a lawyer who expects to win.

Now, excessive modesty is not something they teach you at law school. Still, a lawyer can't very well go around telling people how brilliant and eloquent he is, how he hypnotizes juries and so overwhelms judges with his exhaustive knowledge that they'll let him do whatever he wants.

If, however, he says all those things about his *opponent*—if he presents his opposite number as a judicial Goliath—and then goes on to beat him—well, the client will be free to draw his own conclusions.

Some years ago, IMG was put through a David-and-Goliath scenario on a matter that is rather comical in its sheer pettiness. It so happened that during the same years our client Bjorn Borg was ruling men's tennis, the great nation of Uruguay was going crazy over the sport. The Uruguayans had an apparently unslakable thirst for products—T-shirts, coffee mugs, beach towels—with Borg's name and likeness on them.

The only problem was, no one in Uruguay seemed inclined to take the time or trouble to license that name and image, or to look into the inconvenient fact of international trademarks and copyrights. The abuses were so flagrant that we had no choice but to hire an Uruguayan lawyer to try to straighten out the mess.

This lawyer was a character. He had an incredibly high-flown way of talking and writing, and from the start he made it sound as if the entire legal apparatus of Latin America was mobilized against him, and him alone. The fight would be long, hard, and bitter, he warned us. Perhaps he could carry the day, but it would require every scrap of his wit and passion, because the other side was so crafty and so determined.

Forget that this was as clear-cut a case of infringement as could possibly be imagined, and a puny one at that! This fellow insisted on presenting it as a battle royal among the best legal minds of the age.

Eventually, we won the case—and our attorney sent us a bill that was roughly equivalent to two years' worth of the royalties we would see from the new licensing agreements.

At the end of that two years, by the way, the Uruguayan tennis craze was pretty well played out, and that was the end of the Borg beach towel fad!

So I would say, Watch Out if your attorney has too many nice things to say about the opposing lawyers. Chances are, one way or the other, his adulation is going to cost you money.

LAW FIRM ECONOMICS 101

Of all the sorts of information that lawyers don't particularly like to share with laymen, facts and figures on law firm economics come high on the list.

Hundreds of thousands of dollars are spent on research studies on the subject, but the results are virtually never circulated outside the profession.

Why?

Well, maybe lawyers are concerned that the general public will resent them even more than it already does, if people find out, for example, that:

Median *after-tax* income for partners of large law firms is closing in on the $250,000 mark. Reckoning by median minimizes the impact of partners' compensation at the very top firms, where annual incomes are often in the seven-figure range.

Many people, myself included, are outraged by the runaway judgments routinely awarded these days in liability cases. But do you know how much of every judgment actually ends up going to the plaintiffs? *Thirty-seven cents* of every dollar awarded. The rest is gobbled up in legal fees and expenses.

In the typical instance, law firms shell out roughly $65,000 per lawyer per year for rent and other operating expenses— meaning, of course, that clients foot the bill for that egregious overhead *before* an attorney does one single thing on their behalf.

In spite of this whopping overhead, law firms operate at an average profit margin of 42 percent. For most businesses, a margin of 10 percent is comfortable, and 20 percent is considered excellent. But then, a law firm is a different kind of store.

CRACKING THE NUT

Meeting the overhead is, of course, the first item on a lawyer's economic agenda.

No client should overlook the role played by operating expenses in determining what his legal costs will be. No client should kid himself about who pays for the signed prints on the wall, the teak desks, the creamy stationery.

As evidence of just how crucial overhead is, consider this tale of two closings.

Recently, one of our broadcasting clients was in the process of simultaneously selling a Manhattan co-op and buying a house in a quiet little town on the east end of Long Island.

A house closing is considerably more complicated than a co-op closing; there are title searches and surveys to be done, on-premises inspections, and so forth. Further, the lawyer's role on behalf of a seller is almost always less complicated than on behalf of a buyer. Finally, the price tag on the house was just more than double the apartment's.

For all that, legal fees on the co-op closing were *four times greater* than on the house purchase.

Why?

Because the attorney on the house closing was a local fellow who had a perfectly decent office above a hardware store on Main Street, and the attorney on the co-op closing had a suite on a high floor in a building on Madison Avenue.

Both lawyers gave competent service in what were, after all, totally routine procedures.

This fellow didn't *need* a fancy lawyer for the apartment transaction any more than he needed his Rolls-Royce to drive to the corner for a quart of milk. But this leads me to give the following warning:

McCormack's Axiom of Location, Location, and Location

If you insist on doing business in an expensive neighborhood, you're going to end up paying your lawyer's exorbitant rent.

HOW DO YOU SPELL CHUTZPAH?

In most businesses, there are limits as to how much overhead can be passed along to consumers. But lawyers have succeeded in pushing that threshold practically to infinity.

The bottom line is that *unless you ride shotgun on them, lawyers will charge you pretty much whatever they want for whatever level of service they feel like providing.*

There's a great story about a man named Ben Sonnenberg, who was one of the inventors of modern public relations as well as one of the greatest self-promoters of all time. Back in 1958, when the Ford Motor Company decided to close up shop on the disastrous Edsel, company executives were frantic about the long-term damage being done to corporate prestige.

They went to Sonnenberg and asked his advice on the best way to restore the patina on the company name.

Sonnenberg told them that, for $50,000, he would think about the problem and bestow upon them the benefit of his wisdom.

So Ford forked over the cash, and Sonnenberg went home to ponder. A week later, he told them, "Do nothing."

That's what Ford got for its fifty thousand.

I mention this story because while lawyers' fees are seldom quite so unconscionable on a piecework basis, their method of charging has several things in common with Mr. Sonnenberg's:

Typically, a lawyer simply names his price, and the client has no choice but to take it or leave it.

Except in contingent-fee cases, the client pays dearly regardless of result.

The practitioner bills virtually without accountability, and does so in a climate where there is almost no standard for judging whether his price is fair.

MONITORING THE METER

Are there ways to make lawyers more accountable in their billing?

The answer is yes and no.

A client should always demand a complete and detailed bill from his attorney, and should review the document carefully.

Ideally, the bill should be issued *monthly*—before fees can get too far out of control.

It should reflect the charges and contributions of everyone—associates, paralegals, secretaries—working on your case.

It should include all items like telephone bills, photocopies, messengers.

A lawyer's bill, in short, should be as airtight as the cash register receipt you get from the supermarket.

THE ILLUSION OF PRECISION

That said, however, the terrible truth remains: *reviewing* a lawyer's charges is not the same thing as being able to *control* a lawyer's charges.

It is still in the lawyer's sole discretion, for example, to bill a full quarter-hour "unit" if he leaves a thirty-second message on someone's answering machine.

A lawyer may still bill you full rate for the five hours he sits on an airplane on your behalf—and you have no way of knowing if *another* client's file was on his lap during the flight, and if *that* client is being billed as well.

Even in a detailed accounting, there will be places to hide such oddments as (true story!) the dry-cleaning bills of paralegals who view business trips as opportunities to have their entire wardrobes cleaned by the hotel valet service.

As ever, then, in the war between clients and lawyers, the lawyers have a broad range of tactical advantages on their side. Still, there are moves that clients can make to give themselves a fighting chance—and in the chapter that follows, we'll talk about some nuts-and-bolts prescriptions for evening up the odds.

4

A PRIMER FOR CLIENTS

There's an old quip about the businessman who is asked by a colleague to recommend a good lawyer.

"I can't," the fellow says, "because there aren't any. There are only *effective* lawyers—and, come to think of it, I can't come up with many of those either."

Turning the joke around, the same thing could be said of clients.

There are effective clients and ineffective clients; clients who promote their own best interests and clients who shoot themselves in the foot; clients who save themselves money on legal fees and clients who unwittingly conspire in running up their bills.

How and why do some clients make their lives even more miserable than necessary when dealing with lawyers?

Usually it comes down to not knowing the right questions to ask. Or being afraid to ask those questions. Or failing to understand the answers.

It's understandable that these difficulties might affect clients who have recourse to lawyers only a few times in their lives. Less understandable is the fact that even sophisticated clients are often hamstrung by the same uncertainties and lack of self-assertion.

Why?

Basically because lawyers—not all, but many—are happy to preserve their aura of mystery and their stance of subtle intimidation.

They aren't taught that stance in law school, you understand. But, boy, do they ever learn that it comes in handy in real life!

NOT JUST ANOTHER PRETTY FACE

Many clients put themselves behind the eight ball by the sheer lack of thought with which they choose an attorney in the first place.

They hire someone because they have a passing acquaintance with him at the squash club.

Or because he once represented their brother-in-law in some entirely different sort of procedure.

Or because his office is convenient to where they have their poodle groomed.

Most of IMG's clients have personal attorneys, and while I obviously can't name names in this connection, I have sometimes been appalled at their choices.

We have had boxing clients who apparently picked lawyers because they were fight buffs; these attorneys might *literally* have been good to have in your corner, but you wouldn't want them standing between you and the American legal system.

Similarly, we have had skiing clients who apparently chose lawyers because they would be comfortable meeting them on the slopes.

It is human nature, I suppose, to want to do business with

people who share in your passions and who flatter your vanity by being your fans. But this is no way to pick an attorney; and in fact it leads me to propose another rule.

McCormack's Hardnosed Axiom of Lawyer Selection
Hire the person who can do the job—and accept that the person who can do the job isn't necessarily the person you want to be best friends with.

Keep in mind, too, that the right lawyer for one job may not be the right lawyer for *every* job.

A fresh-scrubbed, horn-rimmed Ivy Leaguer might be just the fellow to ease you through a deal with an investment bank, but chances are he would get eaten alive in a battle with an inner-city D.A.

A gritty sole practitioner might do just fine in a toe-to-toe with the D.A., but wouldn't win you points with the investment bank.

You don't have to know one single thing about the law itself to be able to make these judgments. You just have to pay attention.

ASK AND YE WON'T BE TAKEN

But again, paying *effective* attention is easier said than done.

Most people who fail to get themselves the right lawyer, do so for one of three reasons:

Either they're too lazy to make inquiries or shop around, even though in most cities three or four well-placed phone calls will get them all the information they need.

Or they're so insecure that they don't believe they can judge a lawyer's competence.

Or they're so misguidedly impressed with lawyers that they assume that since Mr. Yale or Ms. Cornell has passed the bar, he or she must have a handle on every entry in the legal lexicon.

This, if you think about it even for a moment, is a bizarre assumption. In fact, there is no one on earth who knows all the law.

There is no one who knows half the law, and I would venture to say that a person with a real, intimate working knowledge of even one thousandth of the law has a claim to be thought of as a giant of jurisprudence!

The law has become a profession of specialties and subspecialties, with the subspecialties getting more fine-tuned every day. It is therefore more crucial than ever to *find a lawyer whose technical abilities suit your present needs.*

Don't be afraid to ask a lawyer head-on if he or she has expertise in a particular matter.

Don't be afraid to ask if he or she has handled similar cases before.

Ask for specific examples.

Lawyers, like the rest of us, enjoy a new challenge and welcome the opportunity to expand their professional repertoire. If you don't *force* them to go on the record with an accounting of their experience, chances are they'll keep mum on the subject of their *in*experience.

Remember: You're not shelling out good money for the privilege of being a guinea pig.

Don't put yourself on the line so that the *next* person can have the benefit of an experienced attorney.

HOME COURT ADVANTAGE

Just as different lawyers stake out different specialties within the law, they stake out different geographical turfs, too; and usually it is to a client's advantage to have local representation.

There are several reasons for this. One is that, especially in smaller cities and towns, there tends to be a prejudice against the "city slickers" and in favor of the native sons or daughters. It is also true that local counsel, generally speaking, will be better able to monitor a given situation, especially if that situation is susceptible to changes in the political or economic climate in their particular area.

Let me give a few examples that underline the importance of being "turf-sensitive" where legal matters are concerned.

A WIN IN PITTSBURGH

IMG was involved in a major legal action concerning a professional sports team in Pittsburgh, and we were debating what sort of firm we should hire to represent us.

The matter was a complicated one and the stakes were high, and my first impulse—call it a prejudice, if you like—was to retain one of the most high-powered New York firms.

Before taking this step, however, we spoke with a partner of one of Pittsburgh's leading outfits, who gave us an account of a horrendous experience *he* had had when trying a case in North Carolina. The judge and the opposing lawyers had known each other for years, and everything that happened in the courtroom made him feel not just that he was from another state, but from another planet.

The implication was plain enough: Although they don't teach it this way at law school, the rules of impartiality always have enough slack in them to give an edge to the home team.

This attorney suggested that, while Pittsburgh wasn't small-

town North Carolina, we would still be better off aligning ourselves with a firm that was familiar with Pittsburgh judges,
Pittsburgh clerks, and "the Pittsburgh way of getting things
done."

We were persuaded to retain him, and in fact the hometown
nature of the resulting legal work was more than satisfactory.

A DISASTER DOWN UNDER

To illustrate what can happen when a client *isn't* sensitive to the
question of a lawyer's turf, I must pass along an account of
perhaps the costliest tactical error I ever made in the selection
of an attorney.

A number of years ago, I and a group of IMG clients invested
in a leasehold on 1.2 million acres in the Northern Territory of
Australia, not far from the town of Darwin. This parcel of land
was almost the size of Holland, and we leased it long-term for
less than a dollar an acre.

The government of Australia was the lessor on the property;
its goal, of course, was to promote the development of the Northern Territory. Accordingly, the government wrote a provision
in the lease stating that the land had to be improved by a certain
amount of investment each year, for the building of fences and
so forth, so that the property could be used for cattle.

Now, we had no intention of getting into the ranching business. We had bought the property as a speculation—and had
made this very clear to the prestigious Sydney-based lawyer who
handled the transaction for us. The lawyer, in turn, assured us
that we had nothing to worry about. No one had ever paid any
attention to the land-improvement clauses. They were in the
nature of a mere formality, and no one ever inspected the
property.

Besides, would anyone really insist that we build a fence around
a piece of property almost the size of Holland?

As it happened, someone would.

Shortly after we acquired the lease, a man named Gough Whitlam became prime minister of Australia. He had run his campaign on an Australia First theme, and one of his promises was to discourage foreign investment and foreign ownership of Australian property and assets.

This was going on half a world away from where we were based, you understand, and with all due respect to the importance of Australia's domestic politics, Mr. Whitlam's sentiments were not exactly making world news. We were dependent on Our Man in Sydney to keep us posted.

But here we had made a terrible misjudgment. Sydney is about as far from the Northern Territory as, say, New York is from Nevada, and, as the saying goes, all politics is local politics. Our cosmopolitan attorney simply didn't understand how virulent (and how opportunistic) was the nationalist feeling in the frontier north.

So it took us absolutely by surprise when we were suddenly informed that our Holland-sized piece of land had reverted to the state because of our failure to develop it! We were given no warning of this turn of events, and no chance to correct the situation. It was just handed to us as a fait accompli.

Eventually we went to court in northern Australia and, after great trouble and expense, managed to reach a reasonable settlement with the government.

But matters should never have come to that. All along, we would have been better served by a sole practitioner in a dusty office in the northern boondocks—someone who *knew the turf and was in a position to sense the changing climate*—than by our fancy lawyer who was hopelessly out of touch with the local realities.

VICTORY AT SEA

Before leaving the subject of geographical leverage, I would like to relate another anecdote that has a happier note. A good friend of mine charters a yacht each summer in the Greek islands for a month. This friend happens to be one of the world's leading experts in the laws of admiralty and shipping, and someone who is intimately acquainted with the courts of Greece.

One day, while my friend was happily sailing along with his family, the owner of the yacht called the ship's captain on the radio and informed him that he needed the boat for his own use. The owner ordered the captain to disembark my friend and his family at the nearest port. The captain was quite embarrassed, but passed along this unfortunate message on behalf of his employer, the shipowner. The unfortunate owner, of course, had no idea what he was getting involved in.

Within three days, my friend had filed a suit for harassment and damages in the courts of Corfu, had obtained a judgment for several hundred thousand dollars, and ultimately ended up getting a luxury cruise in the Greek islands for nothing, as well as the money.

It pays to know the local customs.

STYLE AS WELL AS SUBSTANCE

Not long ago, a writer friend called me for advice about changing literary agents.

She had just signed a contract for her second book, and was receiving an advance more than double the amount she had received for her first.

She was being paid top dollar and was often getting cover credits from several major magazines.

In all, her career was going swimmingly, and I asked her why in the world she was thinking of dropping her agent.

"Because he embarrasses me," she said. "He's got this fast-talking, Hollywood style, and when I meet editors he's dealt with, I often feel that the first thing I have to let them know is that I'm not like him."

Her story really hit home, because I still have a very sharp recollection of the first time I was made to realize **the importance of personal style in maintaining a business relationship.**

Back in my very earliest days of representing athletes, I was at a beach club in Santa Monica with Arnold Palmer. We were standing at the service counter, waiting to be given towels. For no good reason, the simple process of getting the towels and having our changing facilities arranged turned out to be slow, complicated, and annoying.

Back in those days, I was very aggressive, impatient, and apt to be abrasive and sarcastic. I let it be known—to the checkout clerk himself and to everyone within earshot—that I thought he was a bit of an idiot.

I was nasty, but I was right.

Later on, in private, Arnold gave me a more than stern talking-to. He didn't like to treat people that way, and he didn't want those associated with him treating people that way.

He felt it was a reflection on him—and he was right. Ever since then, whenever I do anything with or on behalf of a client, I keep in mind that the top priority is not how *I'll* feel about it but how *the client* will feel.

With lawyers as well as with agents, personal style matters deeply, and there's no sense hiring someone who has the technical ability but who sets your teeth on edge.

Clearly, if you're hiring an attorney to represent you in a hostile procedure in which everybody hates everybody and you'll never do business again, you may as well get the toughest, gruffest bulldog you can find. As the saying qoes, *"If you're hiring a gun, get one that can shoot."*

Often, however, your lawyer will be representing you *vis-à-vis* people you'll be dealing with in future.

If he's sleazy, you'll be sleazy by association.

If he's intractable on a given issue, chances are you'll run into intractability from the other side somewhere down the road.

So try to find someone whose approach is consonant with your own. But as I said earlier, the idea is not to be sentimental or to pick a lawyer because he's a friend. That's a mistake.

Keep in mind this rule of thumb:

McCormack's Axiom of Association

If you're not comfortable with the idea that someone might *think* the lawyer is a friend of yours, then you probably shouldn't do business.

AVOID THE QUICK DISSATISFIERS

If you hire an attorney to represent you in a lawsuit, and the lawsuit takes two years to conclude or reach a settlement, it will probably take you the same two years to reach a final judgment on whether you were happy with the lawyer's services: in the end, it's results that matter.

Along the way, however, there will probably be hundreds of small details in which the lawyer will satisfy or frustrate you, win your confidence or make you angry.

Does he return your phone calls?

Does he explain things to you in a manner you can understand?

Does he make an effort to be available when *you* are?

Does he keep you posted about important developments in the case, or does he leave you in the dark?

These are the kinds of issues I tnink of as the potential quick dissatisfiers—and *avoiding them is the client's responsibility as much as the attorney's.*

Different clients have different needs—emotional as well as practical. And a great deal of trouble and ill feeling can be avoided if a client is clear and explicit about his needs from the beginning.

Are you the type of person who requires a fair amount of hand-holding?

If so, ask your lawyer if you would be able to reach him, if need be, in the evenings or on weekends. Ask him if he tends to be away for weeks at a time, and how his office is covered when he's gone.

Do you get paranoid if you feel you're losing control of things?

If so, you should make a point of asking to be kept abreast of all procedures, copied on letters and memos, etc.

If, on the other hand, you're happier not being bothered with details, tell your lawyer you want to be shielded from them, and that you want to hear nothing from him except when to appear in court.

For your own peace of mind, let your attorney know where you stand on these basic contact and involvement issues. And make sure he's willing to do things the way you want them done.

Remember, when you're the client, you're the boss, even if sometimes it doesn't feel that way.

Your lawyer should be accountable to you in whatever reasonable form *you* are comfortable with.

HOW SMART IN BUSINESS SHOULD A BUSINESS LAWYER BE?

The crux of being an effective client lies in knowing how to get a lawyer to give you the service you need.

But there is another side of it as well: **knowing how to *prevent* a lawyer from meddling in situations where "the legal approach" just isn't appropriate.**

Giving credit where credit is due, most lawyers are pretty intelligent people.

They have the analytical tools to go after a problem, and they are generally quick studies of the specific requirements, customs, and jargon of a given field.

However, the nature of their intelligence tends not to be the same as the more intuitive, improvising resourcefulness of the business person.

And when lawyers try too hard to apply their smarts to issues that are really *business* issues, the terrible truth is that they sometimes end up seeming not so smart at all.

In situations like that, *it is the client's responsibility to let the attorney know when to back off.*

ANATOMY OF A DEAL

I have no shortage of examples of misguided legal zeal in action —examples that illustrate the value of client oversight.

To understand the cases that follow, however, you need to know just a little about the steps by which a deal is generally concluded at a company like IMG.

To put it very simply, first, one of our line executives negotiates the basic deal points with executives of the company contracting for our client's services. Working out the deal points is often a tremendously delicate process that can take months.

Once the deal points are agreed to in principle, several sets of lawyers become involved—and *that's* where it really gets complicated. IMG's legal department drafts a document reflecting the understanding reached by the executives. This draft goes both to the other company's lawyers *and* to our client's own attorneys.

Now, even if the draft is a perfectly good representation of the agreement, and even if the deal is an advantageous one for all concerned, there is a very good chance that some or all of the lawyers will at this point try to get *something extra*.

Why?

Simply because they have to feel they're serving *some* purpose, after all.

Thus, we end up with lawyers' inappropriate *after-the-fact* meddling in other people's hard-won deals.

This causes potential problems—and we, as savvy clients, have to make sure those potential problems don't become actual problems.

First of all, negotiations, like sharks, have to keep moving forward or they die. *Any time the forward momentum of a deal is stopped in order to rehash things that were supposedly settled, there's a real chance the deal will fall apart.*

Additionally, *bringing in new issues late in the game casts doubt on the good faith of what has gone before.*

If the new requests are legitimate, why weren't they mentioned sooner? And what's to prevent them from seeming sneaky or unfair, like a final jab thrown after the bell has sounded?

"YES, BUT WHO WANTS PICTURES OF THIRTY-YEAR-OLD SNEAKERS?"

Consider this apparently innocent "something extra" sought by the lawyers of the All-England Club in regard to the club's standard licensing agreement for use of the name "Wimbledon."

Wimbledon is one of the magic words in sport, and the All-England Club, owner of the tournament, takes in enormous promotional revenues for allowing the name to be linked to everything from sportswear to soft drinks.

As is perfectly normal in this sort of licensing arrangement, licensees are given access to the tennis stadium to shoot advertising and promotional photographs. Typically, these photographs will be of items like a can of soda sitting in the umpire's chair, or of a model posing in the stands wearing a certain brand of sunglasses.

Well, a number of years ago, a lawyer for All-England came up with the notion that at the termination of a given licensing agreement, copyrights of all pictures taken by the licensee should revert to the club.

On the face of it, this seemed a harmless enough suggestion.

But in fact it placed an unconscionable burden on the licensee. Expensive and unwieldy mechanisms would have to be designed to make sure that all photographs were filed and preserved— for decades, in many cases. Licensees would have to negotiate, in turn, with individual photographers, making it clear that *they* couldn't retain the copyright.

Besides, since in virtually every case the photographs were product shots of what the licensee happened to be selling, what good could it possibly do the All-England Club to have them? Who needed an out-of-date picture of tennis sneakers standing at the baseline?

Nevertheless, this lawyer kept insisting that the photograph-copyright clause be inserted into the standard licensing agreement.

And you know what? We haven't gotten it yet in any executed contract! Every licensee insisted on having it crossed out, and they were usually annoyed that it had even been asked for. So what was the point?

A WAREHOUSE FULL OF BLUSHER

The question of copyrights on photographs is small potatoes compared with the "something extra" that Michael Jackson's lawyers tried to get on a deal they were negotiating with Max Factor.

Max Factor had in mind to launch a major line of Michael Jackson fragrances and cosmetics, and the fees involved were stratospheric. But Jackson's lawyers weren't satisfied with money alone. They wanted a clause stating that if Max Factor defaulted *for any reason*, the company would instantly forfeit its right to sell any licensed products it had in inventory.

This provision was totally unworkable. Max Factor's inventory could conceivably run into the tens of millions of dollars, and no corporate counsel would allow his company to take on that sort of exposure.

Second, insofar as the clause was presumably intended to safeguard Jackson from an intentional reneging by Factor, it was reasonable in theory. In fact, however, the licensing agreement ran to sixty-five pages, and was so complicated that Factor could have been *technically* in default if—literally—a memo blew off someone's desk.

What Jackson's lawyers were asking, then, was for Factor to put a giant club in their hands, the better to clobber the company with later on! They damn near lost the entire deal.

A RUDE BUT VITAL QUESTION

For similar reasons, I happen to believe that a client should give the following reply when a lawyer starts making suggestions on the *business* aspects of a deal:

WHO THE HELL ASKED YOU???

This is not to say that lawyers *never* come up with helpful and even brilliant suggestions. They do—and it will be my pleasure to relate some of those instances in their proper place.

In the typical case, however, when lawyers try to horn in on the business aspects of a deal, the practical result is usually confusion and wasted time.

Keep in mind the following axiom.

McCormack's Axiom of the Division of Labor
Lawyers *formalize* the deal. They shouldn't *do* the deal.

ARGUING WITH THE EXPERTS

This question of legal expertise versus business savvy raises a more general issue that every client should be aware of—the issue of questioning one's own hired experts.

The conventional wisdom, of course, is that if you're paying someone good money for supposedly expert advice, you should either follow the advice or fire the expert; those are the only two acceptable options.

Well, I believe that the conventional wisdom is dead wrong on that score.

The value of expert opinion—legal or otherwise—lies not in following it blindly and absolutely, but simply in having it available as *data*. In that form, it can be factored in with *other* data, including one's own intuition and experience.

In 1984, when *Time* magazine was forced to defend itself against a libel suit brought by the Israeli military leader Ariel Sharon, I had a discussion with *Time*'s managing editor, Ray Cave, which neatly underlined the truth of this advice.

Needless to say, *Time* had hired an absolutely top-notch battery of lawyers to defend it; these were men and women with an impressive knowledge of the libel laws and of First Amendment protections—and they had no shortage of expert advice to dispense.

At the same time, Cave realized that no one was better equipped to offer insight into journalistic procedure and sound reporting practices than the editors and writers of *Time*—i.e., his own staff.

So in this instance, the client, Time, Inc., found itself with two different sets of experts who had divergent priorities and who approached almost every issue somewhat differently. Ignoring either group would have been folly, and the *Time* management had the good sense to realize that both cadres should have a hearing.

The result was spirited discussion, sometimes argument—and

an overall defense that was more intelligent and persuasive than either gang of mavens could have formulated on their own.

LEAVE YOUR EGO AT THE DOOR

It should be said, however, that just as lawyers sometimes do their clients a disservice by meddling where they shouldn't, clients sometimes do *themselves* an injury by believing they are the final authority on everything.

This tendency usually goes by the name of pigheadedness, and it can be a very expensive habit.

It might make sense to argue with an expert who is holding forth on some intimate aspect of *your own business;* it makes less sense to compare brains with someone who is reading you chapter and verse on the quirks of the tax code.

To judge effectively where your own competence fades off into vulnerability, and where your own good ideas tail off into bluster, you've got to leave your ego at the door.

And that's an absolutely basic requirement of being an effective client.

BEWARE OF BEING OVER-LAWYERED

One of the truly terrible things about many Western legal systems is that *the lawyers themselves are given such broad discretion in determining the pace and complexity—i.e., the* cost *—of most procedures by which they make their living.*

Built into the systems are all sorts of incentives for lawyers to be slow, obscurantist, contentious, long-winded. Law schools might deny it, but there is the most obvious temptation for lawyers to do more lawyering than really needs doing.

For a slightly comical example of over-lawyering at its worst, consider these two versions of so-called grant clauses typically included in licensing contracts:

> Licensor hereby grants to Company the right to use Licensor's trademarks on and in connection with the advertisement, distribution and sale of athletic shoes and athletic shoes only.

The above wording is perfectly clear and legally watertight. Now here is what an overly zealous lawyer might add to it (and in fact *has* added to it, this example being from our files!):

> Use by Company of the Licensor trademark on products other than athletic shoes shall result in immediate termination of this agreement and the forfeiture by Company of its rights hereunder, including the right to dispose of any inventory bearing Licensor's trademarks. Company agrees that Licensor shall have the right to enforce this obligation by injunctive relief and Company hereby indemnifies Licensor for any and all costs, expenses, damages, claims and expenses, including attorneys' fees, for any breach by Company of the foregoing obligations.

Just what in the name of heaven is the second version all about? It adds virtually nothing of substance to the first simple clause.

One party to a contract can *always* seek relief if the other party violates the contract's provisions; that's why they call it a contract!

Damages can *always* be sought—again, by definition.

So the second version does nothing except keep the billing meter running while the lawyer belabors basic points of law that are implied in any contract anyway.

The result, however, isn't quite so innocent because the overwriting and the over-lawyering have dramatically changed the whole *tone* of the agreement. The second clause is an example of what lawyers call "confrontational drafting"; I think of it as "dueling word processors."

Based on the second version, it would seem that the Licensor expects the worst from this relationship, mistrusts the Licensee, and is ready to file a lawsuit at the very first hint of justification.

Is this the impression that the Licensor would like to convey at the beginning of a *cooperative* arrangement, the object of which is to have *both sides* make money?

Obviously it isn't. And it is the client's responsibility to make sure that his lawyer's language accurately reflects not just the *letter* of a deal, but the *spirit* of it as well.

OBNOXIOUS BY ASSOCIATION

The damage of being over-lawyered, then, goes beyond the mere fact of being overcharged. The real danger is that your intentions are misrepresented. **If your lawyer is obnoxious, you're obnoxious by association.**

In the worst case, deals fall through, much to the bafflement of the principals, because the lawyers have gotten carried away by their own pugnacity.

In less dramatic instances, positions harden, resentments accrue, and proceedings take on an adversarial flavor when they don't have to.

And of course everyone ends up paying more than is really necessary.

So how can a client avoid being over-lawyered?

Make it very clear to your attorney *from the start* whether you expect difficulty or cooperation from the other side.

If there is a reservoir of trust and goodwill between you and your opposite number, let your lawyer know that—and stress that you want the present business to add to that reservoir, not deplete it.

Review your lawyer's letters and documents along the way, and if you don't think they're appropriate in tone, say so.

Lawyers, like Doberman pinschers, tend to think they were put on earth to act menacing. They've been bred to assume that's what their masters *want. So let your lawyer know when you want him to snarl and when he should try purring.*

LOVE ME, LOVE MY STAFF

I can still recall the first time I was wooed by a New York law firm.

This was roughly two decades ago, when IMG was a far smaller company than it is today. Still, sports promotion was a tremendous growth industry at the time, athletes were achieving celebrity status more and more—and where there's money and visibility, there's litigation. So lawyers began to be interested in soliciting our business.

On this particular morning I went to the offices of a major midtown firm. I'd never been there before, but the receptionist, well briefed, knew my name before I told her. A secretary brought me fresh-brewed coffee in an exquisite china cup. Then, without a moment's delay, I was ushered in to meet with a senior partner—a man who wore the whitest shirt I have ever seen, before or since.

This gentleman impressed the hell out of me. On his office wall, there was a gallery of photographs of himself with various CEOs of major companies, and a couple of heads of state thrown in for good measure. He was a terrific storyteller, with real wit, charm, and a stash of anecdotes stretching back to encounters with FDR, Gary Cooper, and Marlene Dietrich.

He took me to lunch at a place where it was famously difficult to get a table, where he was fawned on and personally visited by the chef. He ordered wine that had been in the bottle longer than I had been in long pants. In short, he was one of the worldliest and most magnetic men I had ever met in my life.

He was so charismatic that I almost didn't realize that *he would have virtually nothing to do with the sort of service I would or wouldn't get from his firm!*

He wouldn't be handling my cases. His elegant shoulders probably hadn't darkened the doorway of a courtroom in fifteen years. He was an ambassador—what is known in the trade as a "rainmaker." He brought in business by impressing, regaling, and tickling the vanity of youngish men such as I was at the time.

I tell this story because it suggests what I believe is a common mistake on the part of clients:

Too often, a client pays too much attention to the image of a firm or to its figureheads, and too little attention to the younger attorneys, paralegals, and functionaries *who actually service the account.*

A client should keep in mind that, in most instances, he or she is hiring not a single individual but a *team.* And the team is only as effective as its least effective member.

The most masterful trial work performed by a partner can be undermined if the associates and researchers haven't adequately prepared the case. A delicate negotiation being handled by a $500-an-hour lawyer can go down the tubes if a $40-an-hour paralegal has missed a deadline or gotten the facts wrong.

BEYOND THE WHITEST SHIRT

Clients, then, should ask at the outset **who at the firm will be responsible for what.**

Clients should not feel shy about asking to meet and interview associates and others who will play a part in their case.

If personnel change, as often happens, during the course of a legal action, clients should be advised of the change; you don't want the second-string coming into the game at a crucial juncture.

Don't let the impressiveness of the person in the corner office blind you to the necessity of having quality reflected *throughout* the firm you're dealing with.

THIS LITTLE MATTER OF MONEY

One of the shrewder observations of human nature was made by a humorist named Kin Hubbard. "When a man says it hain't the money but the principle o' the thing," this fellow commented, "it's th' money."

So it tends to be with legal actions. And so it certainly tends to be with relationships between clients and lawyers. At law school they teach you that the best attorney is the one who gets straight As and makes *Law Review;* out in the world, most people consider the best attorney to be the one who rakes in the most lucre.

Lawyers are obviously concerned with how much money a given client or a given action will bring in to the coffers. Clients are just as obviously concerned with how much a given procedure is going to cost them, and whether, on balance, they will gain or lose by the time the thing is over.

For all that, however, clients and lawyers, in the typical instance, talk about fees and costs surprisingly little.

They don't talk about them soon enough, openly enough, with enough creativity, or in enough detail.

Why?

Because such discussions tend to make everyone uncomfortable, and clients therefore avoid them—usually to their cost.

The legal profession takes the quite explicit stance that **fees** should be candidly discussed at the beginning of a relationship; however, no one says the attorney has to be the one to initiate the discussion.

Usually that responsibility devolves upon the client; and usually the lawyer is just as happy if the client doesn't quite know how to broach the subject.

What, then, are the questions that a lawyer should be asked? Here's a brief list:

What Is Your Hourly Rate, and What Are the Hourly Rates of Others Who Will Be Working on the Case?

This, of course, is an absolutely basic question. On the other hand, it is one that clients get fixated on when they shouldn't.

If a lawyer tells you he charges $500 an hour and bills in quarter-hour segments, you'll probably swallow hard when you realize it's going to cost you *at least* $125 every time he lifts a pencil or a telephone on your behalf.

But if that lawyer is skillful enough to find a shortcut so that a potentially drawn-out lawsuit is settled in a month, he is a bargain at his price.

Keep in mind, too, that top-ticket lawyers are charging you not just for *what* they know, but *who* they know.

A couple of years ago, a friend of mine was involved in a very delicate import-export matter that involved negotiations with the upper echelons of a foreign government. He hired an attorney who charged him $1,000 per hour—but who was able to get a former vice-president of the United States to stand in as an intermediary in the discussions.

During my early days at Arter, Hadden, I recall a client being told that senior partners at the firm billed at a rate of $175 an hour—which was very much the high end of the market at the time. "How fast do they work?" the client asked. The remark was facetious, but there's wisdom in it.

Hourly rates should be appraised with a full awareness that

one lawyer's hour can be another lawyer's week, and that some lawyers can accomplish with a single phone call what others couldn't pull off in a lifetime!

What About Expenses?

I will never forget the first time I saw a pack of lawyers gleefully squandering a client's money on limos, champagne, and over-priced food at the most expensive restaurant they could find.

I was serving as co-counsel on this case; a glitzy New York firm provided the lead attorneys, who were in charge of handling expenses For them it was all first-class air travel, deluxe hotels, and *foie gras*.

Frankly, I don't think they really enjoyed the luxuries they lavished on themselves. I think the fun just lay in the childish thrill of seeing how much they could get away with. They loved playing the big spenders—as long as it was with someone else's money.

I'm certainly not suggesting that that sort of decadent behavior is typical of lawyers. The champagne-and-truffles banquet, however, neatly illustrates a point that every client should be aware of: the question of "expenses" for legal work can cover a multitude of sins, and boundaries should be set as early on as possible.

If the work entails air travel, will the lawyers fly first class or coach?

Will they stay at the priciest hotel in town or be content with something less grand?

Will there be a cap on expenses for meals?

Also, if a lawyer is traveling on your behalf, how many hours will he bill? Some lawyers may do two hours of work for you while traveling and bill you for eight, on the grounds that they *would* have worked eight if they were home. By the same reasoning, some lawyers might bill *twelve* hours, claiming that's their normal workday.

Clients should understand that some lawyers—especially when working for a company presumed to have deep pockets—operate on the premise that they can get away with this sort of padding because their bills won't be closely scrutinized anyway.

A couple of years ago, I heard a terrific story that illustrates what a dramatic effect it can have when lawyers' bills *are* closely examined.

Company A and company B were engaged in a bitter and drawn-out lawsuit. The lawyers for company B wanted to settle, but the lawyers for company A refused: They were having too good a time, flying first class to Europe to take depositions in Geneva and Paris, lapping up caviar on the Concorde, and shopping for their wives and girl friends on the client's time. Obviously, the general counsel of company A had given them a long leash and was not watching the meter.

During the discovery phase of the lawsuit, however, the attorneys for company B pulled off a masterstroke. They managed to convince the judge that the billing records of company A's lawyers were germane to the case, and therefore should be handed over to be examined by all parties!

When the extravagant attorneys realized *everyone* would see the blatant evidence of all that chateaubriand and vintage Burgundy, they promptly agreed to settle.

Clearly, the abuses in this story were extreme. The fact is, however, that lawyers are generally not averse to spending their client's money. And keep this in mind:

McCormack's Axiom of Inverse Proportions
They'll spend more of it, the less the client seems to care.

So let your lawyer know you *do* care. Make it clear from the outset that you'll be reviewing all expenses, and that you expect your attorneys to be reasonable and prudent. By doing so, you'll save yourself some most unpleasant surprises when the bills come in.

Is There a Retainer, and If So, What Does It Cover?

Some lawyers—in a practice that is analogous to charging admission to a department store—charge clients a "retainer" merely for opening up a file in their name.

Other firms charge a retainer that s essentially a guarantee of a certain amount of billed time per month or quarter, and against which actual billed time is credited.

Other firms charge no retainer at all.

Find out from the start how a prospective lawyer handles this issue. If there is a retainer, ask how it is justified; if nothing else, it is highly entertaining to note the ingenuity with which attorneys answer this question.

Is There a Contingent-Fee Arrangement?

As I have said before and will say again, I believe that the contingent-fee system, as it applies to liability cases, is one of the things that is disastrously, catastrophically wrong with the American legal system.

In *some* instances, however, hiring a lawyer on a pay-for-results basis makes sense for all concerned—for the client, for the attorney, and for that vague entity known as the common good.

If, for example, one of IMG's clients is in a position to file suit for unpaid royalties, it might make sense to pay the lawyers not an hourly fee, but a percentage of moneys collected, regardless of how much time or work it takes. This creates an incentive to get the matter resolved expediently and a *dis*-incentive to drag it out; in most cases, it leads to an out-of-court settlement that allows one more trial to vanish from the docket.

There are certain issues a client should address in *any* sort of contingent-fee arrangement:

What will be the lawyer's percentage of the take?

What sorts of costs and expenses will come off the top, *before* the pot is divvied up?

Who will bear what part of those costs and expenses if you lose?

Don't assume that a contingency agreement means you have a free ride till the judgment comes rolling in. Judgment or no, the terrible truth is that you'll almost always find a bill in your mailbox.

Also, there's no law stating that a lawyer-client relationship must run on either a straight hourly rate or a straight contingency basis.

Everything is negotiable—though this is one of the things that lawyers would just as soon not have clients realize.

All sorts of hybrid arrangements are possible, and, as in any other business matter, a bit of ingenuity and some skill in negotiating can open up favorable horizons.

On occasion, for example, I have persuaded lawyers to *share* in the risk of a lawsuit by accepting a *reduced* hourly rate plus a premium if the judgment is favorable.

Such creative ways of dealing with the question of fees can make a lawyer and a client more effective partners in a legal action, as it brings their respective self-interests more closely into line.

How Much Is This Whole Business Likely to Cost Me?

This is a question you should always ask, even though it is virtually certain that a lawyer will bend over backward to avoid giving you an answer.

The lawyer will say—truly—that a meaningful estimate is impossible because everything depends on what the other side does.

Will the other side be cooperative or hostile? Will the other side move briskly forward or stall? Will *they* want to handle the drafting of documents, or will they leave that responsibility to you? These and other uncertainties are real enough.

Still, a client has the right to be given *some* estimate of probable fees and expenses.

Will it be in the range of $1,000 or $10,000 or $100,000?

These estimates, vague as they are, are valuable because **every prospective client should do a cost-benefit analysis—if only an informal one—before embarking on any legal action.**

My close friend Gordon Forbes, a former South African tennis champion who became most successful in the electrical business, tells an amusing story about his foray into the mystical world of trying to find out what one's legal bill is going to be. It seems that Gordon had a problem requiring the services of a good British law firm, but he was most concerned about what the limits of his costs might be, and queried in a persistent and pointed manner the eminent solicitor handling the case.

The response he got was: "Well, you know, Mr. Forbes, it is a bit like a piece of string, and it's really hard to tell." Upon further persistent questioning, the response became: "I suppose you could be looking at twenty thousand to twenty-five thousand pounds."

Since Gordon had figured that in South Africa the services in question couldn't cost more than 2,000 pounds or so, he said to the rather shocked British attorney: "What I would like you to do is two thousand pounds' worth of work and stop at precisely that moment, even if you are in the middle of a sentence." The stunned recipient of those orders was so taken aback by this approach that, if you can believe it, Mr. Forbes got all his legal work done within the 2,000-pound limit.

There are no hard-and-fast rules as to what is an acceptable ratio between legal fees and total moneys on the table. This ratio, in fact, varies quite widely in accordance with different procedures.

Some years ago, when IMG was in the steepest part of its growth curve—that stage when a business's very success can make it go broke—I decided to beef up our resources and facilities with the help of a quite substantial bank loan. Because of the amount of money involved and the other demands on my own time, I hired counsel to negotiate the transaction.

How much sense did it make to pay for that sort of service? Since the legal fees became, in effect, part of what I would be paying for the use of the loan, I reasoned that costs had to be kept within a point or two of the total transaction.

At the other end of the spectrum, if you are unlucky enough to find yourself the defendant in a liability suit, you may conclude that anything short of 100 percent of the judgment being sought is worth giving to your attorneys; you'll grudge every dollar, and rightly so, but what's the alternative?

The worst thing that ever happened to IMG in a court of law was when we spent $200,000 in legal fees en route to a settlement that cost us $800,000. That settlement, however, was in lieu of a judgment against us of $1,036,760. So, everything being relative, you could say our legal fees were well spent!

Will You Accept a Cap on Fees?

Over the years, I have sometimes used a stratagem which has, I believe, saved our company money. But even more important, it has allowed us peace of mind and the feeling that we were staying in control of our own destiny:

In instances where legal actions threatened to become complicated and protracted, I have tried to persuade our hired counsel to agree to a *cap* on yearly fees.

This cap, to be acceptable to the attorneys, obviously has to be somewhat in excess of the estimated cost; it's meant not as a way of cutting corners, but as protection against a worst-case scenario where outlays really run away with you.

In one instance, our lawyers estimated that a certain matter would cost between $48,000 and $72,000 a year to pursue, and I suggested putting a cap at $90,000.

Now, $90,000 is an annoying sum to have to shell out for lawyers, but it's preferable to worrying that, at the end of the year, you'll tot up the bills and they'll come to $150,000.

Why should a lawyer agree to a cap on fees?

First of all, because if he or she *doesn't* agree, there's a chance you'll take your business to someone who will.

Second, because if he refuses, he'll be placed in the embarrassing position of having to acknowledge that he doesn't place much faith in his own estimates.

And a lawyer wouldn't want to admit that, any more than a car mechanic would. If the estimates can't be relied on, who knows what *other* aspects of the lawyer's services might turn out to be dubious.

THE ONE-TIME-ONLY RELATIONSHIP

Most individuals hire lawyers on an *ad hoc* basis.

They are buying a piece of property. They are getting a divorce. They have been involved in a fender-bender and are entertaining visions of a big "pain-and-suffering" judgment.

In cases like these, lawyer-client relationships tend to be short-term, with repeat business expected by no one and loyalty accruing to neither side.

Why, then, should attorneys work hard at doing a good and timely job for one-time-only customers?

Except where a contingent fee is involved, the lawyer's only incentives are his or her own professionalism and personal pride, and the client has no choice but to put a considerable amount of faith in those things.

That faith, however, should not be blind or passive.

Clients should monitor their lawyers' work *as it is being done.*

They should question fees and expenses *as the bills come in.*

If an action doesn't appear to be going well, they should demand to know why, *before it's too late for a shift in course, or, for that matter, a change in representation.*

LOYALTY AND LEVERAGE

The dynamic is rather different when a lawyer-client relationship has some history behind it and, presumably, some future ahead of it.

In that case, loyalty and good business sense neatly dovetail with fear to keep lawyers on their toes and to give them plenty of reason for performing well and charging fairly.

Obviously, no attorney wants to jeopardize a long-term relationship by doing a single piece of shoddy work or by some pettiness on the billing side.

Additionally, since a lawyer and a longstanding client will almost certainly have a network of colleagues and associates in common, no attorney will want to risk a damaged reputation by negative word of mouth.

All these factors give a client leverage—leverage he should never forget that he has, but which, in a good relationship, never need be used.

WHEN SHOULD YOU MARRY YOUR LAWYER?

In forging an ongoing relationship with an attorney, however, there are a couple of questions a client should ask himself:

Do I really *need* this relationship?

When and on what basis should I pick *my* attorney?

On the first question, I can only say that common sense must dictate the need. Some people retain lawyers month after idle month simply because it makes them feel important to have a lawyer.

On the other hand, an individual with assets substantial enough to be considered an estate will obviously want a trusted attorney he can talk with through the years. Similarly, anyone responsible for running a business will want to have access to legal counsel from someone familiar enough with the operation so that every conversation doesn't have to start from square one.

Beyond a certain size, businesses seem automatically to spawn a need for in-house counsel, and then, by the curious and distressing mechanism that makes lawyers multiply, in-house counsel always seems to come up with various needs for *outside* counsel.

As to *how* to enter into a marriage with a lawyer, I say do it gradually and with enormous circumspection.

Breaking up with one's attorney is emotionally stressful and logistically daunting, and the more miles you've traveled together, the more wrenching the whole process is. So take it slow until you're sure of the attorney's competence and of your mutual compatibility.

I am a firm believer in letting a lawyer know, early on, that if he performs well, charges fairly, and is responsive to my needs, I will have plenty more work for him in the future.

This is an absolutely basic way of providing an incentive,

and of course businesses use it all the time with regard to advertising agencies, public relations firms, and so forth.

Any professional in a service occupation will work harder if he knows that one well-done job can lead the way to a mother lode of ongoing assignments. Lawyers are no exception.

They may *act* independent. But a smart client should see beyond the professional pose and realize that, diploma or no diploma, a lawyer is a vendor who is in deep trouble unless he can hold on to your business.

PART TWO

LAWYERS AND BUSINESSMEN: THE UNEASY ALLIANCE

5

WHY LAWYERS
DRIVE BUSINESSMEN CRAZY

A number of years ago, a book was published called *The Duke
of Deception*. It was written by a fellow named Geoffrey Wolff,
and it was about Wolff's late father, a fascinating raconteur, con
man, and liar. Wolff Senior was a compelling rogue who had
unfailing insights into what made people tick, and who used
those insights to raise petty fraud to an art form.

The Duke had a credit rating somewhat worse than the government of Mexico's, yet he managed to buy anything he wanted
on credit.

He would walk into the finest men's store, and walk out again
with half a dozen suits charged to a newly opened house account
on which payment would never be made. He would drive con-
vertibles away from used-car lots on the strength of a spurious
promise. He'd "buy" watches, jewelry, television sets, and he
would use a variety of spiels that ranged from the ingenious to
the bizarre.

He got away with it again and again. Why?

He got away with it because he had the genius to penetrate to the deepest truth about how salespeople function. *Salespeople, he realized, are so obsessed with selling that they barely notice anything else.*

In the face of an opportunity for a sale—especially a *big* sale, to an apparently wealthy customer full of swagger and the implied promise of repeat business—other considerations fade into insignificance.

Judgment grows fuzzy. If something doesn't seem exactly kosher, chances are a salesperson will overlook it. Procedures can somehow or other be gotten around if need be.

Priority number one is not to let that customer out the door without some merchandise. The Duke understood perfectly the psychological makeup that correlates with the sales mentality, and exploited it.

To put it another way, he realized that *there are personality types that correspond with different occupations.*

This, in turn, has to do with two factors:

1. What sort of person picks what sort of career to begin with.

2. How people are affected by the pressures and traditions that pertain in various fields.

These observations go a long way toward explaining why businessmen and lawyers drive each other crazy.

Businessmen are like dogs; they're high-spirited, frisky, their tails wag at the thought of a deal.

Lawyers are like cats—careful, coy, and retreating.

Put the two in a conference room together, and anything can happen.

WHAT-IF–ING A DEAL TO DEATH

The best and worst thing about lawyers, from the businessman's point of view, is that they are thorough.

Often it's good that they are, because businessmen, like salesmen, sometimes run the risk of letting their enthusiasm for doing a deal cloud their assessment of the potential downside.

Still, there are times when lawyerly thoroughness just isn't appropriate—when the real danger is that the attorneys will get together and what-if a deal to death.

CLASS WILL OUT

Several years ago I negotiated a contract between Michael Parkinson, the British television personality, and Rupert Murdoch involving a TV series to be broadcast in Australia. The major points of the deal had all been discussed and agreed to—we knew how much Parkinson would be compensated, who would actually own the program, how foreign rights would be divvied up, and so forth.

Appended to these crucial matters was a simple provision that Parkinson's expenses to, from, and within Australia would be paid for.

Well, this made both sides' lawyers very nervous.

Would Parkinson be content with a single room in a hotel, or would he expect a large house with a staff, chauffeur, and cars for himself and his family? Shouldn't everything be spelled out? Shouldn't a floor and a ceiling be placed on the expense budget? What if he stayed longer than expected? What if he went shopping?

What if, what if, what if?

Had all these what-ifs been addressed in the kind of detail the lawyers felt necessary, deadlines would have been missed, enthusiasm would have dissipated, and there would have been a real risk of losing the contract altogether.

Lawyers like things to be as explicit and airtight as they can ever be. Both their personality and their training point them toward fastidiousness; and of course they live in terror of the day when something goes wrong, and a client turns on them and says: "You idiot! Why didn't you tell me that could happen?!"

But it is my contention that, in many if not most contracts, **there are certain things which, by their very nature, have to be left and *should* be left to trust, goodwill, and common sense.**

Murdoch's lawyers had to realize—as Murdoch himself understood, of course—that Parkinson was a professional doing a job, not a freeloader off on a joyride.

And Parkinson's people had to trust that Murdoch would not simply be Parkinson's employer in Australia, but his *host*, and would therefore be nothing but generous and gracious.

To put it simply, *each side had to trust that the other had some class.*

Eventually, despite the typical "O.K., but don't blame me" objections of the lawyers, the contract was signed with the "fuzzy" language still intact.

Needless to say, it didn't turn out to be a problem for anyone concerned. In fact, it provided an opportunity for reaffirming the goodwill and mutual regard between our company and Mr. Murdoch.

Eight months after the deal was done, at a time when the precise discussions were not very fresh in anybody's mind, Murdoch simply made good on Parkinson's expenses.

No one, with the possible exception of the lawyers, was surprised at this civilized and gentlemanly conclusion of the business.

THE END RUN AROUND THE LEGAL BEAGLE

It is an absolutely basic rule of conducting business effectively that to get a favorable result, **you've got to get to the decision maker.**

Of all the many ways that time, effort, and money are wasted in business, probably one of the worst is talking to people who can't really help you even if they wanted to.

Getting to the decision maker is not always easy, of course; in fact, I would argue that the true meaning of the word "clout" is *access*.

There are any number of obstacles that can interfere with access—and lawyers happen to be one of them. **One of the main things that drive businessmen crazy about lawyers is that lawyers will generally do everything to prevent you from talking directly to their clients.**

Their reasons for doing this are several, and some are more praiseworthy than others.

Lawyers would like you to *think* they are keeping you away from the principal because they have a sacred obligation to do so; they have been hired to protect the client from complications and annoyances, and to advance his interests without causing him any bother.

And of course there are some clients who instruct their attorneys to do exactly that.

At the risk of sounding cynical, however, I would have to say that, in my experience, when lawyers keep you away from their client, *it has at least as much to do with their own desires and convenience as with their role of protectors.*

As long as the lawyers know more of what is going on than do the actual players, they are in control. They control the pace of the proceedings—which is to say, they have a large role in determining how much will be rung up in hourly fees.

They control the *tone* of the proceedings—whether the at-

mosphere will be friendly and cooperative, or will take on the
hostile overtones that waste time and erode goodwill.

Unless a businessman is content to leave his fate in the hands
of the attorneys, then, there are times when he has to end-run
around them, protocol be damned.

FIRST, KNOW WHO THE
DECISION MAKER *IS*

Complicating matters is the fact that, even without stonewalling
by attorneys, tracking down the decision maker can be a bedeviling process. It's such a crucial aspect of doing business,
however, that I think it's worthy of a brief digression.

I still remember when, back in the early days of IMG, the
person I most wanted to meet in the entire world was the chairman of the board of General Motors International. Here was the
man who headed up the biggest company on earth, who controlled resources which, for all practical purposes, were infinite;
here, in a word, was the man who could afford to buy absolutely
everything I was so intent on selling.

Well, to make a long story short, I worked for *two years* to
get a meeting with the chairman. I angled for introductions; I
cashed in favors owed me.

When I finally got my meeting, he greeted me with a fraternal
handclasp and motioned me into an enormous leather chair.
"What can I do for you, Mark?" he asked, and I felt as if I had
died and gone to heaven.

It took me about two minutes to realize he could do *zero* for
me, and that my grand ideas about having him as an ally had
been a fantasy.

In fact, the chairman operated solely in a staff capacity. His
job, essentially, was to pass along corporate policies to the various GM subsidiaries, whose general managers were almost au-
tonomous when it came to decisions of interest to IMG.

The time I spent trying to get that meeting was not altogether wasted, however. I learned a valuable lesson from it: **Take nothing for granted about where the decision-making authority actually lies. Look for the subtleties. Assume nothing.**

And understand that every organization is different.

Consider Rolex. For many years, IMG has had a terrific relationship with Rolex, whose brilliant chairman and managing director, André Heiniger, is a businessman for whom I have the very highest regard.

Heiniger, like any good executive, is consistent—but consistent *in his own way.* He leaves most marketing decisions to his local representatives and managers around the world; *however,* on issues that are clearly multinational in scope, he insists on personally handing down the final word from Geneva.

The challenge is figuring out where, with a global firm like Rolex, you draw the line between what's "multinational" and what isn't. You have to try to think along with the person on the other side—and thinking along with Heiniger is a strenuous but worthwhile exercise!

These intuitions get trickier the farther afield you go, culturally speaking—as I learned some years ago at a tiny conference table in Japan

At this point in time, any Western businessman with any sophistication at all is aware that to do business successfully with the Japanese, it's helpful to lay aside one's usual assumptions, biases, and habits of mind. Still, in the heat of selling or negotiating—and under the influence of trans-Pacific jet lag— that is not so easily accomplished.

I had flown to Tokyo, at the request of Toyota, to discuss Toyota's possible sponsorship of the women's professional tennis circuit. An executive from our Tokyo office joined me, and we were escorted to a cramped and totally unadorned conference room with a puny table and four simple chairs.

In walked a Japanese gentleman named Soe, who handed me a card that read: "Assistant Manager."

I saw that title and a wave of unpleasant emotions swept through me. First of all, though I make it a policy to leave my ego at the door when embarking on any negotiation, it was difficult not to feel insulted about traveling fifteen hours to meet with a someone from lower-middle management.

More to the point, I couldn't imagine that this fellow would possibly have the authority to say yea or nay on the multimillion-dollar package I had come to discuss. But I put on a brave face, and made my pitch.

To my great surprise, within a few weeks IMG got a Telex from Toyota, confirming that it had decided to sponsor women's tennis on a worldwide basis.

The "assistant manager," Japanese-style, had in fact had discretion far in excess of anything an American would have expected.

As a bit of practical advice, I would urge you to be sensitive to the Mr. Soes of this world, who wield their clout quietly without the armor of a fancy title. Sometimes they can do more for you than the chairman of the board!

SHOWDOWN AT PEBBLE BEACH

But again, when it's the lawyers who are screening out the person in charge, there are times when they have to be gone around or bulldozed.

Back in the 1960s, in the early days of our company, I had an object lesson in this which still strikes me as valuable.

In those years, IMG's main involvement was with golf, and we were fortunate in having as clients both Arnold Palmer and Gary Player. Aside from being superlative athletes, Arnold and Gary were highly poised, attractive, and utterly professional; they were constantly in demand and it was a great pleasure to handle their business.

At some point we were asked to arrange a deal between the

Lincoln-Mercury division of the Ford Motor Company, as sponsors, and the Revue Studios subsidiary of MCA, as producers, to do a series of shows called *Challenge Golf*, in which Palmer and Player would compete against other two-man teams.

The negotiations were highly amiable, and a contract was soon signed which provided, among other things, that the matches would be filmed during a ninety-day period at various golf courses within the state of California. In the course of the discussions, some specific venues had been talked about, but in the spirit of reason and cooperation that then prevailed, there seemed no need to spell them out in the written agreement.

The plot thickened, however, when the bean counters from Revue sat down with their adding machines and figured out that the studio could save a fair amount of money by filming all the matches on courses in and around Los Angeles. There would be less overtime to pay, and no travel and lodging expenses for crews and production executives.

So Revue's lawyers scoured the contract, and—what do you know?—there was nothing in it that said the matches *couldn't* all be played right there in Los Angeles and Orange counties!

There was only one small problem with this plan. Lincoln-Mercury's general manager, Chase Morsey, remembered quite specifically that during the negotiations it had been clearly understood that some of the matches would take place in northern California, and that one in particular would be played at Pebble Beach—a glamorous and upscale club with which Lincoln-Mercury wanted, understandably, to be associated.

Now Morsey got *his* lawyers on the case, trying to find something in the contract that gave Lincoln-Mercury the right of approval on the choice of courses, or, if need be, to tank the agreement altogether.

By this point everyone was getting mad at everyone, and a deal that had begun as a love feast was giving everybody headaches.

As it turned out, however, the stalemate was easily broken

by a single phone call from Morsey to Lew Wasserman, the chairman of MCA.

Morsey told Wasserman his side of the story, and Wasserman, in turn, confronted his people with a single question: "Did you or did you not lead the executives of Lincoln-Mercury to believe there would be a show produced at Pebble Beach?"

He didn't want to know what the contract said.

He didn't want to know about his company's legal rights.

He didn't want to hear about what the change in venue would cost.

He just wanted an answer to that simple question.

When MCA's people acknowledged that there *had* been talk about a match at Pebble Beach, Wasserman told them to apologize to Morsey, dispatch a crew to Carmel pronto, and stop wasting everybody's time.

In that single exchange, Morsey and Wasserman not only got *Challenge Golf* back on track, but cemented the relationship between their two companies by making it clear that each would stand by its commitments, whether or not those commitments were expressed in letter-perfect legal form.

TELEPHONE

Two factors enabled Morsey and Wasserman to resolve their problem so efficiently: good faith and good communication.

Both are essential for mutually advantageous business dealings. **Both are often mucked up by lawyers.**

Remember the childhood game of Telephone? In that pastime, player A whispered a message to player B, who passed along what he *thought* he had heard to player C, and so on down the line. At the end, player Z would recite the communication that he or she had ended up with, and everybody would laugh at how much the original message had changed.

Well, going back and forth between lawyers who won't let

their clients speak directly is a lot like that—but with two significant differences.

One difference is that it's hard to laugh when the garbling of the message is costing you cash, credibility, and maybe a relationship.

The second difference is that the garbling doesn't come about by simple mumbling, but by *a clash of differing styles and agendas*.

Let me give you an example of how this game of poor communication works in practice.

A few years ago, IMG negotiated a deal with Sony, whereby Sony would sponsor the world computerized ranking system of men's professional golf. Among the provisions of the deal was a perfectly clear understanding that Sony and IMG would work together to stage *three simultaneous press conferences—in New York, London, and Tokyo—to launch the new arrangement.*

Then the deal, as drafted by executives, went to the attorneys.

Here's what happened to the press-conference provision once the lawyers got hold of it:

First it got garbled so that three *separate* events were staged in the cities mentioned above, so the impact of simultaneity was lost.

Then it was misinterpreted to mean that Sony and IMG had an ongoing responsibility to hold press conferences together— a responsibility that *neither* side particularly wanted.

Then it became mangled to the point where it was thought that IMG and Sony were supposed to hold a press conference before *every* event on the pro tour!

I would never even have *known* about this last distortion, except I got a call one day from our New York office, informing me that the Sony people were very upset with us.

"Upset about what?" I asked.

"Upset that the press conference in Chicago was a flop."

"*What* press conference in Chicago?"

And so it went, until we struggled our way back through the

morass of legalese and finally uncovered the original message.
To quote the famous old advertising slogan, "Is this any way to
run an airline?"

NOT BY LAW ALONE

Just as sound business judgment dictates that there are instances
when the best move is to go around the lawyers, there are also
situations when the wisest action is to go around the law itself.

By this I certainly don't mean that it's acceptable to *break* the
law. It's only that, **in certain situations, an issue that seems legal
at first glance is in fact more effectively approached in pragmatic and nontechnical business terms.**

SELLING THE CUP

The truth of this notion was demonstrated recently by a contro-
versy involving the Royal Perth Yacht Club, which we represent.

When the Australian sailors defeated the Americans at New-
port, Rhode Island, in 1983, the ownership of the famous America's Cup moved to Perth. For the New York Yacht Club, the
loss was more than just a psychological blow: The licensing of
the America's Cup name and logo is quite a considerable revenue
source that goes a long way toward underwriting the races and,
in fact, toward keeping the entire sport of competitive yachting
afloat.

The New Yorkers, for whom lack of confidence has never been
a problem, had apparently never given a thought to what would
happen to their cash flow if they ever lost the Cup, apparently
because it never dawned on them they might be beaten.

Having lost the trophy, however, and in keeping with their
habit of changing the rules when the game was no longer going
their way, the New York Yacht Club began refusing to assign

trademark applications around the world for the exclusive licensing rights to the name and the logo of the America's Cup.

At first glance, what was developing seemed to be a legal battle, and a fascinating one at that. In some jurisdictions, ownership of a trademark is determined by first use, irrespective of first filing; in other places, rights go to the first filer, regardless of who was the first user. Then there was the intriguing question of whether licensing rights automatically went with ownership of the Cup itself or were to be regarded as a separate entity. The issues were complex and juicy enough to keep several batteries of copyright and trademark lawyers busy for many months, if not for several years.

In the meantime, however, the Royal Perth Yacht Club had a multimillion-dollar event to stage, and, because of the New York Yacht Club's filings around the world, Perth was running into obstacle after obstacle in arranging the fees and royalties to which, by common sense and simple justice, it was entitled as host club of the races.

With time before the 1987 Cup defense growing ever shorter, it became clear that in regarding the trademark business as a legal squabble, Perth was agreeing to fight the battle on New York's chosen turf, and by doing so was effectively conceding defeat. *Time was the real enemy, as it so often is when litigation looms.*

The solution—simple enough once we thought of it—was to stop arguing in legal terms and shift the battle back to business basics.

Accordingly, at a meeting in Australia late in 1985, I suggested to the officers of the Royal Perth that they call off their attorneys and instead write a simple letter to the New York Yacht Club as well as to all other competing parties.

The letter should say essentially this: If anyone did anything to hamper the Royal Perth Yacht Club's efforts to market the 1987 defense *in exactly the same way that it had been marketed in years past by the New York Yacht Club,* that party would be barred from racing at Perth. Period.

Would such a prohibition be legal? My contention was that it would be; it would certainly be just.

But I knew that the threat of disqualification would never be put to the test because now it would be the *other* side racing against time and taking on the risk.

Would the New York Yacht Club, having spent millions on new equipment, jeopardize its chances of being allowed on the starting line Down Under—especially knowing that if it challenged the validity of the Royal Perth edict, the matter would have to be tried in the jurisdiction of Western Australia?

So, strictly speaking, the trademark issue was never solved; it was simply made to disappear. Perhaps such a resolution might be disappointing to a legal scholar. For a businessman, it was the most expedient and least costly of all possible outcomes.

THE FORCE OF SHAME

A great deal has been written about the real or perceived decline of business ethics, and about the shameless shenanigans of certain highly visible businessmen.

However, I would argue that, as a group, business people are as concerned as ever with their good names—and that *appeals to their sense of shame can sometimes be a highly effective way of avoiding litigation and finding shortcuts out of legal dilemmas.*

Let me illustrate this by way of an anecdote, though it may be significant that the company involved was Japanese, and perhaps more prone to compunction than its American counterparts.

In 1986 Harvard University celebrated its 350th anniversary, and the Harvard Corporation hired IMG to handle the licensing of products and promotions connected with the event.

Accordingly, we did a worldwide survey of how "Harvard" this and "Harvard" that were being marketed. We discovered that there was a company in Japan—where the name is hugely prestigious—calling *itself* "Harvard." This company had been doing about $10 million worth of business a year for the past decade, and had never paid the university a dime in royalties!

At first glance, this seemed like the most flagrant sort of piracy, though there was more to it than met the eye.

Back in the mid-seventies, executives of this Japanese firm had in fact visited Cambridge, with the intention of working out a licensing arrangement with the Harvard Corporation. Prior to the 350th anniversary, however, Harvard hadn't wanted to sully itself with the taint of commerce, and its officials wouldn't even talk to the Japanese businessmen.

Piqued by this rebuff, the Japanese went back to Tokyo, where they discovered that the name "Harvard" had never been filed as a trademark *within Japan*. They registered it and had been operating in accord with Japanese law ever since.

So, once again we faced an intriguing legal situation—one that might have kept a pack of attorneys profitably employed for a good long time.

Our counsel in Tokyo, however, pulled a *business* masterstroke that cut a terrific shortcut through the potential legal morass.

He called a meeting and patiently listened while the other side's lawyers aggressively spelled out all the reasons the company was right. It had *tried* to do business with the university, and been turned away. It had complied with all appropriate local statutes. It had invested time and money, and taken significant risks to make this a successful enterprise—*now* the university was hitting it up for a percentage?

Our counsel heard the lawyers out, and realized that they were trying a little too hard to protest their innocence; there was an undertone of guilty conscience.

So our lawyer calmly announced that he understood their position and wouldn't fight them after all. To clarify matters, however, *he would send a memo to everyone the company did business with, explaining why it didn't see fit to pay a royalty for the use of the Harvard name!*

The licensing arrangement was summarily concluded.

AC-CEN-TUATE THE POSITIVE,
E-LIM-INATE THE NEGATIVE

In 1968 I negotiated a contract with John DeLorean, then the general manager of the Pontiac division of General Motors. The contract involved Pontiac's sponsorship of the U.S. Ski Team and the U.S. Ski Association, and there was a high level of enthusiasm for the arrangement in all quarters.

At a meeting in which DeLorean and I discussed the major deal points, and at which Pontiac's attorneys were present, John turned to his lawyers, waved his finger at them in mock scolding, and said, "I really want this thing, and don't you guys screw it up."

This vignette graphically summarizes another important axiom.

McCormack's Axiom of Checks and Balances

Businessmen accentuate the positive, lawyers are left to wrestle with the negative, and all parties struggle toward a situation somewhere in between.

Since this meeting took place at General Motors, let me put it in these terms: The businessman—the one who wants the deal—is the gas pedal; he provides the forward momentum, the thrust, the push that gets things started.

The lawyer is the brake; his job is to keep things within a safe speed and to stop the machine at any sign of trouble.

When the brake and the gas pedal are in balance, the vehicle of business runs smoothly.

The point I would like to make, however, is this: Until the car is rolling, a brake pedal is redundant. And if the brake is applied from the beginning, chances are the momentum will never get a chance to build.

For that reason, **I am a firm believer in keeping the lawyers out of the early stages of a deal.**

Why contemplate the things that can go wrong before savoring the things that can go right?

Why create the anxiety that inevitably attaches to the presence of lawyers before establishing the enthusiasm that attends the care and feeding of a deal?

Eventually, of course, lawyers do need to get involved, and I freely admit that there is a potential downside to bringing them into a deal late.

Sometimes, inevitably, effort must be duplicated.

Sometimes, for technical reasons, certain deal points need revising.

And then there's the discomfort of dealing with lawyers who are testy about not having been consulted sooner

But I contend that in the great majority of cases, **business ends are better served by stressing the positive up front and dealing with the negative only after the momentum is established and agreement in principle has been achieved.**

WHY BUSINESSMEN DRIVE
LAWYERS CRAZY

But let's be fair.

If lawyers sometimes drive businessmen to fits of rage and distraction, the terrible truth is that the opposite is also true.

If businessmen, in the throes of frustration, sometimes view lawyers as obstructionist killjoys who gum up the works and prevent people from making a living, then it's also true that attorneys, at moments of crisis, think of deal makers as irresponsible cowboys who would all end up bankrupt, or worse, were it not for the intervention of cooler heads.

In this connection, I must relate the sad saga of a man named Chuck Sullivan. Sullivan is a scion of the family that owns the

New England Patriots and is himself the owner of Sullivan Stadium, in which the team plays. He is a highly educated and sophisticated man—and he even has a law degree! In his heart, however, he is a businessman, with all the enthusiasms and occasional excesses pertaining thereto.

A few years ago, Sullivan decided that he was going to make himself a ton of money by aligning himself with pop singer Michael Jackson. At the time, Jackson was the hottest property since the Beatles, and it seemed that *anything*—clothing, fragrances, soft drinks—could be marketed in his name. Accordingly, Sullivan reputedly shelled out around $50 million as promoter of the Jackson family's 1984 concert tour, and committed an additional $30 million for the licensing rights to Jackson's name and likeness.

In fantasy, Sullivan had pulled off a real coup. In reality, he had locked himself into a disaster.

The concert tour entailed such enormous transportation, staging, and insurance costs that in spite of sellouts everywhere, it reportedly lost more than a million dollars.

When the tour was over, Jackson's managers became fearful that he was being "overexposed." This meant that, just when Sullivan was trying to sublicense Jackson's name, no one was hearing as much about Jackson anymore!

Having already incurred losses, Sullivan approached IMG for help in disposing of the licensing rights he controlled. He showed us his contracts, and our attorneys were frankly surprised that a man of Sullivan's sophistication would have gotten himself into unworkable contract provisions.

Sullivan's story perfectly illustrates several classic mistakes made by overfervent deal makers, and points up exactly what businessmen *should* look to lawyers for:

1. He very probably saw dollar signs that were unrealistically large. Whatever the potential windfall, $80 million was too big an exposure to risk in a business as volatile as pop music.

2. He was possibly too intent on being where the action is. It might make great cocktail-party conversation to be able to describe oneself as Michael Jackson's impresario, but level-headed advice would have pointed out the downside.

3. He was perhaps too singlemindedly intent on sealing the deal, and Jackson's lawyers, sensing that Sullivan would agree to almost anything to get the contract, again and again put him on the short end of clauses that unemotional outside advice would not have allowed him to accept.

THE DEAL MEMO TO THE RESCUE

Given, then, that lawyers can bust up a deal if brought in too soon, and that businessmen can get themselves into a passel of trouble if lawyers are brought in too *late*, how can deal makers and their attorneys stay usefully in sync?

One way is by effective use of the *deal memo*.

The deal memo is an integral part of how we do business at IMG. Here's how it works:

One of our executives negotiates the points of a deal—*but* it is made clear to all concerned that he or she does not have the authority to *conclude* the deal.

The executive then writes a deal memo—just a letter, in plain English—to the legal department, outlining the agreement that's been negotiated. This deal memo serves several purposes:

1. Since it will involve the legal department *before* any commitment has been made, it justifies keeping the lawyers out of the early talks.

2. It forces the executive to be *crystal clear* about what he has or hasn't agreed to, since he has to put it in writing.

3. It allows the executive and the lawyers to work together, away

from the pressures of the negotiating table, to put the final document in optimal form.

4. When necessary, it provides a mechanism to let us stall for time or simply pause for breath.

THEORY VERSUS PRACTICE

The theory of the deal memo is simplicity itself, and at our company it is regarded as an absolutely standard procedure.

Yet, at one time or another, practically everyone who negotiates for IMG has given in to businessman's impulsiveness and neglected to do a proper memo.

This drives our legal department batty—and rightly so.

The lawyers' annoyance has to do not with mere protection of their bailiwick, but with substantive issues.

If a deal memo isn't done, or is done improperly, and if the eventual contract doesn't accurately reflect the deal maker's understanding of the terms, whose fault is it?

Worse still, if an account executive skirts the legal department, and unilaterally sends his customer a writing that could be *construed* as constituting a contract, could IMG be held to that agreement?

To avoid this latter possibility, our general counsel, Bill Carpenter, is *constantly* coaching us on exculpatory language that *every* business negotiator should have as part of his or her working vocabulary:

"If this reflects our understanding, I will have contracts drawn up," or,
"If this is correct, I will arrange to have it finalized."

Phrases like those can save an enormous amount of trouble, and will steer you clear of being held to commitments you didn't even *know* you'd made.

DOWN, BOY!

Before leaving the subject of how lawyers can sometimes save overeager executives from themselves, let me give one more brief example of this dynamic in action.

At IMG, as agents we are virtually never in a position to commit our clients to anything: We *advise* our clients; our clients commit themselves.

This is an extraordinarily basic distinction, designed for the protection of all parties; you don't need a law degree or an MBA to grasp either the notion itself or the reasoning behind it.

Still, in the midst of deal lust, it's truly amazing how often even this rudimentary point is overlooked.

Not long ago, one of our junior line executives was approached regarding a lucrative clothing endorsement for a client. Over the course of several long conversations, during which a lot of intoxicating numbers were bandied about, our young executive's ardor grew to the point where he made the endorsement sound like a done deal—regardless of the facts that:

1. The final authority to conclude the agreement rested not with him but with the client.

2. The proposed endorsement, unbeknownst to the eager young executive, was in clear conflict with an agreement signed before he had come on board.

The legal department (by way of a deal memo!) caught the potential problem, and the upshot was nothing worse than some wasted time and some deserved embarrassment on the would-be deal maker's part. Had Legal not been on the case, well, all of us could have had a real problem on our hands.

The point is that while there *are* broad differences in style and priorities among businessmen and lawyers, and while those differences inevitably give rise to tension, *that tension can be a blessing as well as a bane.*

If businessmen and lawyers are natural adversaries, they are natural allies, too.

They temper each other's excesses and compensate for each other's deficiencies.

And when they work effectively together, they can achieve results beyond what either group could accomplish alone.

6

PLAYING AS A TEAM

CAN'T LIVE WITH 'EM; CAN'T LIVE WITHOUT 'EM

So goes the old saying about relations between men and women.

The maxim could apply equally to the difficult but necessary marriage between business people and attorneys.

Yes, the two groups get on each other's nerves practically every hour of every working day.

Yes, members of each profession are only too ready to point out the foibles and pretensions of the other.

Still, lawyers and business types are unmistakably symbiotic. Without business clients, a hefty proportion of attorneys would have absolutely nothing to do. And without lawyers . . . well, I happen to believe that businessmen could get on all right without attorneys, as long as *none* of them had attorneys.

But that's too much to hope for in this life.

You can bet that the fellow across the conference table from you is going to have a legal eagle or two on his side. That being so, you had better have counsel on your team, too.

And you had better make sure that the machinery that connects your lawyer and yourself is running smoothly because, as I've stated below:

McCormack's Axiom of Symbiosis

The successful outcome of a negotiation or a legal fight most often depends not just on the individual savvy of the business person and the lawyer involved, but on how well they function *together*.

THE CONTRACT AS ARTWORK

Of all the many ways in which business people interact with their own attorneys, probably the most usual, *but also one of the most crucial*, has to do with the drawing up of contracts.

Turning a verbal understanding into a written agreement should be a dynamic and creative process. It shouldn't just lock in a deal, but *enhance* it.

Unfortunately, the terrible truth is that contracts are too often drawn up without any creativity at all, and I shudder to think about the opportunities that are lost that way.

Why are those opportunities wasted?

Because of bad communication between the deal makers and the attorneys, or because of arrogance on one or both sides.

In the worst case, the line person who made the deal is pigheaded enough to imagine that he or she has thought of everything, that the deal points that have been negotiated could not possibly be improved upon, and that the lawyer's job consists of nothing more than the passive translation of the deal memo into legalese.

This attitude is in clear violation of the following:

McCormack's Axiom of Inevitable Omissions
No one *ever* thinks of everything.

This kind of deal maker seldom takes the time actually to *talk* to the lawyers—why bother, if the lawyers are expected to have no substantive input?

A similar boondoggle results if it's the *attorneys* who overplay their own particular role at the expense of fruitful teamwork.

Some lawyers, overly proud of their own areas of expertise, take it upon themselves to make substantive changes in aspects of deals that they are not really in a position to understand. This type of lawyer likes to knock off the rough edges, so that the finished contract is a marvel of symmetry and elegance—*regardless of the fact that sometimes it's the rough edges in which a deal's real benefits consist!*

A SHAKESPEAREAN MASTERPIECE

If jealousy, parochialism, and lack of communication can lead to contracts that are less advantageous than they ought to be, then good communication and a mutual regard for each other's skills and resources can bring about the optimal functioning of the businessman-lawyer combination.

Let me illustrate this optimal functioning by way of an example.

In 1965 we were approached, on behalf of our client Gary Player, by the Shakespeare Company. Shakespeare, for many years a leader in the manufacture of fishing rods, had decided to get into the golf business with a line of fiberglass clubs.

They wanted an endorsement from Player and in exchange were offering him royalties on all fiberglass clubs sold under the

Shakespeare name, as well as on all fiberglass shafts sold by Shakespeare to other manufacturers. The royalties were to be applied against very substantial guarantees, and by the standards of 1965, the whole package constituted a huge commitment to Gary. Shakespeare's management was very high on the new golf venture, and negotiations were proceeding with great enthusiasm and goodwill.

Still, there are certain technicalities that must be dealt with in every contract. For one thing, terms must be precisely, *legally* defined. But how exactly does one define a golf club?

Our lawyers defined it as "a shaft connected to a head with a hossel." As it turned out, that careful and painstaking definition benefited our client by some thousands of dollars—and also gave us an opportunity to cement our relationship with Shakespeare.

Shortly after the Shakespeare deal was completed, Player was approached by the Lampkin Leather Grip Company, which wanted him to endorse its grips on *whatever* clubs he used.

Now, we knew that Shakespeare had no plans to get into the golf-grip business, so there was no conflict on that score. We also knew that it was established practice for pro golfers to endorse grips separately from clubs.

Still, the deal with Shakespeare was quite unusual by its sheer size, and we felt we owed the company a degree of loyalty. So we went to company executives and told them about the Lampkin offer. We pointed out that our contract—because *it made no mention of grips* in its definition of a golf club—*did* give us the legal right to enter into a separate grips endorsement; we assured them, however, that we wouldn't take the Lampkin offer if Shakespeare felt it was a violation of the *spirit* of our agreement.

Putting it that way, of course, brought human nature into the equation. The executives of the Shakespeare Company appreciated being consulted and our willingness *not* to take selfish advantage of technicalities in the contract. In the end, they graciously gave us permission to enter into the Lampkin deal.

Far from breeding ill will—which might have resulted if the Shakespeare executives felt we were trying to "get around" them —the incident set a tone of aboveboard dealing and mutual consideration.

And it all came about because the lawyers foresaw all sorts of possibilities in the orginal wording of the contract.

"GOOD COP"/"BAD COP"

Cooperating in the conceiving and drafting of contracts is one of *many* ways in which lawyers and executives can help each other shine.

Another way has to do with the roles they adopt in negotiations.

Consider the "good cop"/"bad cop" scenario—one of the most brilliant and versatile negotiating tactics ever devised.

The name derives from the classic instance of two police investigators working together to get a suspect to confess. The "bad cop" plays the heavy, the one who bullies, needles, and threatens the suspect, acts utterly convinced of the suspect's guilt, and tells the hapless interviewee that he is certain to "get the chair."

The "good cop," on the other hand, is all patience and compassion. He soothes, he mollifies, he acts as if he believes the suspect's story. He even tells his partner to "lay off the poor guy."

In the quintessential case, what happens is that the bad cop leaves the room to get a pack of cigarettes, and the suspect confesses to the good cop!

In part, the criminal has let himself believe that the fellow is really on his side. On a deeper psychological level, however, what motivates him to confess is probably that the pressure applied by the bad cop has given him an irresistible need for a sympathetic ear. In precinct-house parlance, he has been "softened up."

For business people and lawyers, too, the good cop/bad cop strategy can move mountains—if you know how to use it.

Few things in the world are easier than casting a lawyer in the role of villain. Let's face it—the other side is generally inclined to think the worst of your attorneys, and the attorneys themselves, with a kind of bulldog glee, seem to delight in being thought of as the bad guys, the street fighters, the stalwarts who won't give an inch.

The subtler part of the equation lies in how the businessman plays *his* part—how he uses the lawyers' toughness to make his own softer sell seem that much more appealing.

A few years ago, I suggested to the All-England Club that we undertake a worldwide program to license the Wimbledon name on tennis-related products.

This, as you may imagine, was vastly complicated. Hundreds of products called "Wimbledon" something or other were already being marketed in dozens of jurisdictions around the globe. Some companies were paying royalties and some were not. Some had registered trademarks that might or might not stand up in court, and some were going blithely along with no trademark at all.

Further complicating the issue was the fact that "Wimbledon" is not just the name of a sports championship, in the way that the U.S. Open means just that and nothing more; it is also the name of a borough in London as well as a well-known soccer club.

If the legal issues were hazy, the moral and economic ones were crystal clear: people were unfairly cashing in on the Wimbledon name, and it was costing the rightful owners of the name a lot of money.

We decided on a two-pronged strategy to remedy the situation: our lawyers would play the bad cop, harrassing the unlicensed users of the name, bringing suit where necessary.

Meanwhile, I would play the good cop. I would gently try to persuade the companies, first of all, that what they were doing simply wasn't right, and second, that they would in fact do much better if they paid a proper royalty, in exchange for which they would gain the prestige, expertise, and marketing clout of the entire Wimbledon machinery.

Part of the beauty of this arrangement was that it really didn't have a downside: The All-England Club and IMG agreed from the start that at no point would more money be spent on lawyers than was brought in from fees made on licensing arrangements.

From the beginning, we understood that neither aspect of our approach was likely to succeed without the other. Without my dangling the carrot of greater revenues that would result from the full cooperation of All-England, the lawyers' stick would not have been impressive. At the very least, unlicensed users of the Wimbledon name could have stalled for several years, and in certain jurisdictions, frankly, they probably would have won the right to keep on using it.

On the other hand, without the threat presented by the lawyers, people already making money from the tournament would have been less inclined to listen to my sales pitch—why give up a piece of the pie if you don't have to?

By working together, however, the lawyers and I were able to shift the terms of the discussions. Instead of deciding *whether* they were going to bother to deal with us at all, our target companies now had a choice as to *which part of our team to deal with*.

Psychologically, I think the decision-making process on the part of the manufacturers came down to this: The lawyers are saying bad things about us and threatening to make trouble, and this McCormack guy seems polite and cooperative by comparison, so we may as well play ball with McCormack.

The upshot of the strategy was a welcome clarification in the rules for use of the Wimbledon name, as well as a tremendous increase in revenues accruing to the All-England Club.

And, in fact, at least some of the manufacturers that had been using the Wimbledon name without permission actually went on to make far more money once they had come into the licensing fold.

The most dramatic instance occurred with the Nike shoe company, which had been marketing a "Wimbledon" tennis shoe in a very lukewarm way. Once the relationship between Nike and the All-England Club was made explicit and mutual, however, promotion of the shoe became far more sophisticated and sales burgeoned.

So the story ends well for all concerned—and *it would not have happened that way unless the lawyers were standing by snarling, subtly persuading people to deal with me instead of them.*

WAYS TO SKIN A CAT DEPARTMENT

Look at almost any sort of legal contract, and what do you see?

Chances are you see a thick and inscrutable document, written in a language never spoken by the human race, and weighed down with all sorts of standardized clauses, disclaimers upon disclaimers, and riders that seem to unsay half of what has already been said.

Probably the last word that would occur to you to describe this sort of contract is "playful."

Yet I would argue that "playful" is exactly what a well-thought-out contract ought to be—or *can* be.

I certainly don't mean playful in the sense of frivolous; any businessman or lawyer who approaches contracts in that spirit won't be around for very long.

I mean playful in the sense of imaginative.

They don't teach it this way in law schools, but contracts, like negotiations, call for an ability to improvise, to implement strategies, to arrive spontaneously at a way of doing things differently than they have been done before.

YOU CAN'T BLAME ME FOR TRYING

In drafting a contract, for example, sometimes it's a playful and also useful tactic to include certain things you *know* you won't get.

Some years ago I negotiated a contract with Dunlop, in Australia, on behalf of one of the world's leading tennis players.

The opportunity to do this deal came about essentially because of the enthusiasm and vision of the then manager of Dunlop's tennis division Down Under. He saw the tennis boom coming sooner than most. He wanted to invest heavily in promotion, and he wanted our client.

We were so impressed with his attitude that we wrote in a clause saying that if he, at some future date, no longer ran the tennis division, our client would have the option of terminating the contract.

We were well aware, of course, that no sane legal department or upper management was likely to agree to such a provision— from their perspective, it was nothing but downside.

Still, we felt that there was a twofold psychological advantage in including it in our draft.

First of all, *it was hugely flattering* to the manager; it made him look great in the eyes of his superiors and thereby cemented his alliance with us.

Second, *it sent a message* to others at Dunlop that we expected this person's level of commitment to be carried through by anyone we dealt with at the company.

Eventually the deal was concluded minus that playful clause, but the thinking behind it had registered with all concerned.

PULLING THE PLUG

To say that a contract is playful is essentially the same as saying it is **responsive to the realities of human nature.**

Human nature is *partly* logical. It is also partly motivated by hopes and fears, vanities and insecurities, needs for reassurance and the possibility of escape.

A well-thought-out contract should address *all* of those facets of what makes people tick.

Let me illustrate this by describing a contract provision that has proved so useful over the years that we have given it an unofficial name: the "Australian Termination Clause."

This clause was born during a negotiation we were handling on behalf of Jack Nicklaus, with Slazenger of Australia. All the major deal points had been hashed over and agreed to—with the exception of those clauses setting forth the term of the contract, circumstances under which the agreement might be ended, and the amount of notice required for its termination.

These were sticky issues because Slazenger was gambling on a new line of products to be released under the Nicklaus name. The company was throwing a lot of money into the launch, and it was paying Jack very sizable guarantees.

If, for any reason, the new products didn't fly, Slazenger didn't want to be locked into paying the annuities on top of other losses it might possibly sustain.

Our position in the negotiation was the opposite, and equally valid. Nicklaus was one of the most marketable names in all of sport. Why should he risk sudden termination of an income-producing deal if a sales campaign flopped through no fault of his? If the Slazenger arrangement fizzled, years might go by before another similar deal offered itself in the Australian market.

How could these two positions be reconciled?

Our solution was a clause that stated that the agreement could be terminated by either party at any time *but on five years' notice*.

This was acceptable to Slazenger because it put a cap on the company's liability; in exchange for the option to call it quits, Slazenger was willing to commit to five years in guarantees, during which period it would most likely have inventory to dispose of anyway.

But while the deal made sense for the manufacturer, I frankly think we got the better bargain for our client. That five-year window would have been more than enough time to find a new endorsement for Jack.

More than that, however, we felt sure that the necessity of paying off five years' worth of hefty guarantees would be a strong inducement to Slazenger not to terminate the deal. Slazenger's strategy was a defensive one; it wanted an escape hatch against worst-case possibilities—and it was willing to pay for it. But the company paid so much for that escape hatch that, in turn, it had to protect itself by making sure the Nicklaus line of products succeeded.

This, by the way, is exactly what happened. Slazenger, using its obligation to Nicklaus as a measure, put appropriate sums and energy into promoting and marketing the line, and the arrangement between the company and Jack in fact lasted for decades.

The beauty part of the Australian Termination Clause, then, is that **by making it expensive to pull the plug, it goes a long way toward assuring that the plug won't be pulled at all.**

LETTING DEALS BREATHE

As I said before, it is a common but costly mistake to regard a contract as a totally formal, standardized, matter-of-fact document.

In actuality, **a contract is an ongoing** *process*, **an arrangement whose nuances are constantly changing.**

Obviously, the *words* of the contract stay the same.

Nonetheless, the *implications* of those words are always evolving.

And among the crucial tasks that lawyers should perform on behalf of businessmen, are:

to fashion contracts in such a way that they can accommodate

growth and change while maintaining a dynamic balance between the parties' advantages; and

to monitor and act upon the opportunities that arise once
contracts are in effect and have taken on a life of their own.

A comparison to child rearing seems irresistible here: If you
simply "give birth" to a contract, then walk away, you have
shirked a very major responsibility; the other part of the job lies
in the care and feeding of the contract.

MILKING THE PENGUIN

Maybe the best way to illustrate the importance of creating
contracts that can "grow" is to point out what happens to those
that *can't*—arrangements that are brittle, rigid, and incapable
of flowing with changed circumstances.

Back in the late fifties, when pro golf was rather an infant
enterprise, and before Arnold Palmer had become a client of
ours, he entered into a long-term endorsement contract with
Munsingwear, the clothing manufacturer with the familar penguin logo.

The contract called for an incredibly puny guarantee—$1,000
or $2,000 a year, as I recall—which was fairly standard at the
time the agreement was made, but which became increasingly
absurd from year to year.

Had Arnold been a client at the time the Munsingwear deal
was offered, we would have strenuously advised him against
accepting it—not necessarily because of where the contract *started*,
but because there was nowhere for it to go. As it was, we spent
a lot of time thinking about how best to extricate Palmer from
an arrangement that had ceased to have any relation to his value
on the open market.

But Arnold happens to be an exceptionally loyal person, and
he wanted to stay with Munsingwear, if at all possible. So he

asked me to try to negotiate a long-term licensing arrangement with the company for a line of Arnold Palmer autographed sportswear. This would have been a deal that could *breathe*— Munsingwear and Palmer would truly have been partners who benefited proportionately from the success of the line.

But Munsingwear stubbornly insisted on keeping things as they were. In the short run, it had a very sweet deal.

Meanwhile, not surprisingly, given the growth of golf and Arnold's phenomenal success on the pro tour, other offers kept coming in. Other companies were begging Palmer for exactly the sort of license deal that Munsingwear declined to enter into.

And this raises a point that I cannot stress too highly. In fact, as a service to all business people and all lawyers and all arbitrators and all mediators, I would like to paint this simple message across the sky:

LOPSIDED DEALS DON'T LAST

I must take a minute to expand on this point. False modesty aside, I have a reputation for being a tough and effective negotiator. I enjoy that reputation tremendously and, needless to say, it helps me a great deal in my work.

However, I am sometimes astonished at the misunderstandings that surround the question of what being a good negotiator *means*.

Some people seem to think that negotiating means splitting the world up into Us and Them, getting as much as possible for Our side, and sticking it to the other guys at every opportunity.

That, in fact, is not negotiation; it's war.

Negotiation consists of devising means such that *all* sides feel they are profiting from a deal.

And not just profiting to some arbitrary degree, but *in accordance with fair market value in whatever arena they are operating.*

As long as no one was offering a better shake than Munsingwear, the Munsingwear deal was acceptable; as soon as offers worth ten or a hundred times more started cropping up, the Munsingwear deal had to adapt or it was doomed.

I sometimes see both business people and lawyers—especially young ones—come away from the negotiating table congratulating themselves for striking a bargain in which a clear disproportion of the benefits are on their side. They feel that they have been brilliant, they feel that they have *won*.

Yet, in the great majority of cases, that victory will sour, and it will sour sooner rather than later.

There is virtually no such thing as a deal that can't be wriggled out of somehow or other. A corollary to that is:

McCormack's Axiom of Proportionate Wriggling

The more lopsided the contract, the greater the incentive for one side or the other to wriggle out of it.

The truly victorious negotiation, then, is the one that leads to a deal with which all parties are happy *over time*.

In the Munsingwear situation, we were increasingly unhappy, and since the manufacturer was disinclined to bring the contract into line with market realities, we had no choice but to look for ways to end the deal.

We offered to buy our way out, but were turned down.

We made certain concessions in a possible licensing arrangement, but met with no interest.

So we went back to the contract in search of a fatal flaw such as overly rigid deals so often contain. And lo and behold, we found one.

In Arnold's contract there was a clause—presumably the brainchild of one of Munsingwear's bright young lawyers—which stipulated that the golfer would receive a bonus of $500 every time the penguin logo on his shirt appeared on national TV. Originally, this clause was designed to reward Arnold for golfing well enough to be in camera range during those Saturday and Sunday telecasts when the tournament leaders were followed around the course.

However, in those years it was still legal for cigarettes to be advertised on TV, and in those years Palmer was still a smoker. Specifically, he smoked L&Ms, and Liggett and Myers, the manufacturer, was so pleased that it decided to make Arnold the star of a major ad campaign.

Now, the folks from L&M only cared about what Arnold smoked; it didn't matter to them what he *wore*. So why not do the commercials in a nice sport shirt with the penguin logo on it?

This would have resulted in many hundreds of "bonusable" exposures on the tube, and it would have cost Munsingwear a great deal of money. It would, in fact, have cost Munsingwear *more* than we had been asking for a licensing deal, and they wouldn't even have gotten the benefit of a license!

So they sheepishly changed their tune and let Arnold out of his contract after all.

If our lawyers deserve the credit for freeing our client from such a terrible deal, then Munsingwear's attorneys must bear the blame *for fashioning an arrangement that had no bend in it.*

In making a deal that was too good to be fair, they lost out on the possibility of a more mutually valuable arrangement in the longer term.

WHAT'S IN THE BLACK BOX

I hope I have managed to convey that the drawing up of contracts should really be thought of as an art form in which business people and lawyers collaborate. The business person forms the concept. The drafting lawyer gives it shape. Both should take credit for the beautiful artifact that results.

Contracts, however, are not the only aspect of business in

which good communication between line executives and attorneys is essential. There are all sorts of areas in which one's own lawyers—in-house or outside counsel—provide services that are *advisory, cautionary, or informative.*

To put it bluntly, there are times when lawyers are a pain in the neck, and *should* be.

Take the "Black Box" scenario as an example.

Since IMG is involved in conceiving, producing, and marketing television sports programming, we get a fair number of unsolicited ideas—so-called Black Box items—sent in to us by individuals who are convinced that they have dreamed up the catchiest show since *The Battle of the Network Stars.* These treasures generally arrive in envelopes marked "Confidential" or "Proprietary."

Are these ideas ever any good?

Don't ask me, because I'm not allowed to look at them, and neither is anybody else!

I may be the boss, but my own legal department slams the Black Box shut in my face every time. They would be derelict in their duties if they didn't.

The lawyers are painfully aware that if someone sends us an idea—notwithstanding that we didn't *ask* him to, and never mind that two hundred other people may have already had the same idea; and if we *look* at his idea; and if, at any time in the future, we produce a show that in any way *resembles* his idea, we may be subject to a claim that we misappropriated his idea.

This puts us in a bind.

First of all, let's face it, television is a copycat medium. *Everything* on television resembles something else.

Second, it is at least *possible* that there will be a fabulous idea in one of those unsolicited envelopes—an idea that we would gladly pay for—but how will we know if we don't look inside, out of fear of provoking a claim?

Finally, there's a simple, basic fact of human nature to be dealt with: curiosity. How can you *resist* taking a peek?

In order to resist, you've got to *transcend ordinary human nature*.

This is what lawyers are not infrequently called upon to do; and *it is a large part of why they can be so valuable to an organization*.

At moments when every fiber of a deal maker's being is crying out to look at that idea, the lawyer, like the disembodied voice of conscience, should yell out, **DON'T DO IT**.

This, you understand, is not necessarily a moral imperative but a pragmatic one. Look inside an envelope marked "Confidential" or "Proprietary" and you are asking to be sued.

If you are sued, regardless of the merits, you will almost certainly face a jury strongly biased in favor of the plaintiff.

Plaintiff's counsel will present the case as a righteous battle of a poor exploited individual against a big heartless company with deep pockets, and chances are the company will pay.

It is the lawyer's job to prevent all this from happening by making sure the company is, like Caesar's wife, *not just free of blame but above suspicion*.

In order to do this, IMG's staff attorneys have instituted procedures about as complicated as—but let's hope more effective than!—Pentagon security measures. We have locked files. We return unopened letters by registered mail, double-sealed with metal tape. We get affidavits, waivers, and releases before we will even *talk* to someone.

If these measures seem extreme, they are. But they are necessary.

And the point I want to make is one that is too often underappreciated by business people: **There truly are situations where there is no substitute for the formality, fastidiousness, and even finickiness that lawyers bring to a problem.**

Anything short of these attributes can spell disaster, and that's the terrible truth.

SEE WHAT I MEAN?

In case you think I'm exaggerating the sensitivity of Black Box issues, let me pass along the story of one of the strangest episodes our company ever had the misfortune to be involved in.

A few years ago, IMG's television production subsidiary, TWI, was sued by an individual who had submitted to us, unsolicited, a film treatment whose working title was *The Muscleless Wonder*. Suffice it to say that we were interested neither in acquiring nor developing this opus.

At around the same time, however, TWI was preparing to make a TV movie from an adaptation of a novel called *Addison*. The plaintiff claimed that *his* treatment was in fact the germ from which our screenplay had sprung.

There were only three small flaws in this resourceful and, on its face, not unreasonable argument:

1. We hadn't read this fellow's treatment.

2. The adaptation of *Addison* had been done **before** *The Muscleless Wonder* was even received.

3. There was virtually no resemblance between the two stories!

The plaintiff in this case, who was not a lawyer, decided he would represent himself. Whether this decision was strategic or economic we will never know.

In any event, *his* legal costs were virtually nil, while we, of course, had to assign one of our staff lawyers to deal with the suit in a responsible manner. She had to answer documents, make several trips to New York, and so forth.

Eventually, the suit was thrown out. We had "won"—though, given the quirks of the American legal system, we had no way of recovering the expenses we should never have had to shell out in the first place.

That, however, was not quite the end of the story. The plaintiff ended up in the penitentiary, and while there he wrote us three or four letters a week, still claiming that we had stolen his brainchild. We hear from him occasionally to this very day.

With such people around, it's a damn good thing that lawyers take all precautions!

REPORTS FROM THE FRONT

Most business people, if they are reasonably bright and if they pay attention, will pick up a fair amount of knowledge of the law, as it pertains to their businesses, by osmosis.

If the law stayed still, chances are most people would know about as much as they needed to by the time they had risen to positions of real responsibility within their companies.

For better or worse, however, the law *doesn't* stay still.

It's constantly changing, and, as with so many things in our society, the rate at which it changes seems to be accelerating all the time.

A friend of mine who has been practicing law for many years tells me that there was a time when one referred either to the tax code of 1939 or the one from 1954.

Then there were yearly revisions.

Then monthly supplements were added.

Today there are data bases available that feature new information *hourly*.

In antitrust, in liability, even in divorce and child-custody cases, the law has been evolving at an ever-faster clip—far faster than any business person could keep abreast of, given that most of his or her time and energy is taken up with other things.

One of the key functions that attorneys perform for business people, then, is **to issue reports from the legal front.**

As with any aspect of legal service, this role can be performed well or it can be performed badly. *Any* lawyer can spend his working hours poring over journals and government notices, then write pompous-sounding memos informing the staff that the wording of such and such a statute has been changed.

That's the flat *minimum* a lawyer should do, and it's of only very limited use to the people on the business side.

What an attorney *ought* to do is report not just on the changes in the law, but on the *applications and implications* of those changes.

FOOTPRINTS ON THE EARTH

Let me illustrate. Our company, in its role as a producer of television programming, regularly negotiates deals for the use of that programming. Traditionally, these deals have been made on a country-by-country or, occasionally, a continent-by-continent basis. As long as the programs were broadcast by conventional means, it was fairly simple and straightforward to say, "You can air this program in France, but not in Belgium," or "Your rights to this material end at the Canadian border."

What happens, however, when broadcasts are sent by satellite—a new technology that has nothing to do with national boundaries and, in itself, is subject only to physical laws?

As a matter of earthly jurisprudence, the rules governing the use of satellite broadcasting are still being hashed out. And one of the jobs of our in-house counsel is to keep us informed of what is going on at that busy intersection where law collides with technology—and also collides with the bottom line.

Quite often, we sell sports programming to the cable network ESPN. When we do, we take the stance that ESPN is buying the rights to broadcast in the United States, its territories and possessions. ESPN, however, takes the position that it's buying the rights to use the shows throughout what is known as the network's "footprint."

A footprint is the entire sweep of earth that is within reach of a given satellite's signals. Now, the ESPN footprint happens to include a fair amount of Central America, South America, and Canada—all markets which traditionally would be sold separately.

In terms of established practice in broadcasting, then, we feel that our position is absolutely justified, and that ESPN is trying to get more for its money than is fair. But even if we win the battle to limit ESPN's broadcast territory, we still have the problem posed by the "new territory," i.e., the satellite. What happens is that ESPN notifies these "footprint" territories that they may not show the programming in question. But in fact, it is right up there in the sky, available to them. Do they honor the ESPN instruction or do they simply show it anyway?

The real answer is, most of the time we don't know. Many of these territories are small, distant and difficult to check on. And suppose we find out they did violate ESPN's instructions; whom do we sue? ESPN? The territory? And for how much?

International law on this subject is mostly unwritten as yet. So our deal people continue to argue and monitor the law.

CLOSER TO HOME

Not that the lawyers' role as advance scouts pertains only to such exotic subjects as high tech.

In more down-to-earth ways as well, **a company's attorneys should keep the line executives meaningfully informed on shifts in the legal climate.**

Take endorsements. They are obviously a tremendous income source for the athletes we represent, and advising our clients on what products and services to endorse is an integral part of the service we provide.

Giving this advice responsibly is more complicated than you might imagine, however, because *every endorsement carries with it a potential liability.*

And as our legal system becomes more and more liberal in its interpretation of liability, dangers crop up, like rocks at low tide, where none had been seen before.

THROWN FOR A LOSS

A couple of years ago, for example, Johnny Unitas, formerly the great quarterback for the Baltimore Colts, was sued by two men who had lost money in an investment firm that Unitas had endorsed and that had turned out to be a fraud.

The company, First Fidelity Financial Services, went belly-up, and its founder was indicted on eight felony counts.

Unitas himself had had nothing whatsoever to do with the scam. His sole connection with First Fidelity was that he had accepted a fee of $7,000 for doing some radio and newspaper ads on behalf of the company.

The grounds on which he was sued were actually very touching, though legally shaky. The plaintiffs' attorney argued, essentially, that *everybody trusted Johnny U.*, and that, even if he was not guilty of any wrongdoing, he had a responsibility to check more closely into the soundness of the product he was endorsing.

Johnny Unitas was not a client of ours, and, except for newspaper coverage in Baltimore and some very spotty mentions elsewhere, this case actually received very little publicity. Nevertheless, IMG's legal staff followed it closely, as it had clear implications for people who *were* our clients.

As soon as the suit was filed, our general counsel, Bill Carpenter, started sending us memos about the issues it raised. He went beyond the Unitas affair, to review for us certain low points in the history of celebrity or "expert" endorsements.

In 1978, for example, singer Pat Boone had been hit with a suit for endorsing an acne medicine that didn't work and that had dangerous side effects. The lessons to be drawn from that debacle were writ large in Carpenter's memos: Beware of endorsing anything used on the body, and, for God's sake, don't claim that you or your family actually *use* the product if you don't.

In 1985 Dr. Barry Bricklin was subject to a complaint by the

Federal Trade Commission because of his endorsement of the so-called "rotation diet." The FTC ruled that Bricklin "knew or should have known" that the diet's promised weight loss was a gross exaggeration.

The crucial phrase here, of course, was *"should have known."* As Carpenter pointed out, this suggested that, when endorsing something as an expert, or in a field in which one could be *construed* to be an expert, the endorser should review not just the ads but the *evidence* on which the ads were purportedly based.

The Unitas case raised red flags of its own. Celebrity athletes are quite regularly asked to lend their names and likenesses to various financial services, and financial services routinely make rather optimistic claims about anticipated rates of return.

What if a financial service, even in the absence of fraud, failed to perform as claimed? What if John Madden, say, were paid to stand in front of a new condo development and say it was a fantastic investment as well as a great place to live, and as an investment the development turned out to be a dog? Where exactly does an endorser's liability begin and end, so far as investors' money is concerned?

How much is an endorser required to know—or for that matter *care*—about a product he or she is very obviously being *paid* to endorse?

As it happened, Johnny Unitas's attorneys successfully argued that he could not be held accountable for the misdeeds of First Fidelity's principals.

But the point here is that, by paying close attention to the case, and by *interpreting it in ways that were meaningful to our business*, our lawyers made our line executives a bit more informed and more sophisticated in the matter of endorsements.

They answered questions for us that we might not even have thought to ask.

They made us better at our jobs.

And that, finally, is what playing as a team is all about.

7

THINGS I WISH EVERY
LAWYER KNEW

What the two preceding chapters have really been about are the two sides of McCormack's Central Paradox about businessmen and lawyers:

> Businessmen and lawyers tend to have deep temperamental differences that make conflict between them almost inevitable.
> However, by viewing those differences not in terms of conflict but of *mutual advantage*, both sides can advance their interests.

They can mold themselves into a team that is more powerful and versatile than any single player

KNOWING EACH OTHER'S MOVES

Playing as a team, however, requires unanimity of effort. Achieving that unanimity is our subject now.

I'm reminded of the way that Paul Hornung and Jim Taylor used to block for each other back in the glory days of the Green Bay Packers.

The halfback and the fullback moved so well together that every cut and feint seemed to have been choreographed. It didn't look like the runner was following the blocker; the zigs and zags were too spontaneous for that. Rather, it seemed as if the blocker was somehow seeing the runner with eyes in back of his head. That's how well they *knew each other's moves.*

And that, I think, is the key phrase here.

For a lawyer and a client to get the best results, each should know the other's style, abilities, and limitations.

Each should know the other's goals and priorities.

Each should understand what motivates the other, the sorts of challenges that get the juices flowing, the things that make the other lose interest or lose heart.

And each should know what makes the other mad.

SOME LIKE IT SHORT

Let's start with the things that make me the maddest: wasted time, effort, and verbiage.

A number of years ago, our company was approached by a leading NHL hockey player who wanted us to represent him, and whom we would have been very pleased to have as a client.

There was only one small problem: the athlete was already under contract to another agent.

But he was very unhappy with that arrangement, and wanted our help in getting out of it.

So I asked to see his current contract. He reached into his

attaché case, and of course I expected him to produce the typical five- or ten- or forty-page document.

Instead, he handed over a single sheet of paper. My first response was: Great, no problem. How serious a commitment could possibly be indicated by four or five lines of longhand?

The thing didn't even *look* like a contract. All it said, in paraphrase, was that "I, ———, hereby agree that the XYZ Agency can represent me exclusively with respect to my business activities throughout the world for a period of five years beginning January 1, 19—, and that I will pay a commission of 25% of my gross income for this service." Period.

I passed the contract along to our legal department, asking their advice as to how the agreement might be voided.

They told me there was no way it could be. The contract was perfectly legitimate, binding, and about as airtight as any contract ever is.

This bit of news had two consequences. The first, of course, was that we could not represent this particular athlete.

The second was that I wondered why, if this *haiku* held up fine under legal scrutiny, it was impossible for *me* ever to get anything so short and concise out of *my* lawyers.

That, as I said, was some years ago, and I'm *still* wondering!

PROCESSES AND RESULTS

The seeming impossibility of getting anything *short and fast* out of a lawyer drives me, and I think most business people, crazy. It is one of the central truisms of our culture that business people are chronically—and sometimes comically—pressed for time.

Executives are always running to catch planes or putting abrupt endings to phone calls so they can move on to other phone calls.

Business letters are notoriously terse and clipped, often at the expense of both grammar and graciousness.

For all that, when lawyers draft documents that require a

business person's attention, they act as if their clients had all the time in the world to wade through them. The terrible truth is that lawyers tend to be not just thorough but obsessive.

Why?

The answer has to do with something that *is* taught at law school.

Law schools teach that everything is a *process*—a *chain* of reasoning with a *series* of causes and effects.

Well, that's fine, but business people are generally less interested in the twists and turns than in the *conclusions*—not the process but the *result*.

So, one of the things I wish all lawyers were aware of is that they can spare me the details of their brilliant logical pirouettes *and just tell me what's going on!*

EASY ON THE ADJECTIVES

And while we're at it, I wish that lawyers would throw away their thesauruses.

Consider this gem of legal draftsmanship, taken from our files, pertaining to a suit brought against us in 1983, and which, in spite of all the sound and fury, came to nothing:

> . . . defendant IMG did wrongfully, knowingly, intentionally, wantonly, maliciously, and without reasonable justification or excuse, induce, persuade, and entice the defendant BAT and/or ITF and/or IMG to violate, repudiate, and break the said contract with plaintiff. . . .

What is this fellow talking about and whom is he trying to impress? This ponderous paragraph does nothing more than claim that we broke the contract. *So why not say it that way?*

I think I speak for most clients when I say that I don't hire a lawyer to be impressed with his vocabulary.

A lawyer may *imagine* he's making a big hit with his Latin

phrases and five-syllable words, but in fact I'm likely to be tapping my foot and stealing glances at my watch as he holds forth.

I'm also likely to be resentful of the money *I'm* spending so that he can indulge his verbosity!

Let's face it: Most of the grand rhetorical flourishes aren't really an integral part of lawyering, they're just a way of showing off.

PLAYING TO THE CROWD

Not that drafting is the only area in which lawyers tend to indulge in bravado.

In meetings, too, they sometimes seem less concerned with substantive results than with turning in a flashy performance.

A few years ago, I was negotiating with one of the networks for the U.S. television rights to a major sports championship. At the first bargaining session, the network's head of sports programming brought along his chief of business affairs (who was an MBA) and a pair of lawyers.

About five minutes into the meeting, it became patently clear that all of us were wasting our time. The head of sports programming—the real decision maker—was being perfectly reasonable. But the head of business affairs was determined to show how tough he could be. He rolled up his shirt sleeves, planted his elbows on the mahogany table, and set out to impress his boss by taking the stance that he would make no financial concessions, reasonable or otherwise.

Well, the lawyers couldn't very well let themselves be outdone by the MBA, could they? They were *there*, after all; they had to make a "contribution."

So they tried not only to be cleverer, tougher, and more intransigent than the head of business, but also more dogged than *each other*.

It got to the point where I felt **the actual subject of the negotiation had virtually ceased to matter; what was going on was** simply some unpleasant and unproductive ritual among the members of the other side's "team."

I quickly found a pretext for cutting the meeting short.

Some time thereafter, I phoned the head of sports programming, and told him I had a couple of ideas I wanted to discuss with him.

We got together, just the two of us, and within an hour and a half we had hammered out the basic points of a mutually advantageous deal—acceptable enough to all concerned so that both sides have happily stayed together for over ten years.

Why was it so much easier to get the deal done tête-à-tête?

The issues were the same, and my opposite number and I were equally intent on not giving away the store.

The crucial difference was that **we were talking to each other, rather than playing to the crowd.**

We didn't need to grandstand because we realized something that I wish more lawyers would realize: **The evidence that we had done our job existed *in the deal itself*, not in the posturing and one-upmanship we had indulged in to get it done.**

NOW THE POSITIVE SIDE

So far in this chapter I have been giving vent to a few pet peeves—things I wish lawyers knew *not* to do.

But the other side of the coin—the positive side—is even more important.

I *do* wish lawyers would be less theoretical and more pragmatic.

I wish, for example, that more lawyers would approach negotiation *as a business person approaches it;* that is, not as a rigid and formal process, but as **an elaborate game that involves creativity, close attention to human nature, improvisation, and sometimes, to be perfectly candid, such tactics as bluffing and manipulation.**

This game has only two rules:

1. *Everything* is negotiable

2. *Anything* can be used as a tool in a negotiation.

A Yen for Profits

Even such seemingly extraneous elements as currency considerations can become, under certain circumstances, valuable bargaining chips.

Anyone who does business in a multinational context is well aware of the impact that currency fluctuations can have on profits. But I wonder how many people *use* currency issues effectively.

A couple of years ago, a licensing contract between Bjorn Borg and a leading Japanese knitwear manufacturer came up for renewal.

The Japanese company, whose profits had been declining, hadn't done as well with this line of products as it had hoped to, and came to the bargaining table seeking a reduction in the main guarantee that Bjorn was to receive.

Our position was that our client had more than lived up to his obligations, and that, now that he was a known quantity in terms of cooperation and availability, his guarantee should increase. The company's profits, we argued, would certainly increase in the near future.

How could these two positions be reconciled?

The company, of course, did most of its business in yen. Its contract with us was in dollars. And the yen had recently appreciated substantially against the dollar.

By staying keenly attuned to the currency fluctuations—*as well as to their psychological effects*—we were able to reach an agreement that made the manufacturers happy because it cost fewer yen, and made our client happy because it gave him more dollars!

And we built goodwill for IMG on both sides because it seemed to the casual observer that we had pulled the money out of a hat.

THE MATCH GAME

A crucial and often dramatic sort of negotiation that we have not yet had occasion to discuss features *competitive bidding.* And I wish lawyers knew more about the special psychology that pertains when bidders go head-to-head.

As anyone who has ever attended any sort of auction will testify, there are few scenarios more likely to elicit fireworks than the one in which two or more people want the same item, and at least one of them isn't going to get it!

In auction situations, rationality battles with passion, and the business imperative to buy *at the right price* contends with the more primitive impulse *not to lose at any price.*

At IMG over the years, we have participated in all sorts of "match game" situations—both as auctioneers and as bidders. Experience has taught us a couple of things that all lawyers and negotiators should keep in mind:

1. Never underestimate the role of *theater* in an auction, and never pass up opportunities to raise the stakes by dramatic staging.

2. Don't let the single issue of money squeeze you into an overly "linear" approach to competitive bidding. Winning bids are often those that manage to sweeten the deal in nonmonetary ways.

GOING, GOING, GONE AT LAUSANNE

By way of illustrating point number one above, let me tell you about what was probably the most dramatic auction we have ever been involved with.

This concerned the U.S. television rights for the 1988 Winter Olympics, and the numbers were simply enormous. Our client, the Organizing Committee for the Calgary Games, had trusted our advice on how to conduct the bidding, and it was decided to create as much suspense as possible.

We drafted a contract that included all provisions *except those having to do with rights money.*

We then submitted that contract to *all three American networks.* In order to indicate their acceptance of the non-monetary terms and, indeed, to qualify to bid for the games, they were to sign the documents, without the money provisions.

The IOC then asked them to meet in Lausanne, Switzerland, to fill in the final blanks and to see which network's contract would be completed and which remaining two would be discarded.

Why Lausanne?

Well, the International Olympic Committee is headquartered there, and that fit perfectly into the crafted intrigue: There's nothing like a transoceanic plane ride to let the suspense build up and to underscore that the stakes are high. And besides, *doesn't everybody spend more when they're traveling?*

Prior to our arrival in Lausanne, we entrusted much of the drafting and negotiating strategy to one of our staff attorneys who happens to be a woman. Now, most of the people in our business are fairly progressive and enlightened, but still, sports has traditionally been a male bastion, and some males get a little nonplussed at the active presence of a woman in the proverbial smoke-filled room. This particular woman, Betsy Goff, is nearly six feet tall, totally poised, ultraprofessional, and as tough a negotiator as we have.

Did it bother us that some of our bidders might be nonplussed? You bet it didn't.

What, in the end, did all our dramatics and choreography add up to? A rights fee of $309,000,000, $96,000,000 *more* than was predicted would be bid the day we arrived in Lausanne.

So, if you're ever going to stage an auction, think Broadway.

THE DEAL THE OTHER SIDE
CAN'T MATCH

If you're sitting in an auction room at Sotheby's, bidding on a vase, obviously the only factor under your control is the amount of money you're willing to spend.

You can't explain to the auctioneer how beautifully you would display the vase, or argue that you would care for it better than anyone else. A Sotheby auction doesn't work that way.

But *some* kinds of auctions *do*. And lawyers, as well as *all* negotiators who are involved in a bidding situation, should be aware that sometimes the crucial determinant is not the money, **but something you can offer and the other side can't.**

A number of years ago, the National Basketball Association, which we represented, was due to renew its television contract. Barry Frank, the head of sales of our television subsidiary, TWI, was spearheading the transaction for the league, and he opened the floor to bids.

Now, NBA games had long been aired by ABC, and ABC wanted to keep it that way. In dollar amounts, the network was prepared to match virtually any offer.

But some of the league owners preferred to switch to CBS, so the NBA Television Committee came up with a masterstroke that neatly short-circuited the purely linear approach. They convinced CBS, which also badly wanted the NBA contract, to air a certain number of games on Saturday afternoons in the fall of the year, and argued that this particular form of increased exposure to the sports audience would be of great long-term benefit to pro basketball.

The promise of Saturday afternoon air time was one that ABC *could not possibly match*, because of a longstanding commitment to televise college football.

So CBS got the contract.

And ABC sued, claiming that the "Saturday afternoons in the fall" clause had been contrived *specifically* as a provision they couldn't match, and that therefore ABC had been unlawfully deprived of its right of refusal on the pact.

Now, this was an interesting lawsuit, because everybody within the sports industry *knew* that CBS's gambit had been *precisely* designed to ace out ABC. It couldn't have been more obvious.

On the other hand, however, the judge who heard the case ruled that Saturday exposure *did* add value to the league—and therefore CBS won the case, and airs pro basketball to this very day.

The moral of the story is look for values *other than money* **that can tip the scales in your favor.**

MYSELF ON THE BLOCK

Let me round out this brief account of competitive-bidding tactics with a story about the sale of my first book, which dealt with things you don't learn at Harvard Business School.

We decided to put this book up for auction, and several publishers made bids. In exchange for certain considerations, Bantam Books was given the "floor"—i.e., the right to match any other offer that came in.

The bidding escalated, and everyone dropped out except for Bantam and William Morrow.

At this point, Morrow came up with what seemed a brilliant ploy, in keeping with the idea of the offer that can't be matched: it suggested paying us an exorbitant royalty on paperback sales, a percentage dramatically higher than industry norms.

Why?

Because Morrow, essentially a hardcover house, didn't especially *care* about paperback sales. In theory, it would make its money before a paperback even came out.

Bantam, on the other hand, was *perceived* as basically a paperback house—which of course is what it traditionally had been. If Bantam was thinking of the Harvard book mainly as a paperback, the jumbo royalty would pose two problems: it would force the publishers to set a dangerous precedent as to how much they would pay, and it would make it very tough for them to turn a profit on the book.

Unbeknownst to anyone at the time, however, Bantam was on the brink of a major strategic repositioning, and was about to become a major player in the hardcover game.

So, to the surprise not only of Morrow's lawyers but of us as well, Bantam did match the offer and got the book.

Which leads me to this cautionary note: If you're going to pin your hopes on a supposedly unmatchable proposition, make sure it *is* in fact unmatchable.

FIRST WIN THE WAR,
THEN FIGHT THE SKIRMISHES

A publishing saga doesn't end with the awarding of the contract, however, and the story of the Harvard book deal has other chapters germane to our discussion.

At law school they teach you that a contract, once signed, is binding and immutable—unless formally altered by a subsequent contract. This concept in law is so basic as to be almost sacred, and it's no coincidence that "the sanctity of contracts" is such an often-heard cliché.

But business people realize—and lawyers *should* realize— that in practice matters are much more fluid. A contract reflects an understanding. And understandings between humans are usually imperfect. They often need revising.

In the case of the Harvard book, what happened was this:

Bantam published the book in hardcover form, and I'm happy to say it was quite successful. The publishers and I both more than recovered our investment of time, trouble, and money.

When it came time to publish the paperback edition, however,

Bantam informed me that it couldn't do so under the terms we'd originally agreed to. As we knew all along, it would be virtually impossible for the publishers to make money under the original contract's royalty provision. *Now* they wanted to renegotiate.

I *could* have gotten angry. I could even have accused Bantam of negotiating in bad faith in the first place. However, a number of things prevented my reacting that way:

1. There wasn't anyone around to be mad at. Jack Romanos, the man who made the original deal, had left Bantam and gone to Simon and Schuster. His successors claimed—fairly—that it wasn't *their* fault they had been saddled with a no-win contract.

   Lawyers should understand that, *in practice, these shifts of personnel happen all the time, and while they can be troublesome, they also provide useful pretexts for renegotiating contracts, throwing out contracts, and giving people various ways of saving face.*

2. Bantam was not probably going to publish a paperback anyway, but there was something to be gained by being sympathetic to their position. The publishers felt they could renegotiate with me because they judged—correctly—that *I* wanted the paperback to be published soon and with as much enthusiasm as the hardcover had been. Ultimately, they got the relief that they were looking for, and we both got a successful paperback.

3. In their position, *I probably would have done exactly the same,* in keeping with a philosophy that I wish all attorneys and negotiators would take to heart:

First win the war; then worry about the little battles.

First get the contract; then see if you can live with it.

IT'S NOT AS BAD AS IT SOUNDS

I realize that sounds rather cynical, so let me explain it a bit.

I'm not saying one should take contract provisions lightly, and I'm certainly not advocating making agreements that one doesn't intend to honor.

I *am* saying, however, that in any deal there's the Big Picture, and then there are the Small Details.

At law school they teach you that *every syllable of a contract is equally important.*

In theory, that's true.

In practice, it's nonsense.

The Big Picture is what matters, and the rest is usually nickels and dimes.

Just recently, we were approached by a major corporation on behalf of our new client, America's Cup winner Dennis Conner. The customer was very keen on getting Conner to do a number of speaking engagements for them, but they weren't yet firm on the dates or locations of the speeches involved.

Now, Dennis is a very busy man these days, and he's also a very scrupulous one. His initial response was to turn down the offer because he felt there was a good chance there would be a conflict or two along the way, and he probably wouldn't be able to fulfill all the dates that were being asked of him.

We counseled him to sign the contract and then take the events case by case.

Does this make us bad?

The answer has to do with the question of intent. We certainly didn't intend to mislead the customer. Rather, we intended to make them happy *most* of the time.

If Dennis Conner can give them what they want on thirty-five occasions and has to disappoint them on the thirty-sixth, business people will understand.

And lawyers, too, should understand that all the black-and-white contracts in the world can't eliminate the shades of gray that represent how deals *really* work.

THE BEST DEFENSE IS A GOOD OFFENSE

As we have seen, competitive bidding is a dicey business from the perspective of the bidder. In the heat of battle, prices get jacked up and impulsive promises get made. And a lot of the time, after all the trouble and expense of putting in a bid, you go home emptyhanded anyway.

But what if there were a way of *avoiding* bidding situations?

In fact, there is a way—though too few lawyers take advantage of it.

The way is to **be creative about renewing contracts.**

Obviously, a current contract holder generally has an inside track on a new negotiation. If nothing else, the person often has a first-refusal clause or some other sort of option provision.

What he *also* has, however, and what is really more important, is *the rights holder's ear.* He can talk to the rights holder at any time—and can discuss renewal at any point.

How do most attorneys handle renewal procedures?

The terrible truth is: stupidly.

All they do is flag a file to remind them when a contract is three or six months away from expiring.

Of course, *the people who lost the bidding the last time around are doing exactly the same thing!* So right away you're off to the races again: another time-consuming and expensive auction.

Why not renew *sooner?* And at a time when everybody is *thrilled* with the relationship?

This was a stratagem employed with great success by ABC back in the 1970s, when that network was very aggressively seeking to become the preeminent force in sports programming.

Let's say that back in 1975 the rights to a very attractive athletic event were being auctioned off. At that point, ABC would have had no choice but to bid head-to-head against the other two networks. If ABC offered the best deal—as it often did in those high-flying years—that network might walk away from the table with a contract to air the event for five seasons.

CBS and NBC, meanwhile, having lost in the bidding, would put memos in their follow-up files to contact the rights holder in 1979, and try once again to secure the event for themselves.

What the other networks would often find, however, was that by the time 1979 rolled around, ABC had already renewed for several more years!

Typically, ABC would set about renewing two or three years into a five-year contract. The network would say to the rights holder, "Look, we're doing well with this arrangement and so are you. Let's negotiate an increase in your payments for the remaining years on the contract, and extend it three or four years into the future."

Now think about the psychology of this offer. First of all, it makes the point man for the rights holder—the head of one of the amateur sports federations, say—look awfully good. He can go to his board and impress them with the way he "got" ABC to alter an existing arrangement to the benefit of their organization.

Second, since these sorts of people are fond of erecting monuments to themselves, the rights holder is likely to want to extend the deal so as to increase the lifespan of his legacy.

Further, by jumping the gun on the expected renewal time, chances are that ABC will be able to negotiate unilaterally without the other networks' even knowing what's in the works. Should CBS and NBC become aware of the renewal negotiations, how likely will they be to allocate money for a project that couldn't become effective for several years anyway?

For all those reasons, the aggressive approach taken by ABC's lawyers and producers gave the network a real leg up against adversaries who simply did things by the book.

ONE YEAR TIMES FIVE
OR FIVE YEARS TIMES ONE?

Analogous to the psychology involved in renewing contracts is the psychology that should be used in shaping termination language.

As we talked about earlier with regard to the Australian Termination Clause, the wording of a contract-ending provision can go a long way toward determining if a contract is ended or not.

On the surface, for example, it might seem that there is no difference between a one-year contract with an option to continue for five years, and a five-year contract with an option to terminate after one year.

I believe very strongly that in fact there are significant differences between the two—differences that hinge entirely on human psychology. And I wish more lawyers were more attuned to those psychological resonances.

Let's say that Chris Schenkel has a contract as spokesman for Eastern Airlines, and that the contract is for one year, with Eastern having the option to extend.

Psychologically speaking, it will be very easy for the airline to *passively* cancel the arrangement, just by letting the option date go by and doing nothing.

No confrontations will be necessary, no one's ego will be put on the line or bruised. Unless everyone is absolutely thrilled with the deal, there's a real chance it will just fall through a crack. Ending the relationship will be as easy as *not* making a phone call.

If, on the other hand, the contract is for five years, with Eastern having the option not to extend but to *terminate* it, the airline has to take an *active* stance if it wants out. It has to make a *positive* decision to end the arrangement. Most daunting of all, someone has to go to Chris and say, in effect, "We don't want you anymore."

This is a hard thing for almost anyone to say, especially since there will certainly be personal relationships between Schenkel and the Eastern executives by the time the option comes up.

In practice, then, **the sheer interpersonal discomfort of terminating the contract becomes a real incentive to keep the agreement in force—and to make the agreement work to the benefit of both sides.**

CAN INSURANCE BE CREATIVE?

As everybody in business already knows, there is a bad insurance crisis brewing around the world, and especially in America. Skyrocketing premiums, shrinking coverage, whimsical cancellations—these are problems on which whole books have already been written.

For our purposes here, however, I would just like to make a couple of points about insurance that too few people—and too few lawyers—seem to think about.

Most people view insurance as, well, *insurance*—a hedge against worst-case possibilities, but certainly *not* a source of profit.

However, why *shouldn't* insurance be a revenue center? It certainly is for the insurers!

Often when a promoter puts on a tennis championship, for example, he is actually playing two distinct roles. He can make or lose money from the gate and sale of broadcast rights. He can also make or lose money based on the performance of the top-seeded star players.

A tournament promoter routinely buys rainout insurance. If the promoter's star players get knocked out in the early rounds, the promoter very often will make less money if the finals are played as scheduled than if they are rained out.

I am sure that a lot of promoters have spent more than one Saturday evening praying for thunderstorms!

A couple of years ago, we contracted to stage a series of three races between the great English milers Steve Ovett and Sebastian Coe. We insured the race readiness of both runners, since obviously there would be no event unless both were fit.

To make a long story short, first Coe pulled a hamstring, then Ovett bruised a heel, and then Coe pulled a hamstring again.

No races were run, but we recovered the lost income from the insurers.

INSURING THE POPE

The point, however, is not to insure yourself to the eyeballs and then wait for disaster to make you rich.

Rather, the idea is to be so heads-up about insurance that you will come out all right *no matter what.*

In this connection, I would like to tell you about probably the most complex and sophisticated insurance matter we ever had to deal with.

In 1980, we were approached by the English Catholic Church and the Vatican to represent the commercial aspects of Pope John Paul II's impending visit to Great Britain, which was to take place in about eighteen months' time in the summer of 1982. The problem was that when the pope had visited Ireland several years earlier to perform a Mass before over a million worshipers, the visit ended up costing the Catholic Church and the Vatican almost two million pounds. This resulted from the high costs of setting up a sound system, security systems, hospital and sanitation facilities, etc., for the multitudes, and also from the high costs of air, helicopter, and ground transportation.

What disturbed the Vatican representatives, however, was that when they arrived, they found countless people were going through the crowds before, during, and after the Mass selling everything from T-shirts to religious items to sandwiches. The Catholic Church had two major problems with this. The first was that the quality of the items was generally poor, and the second problem was that none of the proceeds from the sales went to the Church to help defray the cost of the visit.

We had a couple of discussions with the English Catholic Church and Vatican representatives, which resulted in IMG representing the commercial elements of the papal visit, the development and trademarking of papal logos, the supervision of product quality, and the negotiation of a great number of licensing arrangements for "official products of the Papal Tour."

This activity was handled by Ian Todd, who is our senior marketing executive in Britain and Europe, and a qualified lawyer as well as an effective salesman.

Everything about the papal visit was enormously complicated—the security, the transportation, the media access, and the licensing arrangements for dozens of papal-endorsed products.

Not the least bedeviling problem was what would happen if the pope, because of illness, political problems, or whatever, was unable to perform one or more of the six scheduled outdoor Masses? These Masses were the main rationale for the pope's trip. Hundreds of thousands of people would attend, and presumably millions of dollars of products might be sold.

Clearly, we needed insurance coverage for the pope's appearances.

But obviously no such policy existed in ready-made form!

So Ian Todd had to write one. This, in turn, raises a point that every attorney and business person should be aware of: Insurance companies would like you to think that their policies are carved in stone, and all that's left for you to do is fill in the blanks.

That's nonsense. There's no reason why an insurance policy can't be drafted from scratch, just like any other contract. And there's no reason why each and every clause in it shouldn't be negotiable.

In drafting this unique policy for the pope, Ian Todd had a very important priority in mind. He wanted to avoid the usual procedure of first filing a claim, then having to establish the dollar amount of the loss. There would be no precedent to follow if, say, a Mass had to be canceled because of a storm, and so how could damages be fairly assessed?

To solve the problem, Ian did *exhaustive* research *before* drafting the policy. By the time he went to the insurers, he could tell them *precisely* how many worshipers were expected at each stop on the tour, how many articles were expected to be sold, and so forth. His figures were so detailed that he was able to get the insurance company to *spell out and* guarantee payments on almost any contingency.

As it happened, the pope did celebrate six Masses. However, the venue of one of them was changed.

Our insurance policy was so clear and explicit that we had a mathematical formula for determining exactly how much we had lost by the switch in plan! We collected just over $100,000 on the Vatican's behalf, and saved ourselves the time, trouble, and possible conflicts of having to establish a claim after the fact.

OFF THE HOOK

Insurance is one way of dealing with the hard fact that things don't always turn out exactly as planned.

Another way of dealing with things that don't quite pan out is **letting the other side off the hook.**

There are a surprising number of occasions on which one may apply the following axiom:

McCormack's Axiom of Good Pragmatic Deeds
Sometimes there is more money to be made from letting people out of contracts than by holding them to commitments that are disadvantageous to them.

I'm not talking, of course, about cases in which the other party has shown bad faith or gotten into a bind because of their own incompetence. In such instances, we just shrug and collect our money.

But sometimes, let's fact it, things happen that just could not have been foreseen.

Let's say, for example, that the Donnay racquet company enters into a five-year contract with Bjorn Borg to endorse a line of wooden racquets.

Two years into the contract, everyone starts playing with graphite and composite racquets, and wooden racquets of every manufacture are piling up in warehouses.

Strictly speaking, this is not our problem. Donnay owes us three more years of fees.

But at the time we made the deal, everyone thought a wooden racquet with Borg's signature would sell. The people at Donnay who made that judgment are no doubt feeling pretty bad; maybe their jobs are in jeopardy. Borg, of course, would like to do business with Donnay in future.

So, if we agree to cancel their obligation, the executives are off the hook, they will feel that they owe analogous consideration in the future, and chances are they will bend over backward to deal with us again.

This obviously is a *business* judgment, not a legal one, and lawyers sometimes have a tough time understanding it. Yale or Harvard or East Podunk Law School has taught them to work very hard at fashioning contracts that are as complete and as watertight as possible; it's hard for them not to feel subverted if the business side just decides to throw out the contract.

But I would argue that attorneys sometimes become so fixated on the solidity of their contracts that they lose sight of what the ultimate *purpose* of the contract really is:

The ultimate purpose of any contract is not to get a stranglehold on the other party, but to formalize an understanding that is of real and proportionate benefit to both sides over time.

WHEN YOU CAN'T DELIVER THE GOODS

Just as we have occasionally released business partners from obligations they couldn't reasonably fulfill, so now and then we have elected to give a refund where circumstances prevented us from doing the kind of job we like to do.

This is difficult for several reasons.

First of all, it obviously costs the company money.

Second, no one likes to admit he fell short of meeting the task.

But my contention is that **dignity and goodwill are better served by freely acknowledging when you just can't deliver the goods.**

Several years ago, we arranged for Levi Strauss to sponsor a computerized ranking service for joggers. The idea was a very ambitious one that promised to give Levi's a great grass-roots exposure that would be totally appropriate to the company's image.

The plan basically was this: If you were, say, a thirty-five-year-old female who had run a half-dozen 10K races at an average time of forty-seven minutes, you would file that information with the Levi's Runners Ranking Service, and receive a computer ranking by age, gender, geographical area, and so forth. This information, in turn, could be used to qualify you for other races, or just to let you know where you stood.

As the saying goes, it looked good on paper, but it didn't really fly. There were some organizational problems. Creating national awareness of the ranking service was enormously difficult. Worst of all, the runners themselves were either intimidated by the computer or just didn't want to bother filing the forms.

So IMG found itself in a position where legally it had done everything it was obligated to do, and more; yet we knew very well that the sponsor wasn't getting value for its money.

We could have kept our fees and said, Sorry—but that's a no-class way to do business. But we gave a lot of the money back —and I believe we have a friend in San Francisco.

GOING TO EXTREMES

In completing the list of business tactics I wish every lawyer had in his repertoire, I would like to talk briefly about the dynamics of deals that turn out to be either real dogs or *too good*.

Realistically, the degree of success of deals can probably be mapped in keeping with the classic bell curve.

A small percentage turn out to be major windfalls.

Another small percentage are real disasters, ending in default, bankruptcy, and/or litigation.

The overwhelming majority end up somewhere in between. They are neither fantasies nor nightmares. They work about as well as you would expect them to work.

That fact notwithstanding, here's an axiom I would like lawyers and business people to pay heed to:

McCormack's Axiom of Wild Extremes

There are major psychological advantages in approaching a contract with the expectation that the deal in question will be either a *huge* success or a *monstrous* failure.

Both extremes present dangers, and both extremes offer opportunities.

CONVINCE ME

Now, no one *really* goes into any deal expecting it to be a dismal flop.

Still, in almost any negotiation, there is a "courting party" and a party being courted—and of course the party being courted has the leverage.

That leverage can be enhanced by the strategic use of pessimism.

The party being courted can say, in effect, "I'm not convinced this deal is going to work, and if you want me, you've got to give me a great deal of reassurance. *I'm assuming the worst. Convince me otherwise.*"

This was a stratagem we used in 1985 in representing Herschel Walker, when we negotiated an extension of his contract with the New Jersey Generals in the now-defunct United States Football League.

Clearly, Walker had the leverage in this negotiation. He was a known quantity—one of the best players in professional football and the USFL's number-one drawing card. On the other hand, the USFL was still a fledgling enterprise and, as we all know, the history of pro sports is littered with leagues that never quite got off the ground.

So we took the stance that, for all we knew, the USFL might go belly-up tomorrow morning.

Starting from that point, we could argue that Walker should be paid a hefty premium for taking on that risk. We could also reasonably insist on getting Generals owner Donald Trump's *personal guarantee* of the running back's $6 million salary.

What makes this strategic pessimism such a powerful weapon **is that the courting party has no choice but to be optimistic.**

Trump was wooing Walker with rosy visions of the new league's future; he couldn't very well turn around and make it seem like he was lacking in faith.

To be consistent, Trump *had* to give Walker all due assurances. Our job was to make sure those assurances cost plenty.

TANKS FOR THE MEMORIES

In a sense, taking advantage of the newness of the USFL was almost too easy. Anyone with any brains realized that the new league would have to compensate in dollars for what it couldn't offer in security and prestige.

More impressive, then, is the situation where strategic pessimism is applied to deals that *don't* have obvious built-in dangers.

Consider this masterstroke pulled off a few years ago by my friend Bruce Rappaport.

Rappaport is a tremendously successful shipbuilder, maritime expert, banker, financier, oil man, *and* lawyer—in short, one of the more brilliant businessmen in the world. He literally made legal history in his dealings with the Indonesian government and its state-owned oil company, Pertamina.

In striking an agreement with Pertamina to lease from it a number of tankers, Rappaport paid shrewd attention to what then seemed a highly unlikely worst-case scenario: What if the world oil picture radically changed, and those tankers could no longer be run at a profit?

This, you understand, was an eventuality that almost no one was considering back then, so Rappaport had little trouble getting the Indonesian government to co-sign and guarantee the contracts.

Sure enough, the oil glut hit shortly thereafter, overcapacity in tankers became a tremendous problem in the shipping business—and almost everyone *except* Bruce Rappaport got badly hurt. He had been smart enough to anticipate disaster even during go-go times.

TOO GOOD TO BE TRUE

Covering the downside is, of course, a vital part of every negotiation. Less obvious—and therefore more intriguing—is the need to guard against things going *too well*.

Human nature is funny. If you and I are fifty-fifty partners in a deal, and together we make a dollar, you may think, "Hey, that's pretty good—I made fifty cents."

But if we make a *million* dollars, chances are you may say to yourself, "Hey, why should that so-and-so McCormack be making five hundred thousand bucks off *me*?"

This leads me to posit this axiom:

McCormack's Axiom of Geometrical Greed
As the pie gets bigger, people start thinking less about their slice of it than about the *other* guy's.

This is obviously not a logical reaction, but I have seen it happen again and again. People get greedier in accordance with the gross amounts that are being divvied up, *even when their proportional split stays exactly the same.*

People tend not to think about this in the early stages of a deal, of course. They think they'll just get happier and happier, the more lucrative the arrangement turns out to be for all concerned.

For that reason, I am a firm believer in preparing *early* for the almost inevitable conflicts that set in when a deal turns out to be a windfall.

Some years ago IMG negotiated a contract with an Italian clothing manufacturer named Cerruti 1881 Sport, on behalf of our client Mats Wilander.

Wilander was just on the verge of breaking into the very top ranks of pro tennis, and he had the talent to stay very near the top for some years. What this meant, among other things, was that the moneys due him, in bonuses and royalties, would grow to impressive—but dangerous—amounts.

The clothing manufacturer, riding Wilander's growing celebrity, would be making money hand over fist; still, I could foresee that Cerruti would come to resent the outlays, and might very well seek ways of getting out of the contract.

Accordingly, I urged our lawyers, *from the very outset,* to write in language protecting us, ironically, from the deal's possible runaway success.

I wanted a clause stipulating American jurisdiction in case of breach or default.

I wanted a provision allowing us to collect moneys directly from U.S. department stores in the event the manufacturer failed to pay us.

Some of these demands were met, some were not—and I had the feeling, frankly, that even my own lawyers thought I was being overly cautious and too much of a stickler on these points.

But sure enough, just as the royalties due our client were reaching the psychological barrier of the million-dollar mark, the clothing manufacturer made an effort to terminate the contract. We were forced to sue, and eventually won.

I will close this chapter with a sobering lesson not dispensed in law school, but of potential value to every lawyer:

When a deal seems too good to be true, it usually is.

PART THREE

THE TERRIBLE TRUTH

8

SOMETIMES
THE SYSTEM DOESN'T
WORK

If you ever want to see a lawyer squirm, ask him the following simple question:

In what percentage of legal actions is justice ultimately done?

I myself have posed this query to a number of attorneys over the years—sometimes in a friendly way, sometimes less so—and I have never yet received a straightforward and satisfactory response.

Typically, a lawyer will answer by talking all around the subject.

He will tell you, for example, that there is no law school course or law school textbook titled *Justice*.

He will tell you that all of us have to live with the burdensome realization that life is unfair.

He will tell you that no code of laws is infallible, and that the most the laws can do is put a brake on people's natural cussedness.

Maybe he will commit himself as far as saying that justice is done more often than not—though frankly even that hazy claim to 51 percent validity might not stand up to rigorous scrutiny.

To be fair, the question I propose is, of course, impossible to answer; no one can pinpoint the proportion of just results.

Still, stating the issue in that way makes us realize that, in our hearts and in our consciences, we feel that **any answer less than 100 percent is morally, if not practically, unacceptable.**

And it's also safe to say that the percentage of just results in legal actions is dramatically below one hundred.

This chapter is about some of the things that can go wrong in legal proceedings, *not* by chance, *not* necessarily because of malice, *but because the system is made that way.*

Insofar as it is possible to protect oneself from these systemic flaws, I will offer some advice on how to do so.

In situations where there doesn't seem to *be* any way to protect oneself, I will try to provide a map, at least, of what one can expect to encounter in the procedural trenches.

Legally speaking, the terrible truth is that it's a jungle out there.

THE STRANGE CASE OF DR. COLUMBU

Let me tell you about the worst thing that has ever happened to our company in a court of law.

It's a sad tale, and in some respects it doesn't make a lot of sense. But I want to tell it in some detail because our general counsel, Bill Carpenter, maintains that the case provides *a perfect shorthand example of much of what is cockeyed about the American tort, or personal injury, system.*

Back in 1977, our television subsidiary, Trans World International, undertook to produce a show called *The World's Strongest Man.*

The format of the program was a contest among various world-class bodybuilders, weight lifters, and so forth; and the show's "hook"—the concept that would make the show irresistible to a broad audience—was that, rather than throwing barbells around, the participants would perform feats of strength that ordinary people could relate to and marvel at.

For instance, our ideas for events included lifting the front end of a car or pulling a tram loaded head high with cinder blocks.

The *pièce de résistance* of the program was the so-called refrigerator race, in which contestants carried 400-pound refrigerators, in specially designed carriers, over a 40-yard course.

That idea, as filtered through the civil courts of the state of California, went on to cost us a million dollars.

Some background is in order. At the time *The World's Strongest Man* was conceived, we were well covered by liability insurance. Between the time we contracted to produce the show, however, and the time we actually taped it, our insurance was canceled. The insurer, with the smug and unaccountable independence for which the insurance industry has become notorious, had simply and unilaterally decided not to cover us anymore.

(This—for those keeping score—can be chalked up as point number one of why the tort system is in such miserable shape: **The insurance industry has been abdicating its proper role.** Insurance companies *should* help active, wealth-producing businesses function. These days, they tend simply to drain resources and to be so intent on protecting *themselves* that they don't really protect their clients.)

Anyway, the cancellation left us in a bind. We had agreed to indemnify both MCA, on whose lot the program would be staged, and CBS, which would air the program. We had already spent considerable sums launching the project and had already invited the contestants.

We *could* have reneged on our commitments, but doing so would have been costly and embarrassing, and might have damaged our credibility on future programs.

So we decided to go ahead. Factored into this decision was

our awareness that we were dealing with world-class athletes who understood and willingly accepted the risks of their profession, and *who had all signed a very clearly and carefully worded release.*

No one had ever been seriously injured at an IMG event, and we were confident that adequate precautions had been taken so that no one would be injured at this one.

But that was before Dr. Franco Columbu, in the 1978 installment of the show, decided to one-up his opponents by trying to *run* with a 400-pound refrigerator on his back.

No one *told* him to run, and in fact, according to at least some of the testimony at the eventual trial, he was advised *not* to run.

Nevertheless, he ran.

His knee became dislocated.

And suddenly we were all embarked on a very different sort of contest.

I would like to make it clear that I bear no ill will at all toward Franco Columbu. In fact, I admire him. I have a genuine respect for the discipline that made him a great bodybuilder—possibly the second greatest ever, after his close friend Arnold Schwartzenegger.

I respect the intelligence and foresight that led Columbu to become a chiropractor even while pursuing his athletic career. And needless to say, I sympathize with his injury. Who wouldn't?

But sympathy is an emotional concept, not a legal one.

This rudimentary distinction seems to have been utterly overlooked—as it so often is—in the course of his suit against us.

Giving the devil his due, Columbu's lawyer was very intelligent, and had among his tools a number of intuitions of the sort one doesn't learn in law school, and that no attorney, client, or business person can afford to be without.

So central are these intuitions, in fact, that they might be thought of as the Three Truths of the Plaintiff's Bar:

Truth 1: Juries will almost always favor an individual over a corporation, especially if that corporation (like CBS and MCA, which were named as defendants even though *we* were the financially liable party) is perceived to have deep pockets.

Truth 2: Less well-to-do jurors, perhaps savoring a plaintiff's windfall vicariously, are nearly always more inclined to award large sums than are jurors who are better off.

Truth 3: Many and perhaps most judges, from the conscious or unconscious inclination "to stick up for the little guy," will give more slack, procedurally speaking, to a plaintiff's lawyer than to a defendant's.

With these truths in mind, let's look at some of the Columbu case's salient features.

Before the trial itself even started, the judge ruled, at the request of plaintiff's counsel, that Columbu's signed release *be excluded from evidence altogether!*

We simply wanted to include the release as evidence that Columbu, a professional athlete, had been made aware of the inherent risks and had accepted them. The judge disallowed this, purportedly out of a concern that *it might confuse the jury*.

In keeping with Truth 3, however, the judge didn't seem to worry about the jury being confused by the *plaintiff's* side.

Columbu's lawyer took the procedural liberty of asking Arnold Schwartzenegger, *by general knowledge the plaintiff's good friend*, to *speculate* about the economic losses suffered by Columbu on account of his injury.

According to the trial transcript, Schwartzenegger's testimony included admissions that the money to be made from body-building "is quite different from one person to the other," that "you cannot hit it exactly on the mark," and that "there is no way . . . [to] pinpoint it."

In spite of that, Schwartzenegger went on to *estimate*— despite defense counsel's objections, which were overruled— that Columbu had lost more money as a result of his injury than he had ever made in his life; more money, actually, than any bodybuilder, except Schwartzenegger himself, had ever managed to earn from the sport and its resultant publicity.

Additionally, while the plaintiff had claimed that the design of the refrigerator carrier was faulty, the jury ended up acknowledging that it was *not*. In fact, a case could be made that the mechanism had saved Columbu's life because when his leg buckled, the carrier device did its job and suspended him in mid-air rather than letting him fall to the ground with the refrigerator on top of him.

Shortly after the accident, Columbu had acknowledged to commentator Brent Musberger that the mishap was his own fault and he should not have tried to run.

For all that, in keeping with Truth 1, the jury's sympathies were with *the individual who* admitted *he had made a mistake, rather than with the corporation that had been* shown *not to be negligent.*

And the judgment? Well, that fell in squarely with Truth 2.

What sort of damages would you expect to have been awarded? Fifty thousand dollars? A hundred thousand dollars? Well, it was $1,036,760—and you'll forgive me for saying I believe the jurors probably took more vicarious satisfaction from Columbu's payday than was seemly.

One more detail: By the time the trial took place, in 1982, *Columbu had made such a complete recovery that he had won the 1981 Mr. Olympia contest.*

Sworn witnesses had also seen him lifting up cars in the Los Angeles area.

The jury knew all that. It didn't seem to matter to them.

As a postscript to this odd tale, I should mention that we filed an appeal. Two hundred thousand dollars in legal fees brought us *halfway* through the appeals process, at which point we settled for $800,000. The total made a nice round number.

YOU THINK YOU GOT TROUBLES?

A million dollars for a temporarily hurt knee is a pretty high ticket. But we don't kid ourselves that we were anywhere near the pinnacle of absurdity, so far as liability handouts are concerned. Consider these recent awards:

> In 1984 a California woman, who was driving her husband's Porsche after having had several drinks, had an accident in which her passenger was killed. She had been driving 60 in a 25-mph zone. Porsche was ordered to pay $2.5 million for having designed a car deemed too high-performance for the average driver.

> In 1985 an overweight man with a heart condition bought a lawnmower from Sears. He later had a heart attack while starting the mower and was awarded $1.8 million.

> While in the process of attempting to burglarize a school, a man fell through a skylight. The company that insured the school was ordered to pay $260,000 in damages and to give the would-be burglar $1,500 a month for life.

> In Maryland two men tried to dry their hot-air balloon in a commercial-laundry dryer. The dryer exploded, injuring them slightly, and they ended up winning almost $900,000 in damages.

> Back in sunny California, a man was injured when a drunk driver rammed into the phone booth in which he was making a call. The state's chief justice ruled that the company that designed the phone booth was liable for the man's injuries.

THE LAW AS LOTTERY

Odd stories like the above, by their sheer illogic and craziness, make headlines and may even elicit grim smiles from many of us.

But they suggest a situation that is not funny in the least.

The terrible truth is that the American tort system is raging out of control, operating less like a cogent mechanism for redressing wrongs than like a lottery in which "lucky victims" find themselves with windfall profits.

The problem, of course, is that those windfalls come at *our* expense. Juries tend to give away corporations' money as if it came from thin air. In fact, it comes from consumers like us.

How does this dynamic work?

Consider the ripple effects of a case like Columbu's.

Having been badly stung on the Columbu lawsuit, we have to be that much more intent on covering ourselves next time around. Either we buy coverage *at whatever price an insurer will deign to sell it to us,* or we "go bare"—that is, proceed without insurance—in which case we need to keep a reserve fund against possible disaster.

Either way, our operating costs have been jacked up.

Maybe we can swallow some of the increase; we can't swallow all of it. So we go to the network—ABC, say—for which we're preparing the program, and we tell them that we need to charge a little more than we did the last time.

ABC, being realistic and well aware of the judicial and insurance climate, is sympathetic and agrees to the higher price.

The network, in turn, goes to the show's sponsor—Ford Motor Company, let's say—and tells them that, since the network is paying more for the programming, commercial time is going to cost a little more, too.

What is Ford going to do—stop advertising on television? Obviously not. Ford understands the fiscal pressures behind the increased cost, and passes that increase right along to the consumer in the sticker prices of its cars.

Taking the ripple effects one step further, for a certain number of consumers that raised sticker price will be the last straw that convinces them to keep their old car for another year, and there go a few more American jobs.

If jurors thought a little more about this whole chain of events, they might realize that their "generous" awards aren't really very generous.

THE REAL VILLAINS

But jurors come and jurors go, and it doesn't make much sense to blame *them* for the basic flaws in the legal system.

On the contrary, the basic flaws were put in by the people who *made* the legal system—i.e., the lawyers.

And since lawyers made the system by which they make their living, it shouldn't come as much of a surprise that **most of the most profound flaws in Western jurisprudence have to do with giving lawyers too much power and control.**

This excessive and misplaced power exists at several levels.

Obviously, it pertains at the level of *individual* cases, as we will shortly illustrate.

But it *also* applies at the *political* level—the level at which reforms can be made, or squelched.

There is no great mystery about what can and should be done to help bring our liability system into line with sanity and fiscal responsibility:

1. A cap should be placed on jury awards for physical harms, and such hazy concepts as "pain and suffering" should either be more clearly defined or gotten rid of.

2. Contingent fees should operate on a sliding scale—for example, 25 percent on the first $100,000, 10 percent thereafter—to remove some of the incentive for the "moonshot mentality."

To their shame, the men and women of the plaintiff's bar have consistently lobbied against these reforms.

So intent are they on preserving their turf that they have managed to subvert even the one reform that *has* been legislated: no-fault car insurance—which has turned out not to be no-fault at all!

And just in case there is anybody out there who harbors illusions about the general moral tone prevailing among the plaintiff's bar, let me report on the results of an interesting experiment conducted recently by *The American Lawyer* magazine.

The publication sent one of its reporters, posing as an accident victim, to thirteen attorneys. She told each one that she had taken a fall *near* a construction site, *but that the fall was in no way caused by or connected to the construction.*

Five of the thirteen lawyers advised her to change her recollection of the mishap, to bring it closer to the site so they could sue!

THE SERVANT AS MASTER

Akio Morita, the founder and chairman of Sony, is one of many non-Westerners who have been shocked by the arrogance and pushiness of American attorneys, and in his recent autobiography Morita tells a story that illustrates perfectly what can happen when lawyers are too much in control in specific cases.

Way back in 1968, an American trade group called the Electronic Industries Association filed a complaint with the U.S. Treasury Department, accusing Japanese firms of "dumping" television sets—that is, selling them below cost in order to destroy competition—on the U.S. market.

This was a long, bitter, and complicated suit, and Sony was eventually omitted from the list of firms under investigation, for a very simple reason: *as purveyor of one of the highest priced brands on the market, Sony couldn't very logically be accused of unfair low-balling!*

That, however, didn't stop an American television maker, National Union Electric Company (whose brand name was Emerson), from filing a *private* suit against Sony. Notwithstanding the Treasury Department findings, NUE pressed its suit with such thoroughness that it dragged on for twelve and a half years.

Now, Akio Morita is a practical man. He is not easily angered, nor does he stand on ceremony.

He was confident that Sony would "win" the suit—which eventually it did. But he also understood that the "victory" would be meaningless.

The lawsuit was *an unproductive sort of competition.*

It improved neither company's products. It benefited neither company's employees or shareholders.

By draining energy and funds, it weakened *both* companies *vis-à-vis* the open marketplace.

So Morita paid a personal call on Hans Werthen, the chairman of Electrolux, which in turn owned NUE. Morita politely explained why he felt the lawsuit should be laid to rest.

Werthen told him that he might be interested in settling, *but that he couldn't commit to it because he was afraid his own lawyers might sue him!*

NUE's attorneys, you see, were working on a contingency basis, and the suit asked for damages in the amount of $360 million. If the suit were dropped on orders from Electrolux, the lawyers could, in theory, sue for the money they *might* have made *if* they had won the original battle.

In other words, the chairman of the board was powerless to call off his own attorneys. The servants had become the master.

Morita was floored by this turn of events, which could never have happened in Japan.

The terrible truth is that once a certain threshold of complexity and expense has been crossed, there is a real danger in American business life that attorneys will take over decisions that *should* be left to executives.

TENNIS SCHIZOPHRENIA

Let me give another example, closer to home, of this dynamic in action.

At this writing, IMG is involved in a tremendously complicated antitrust suit, the subject of which is nothing short of who does and can do what in the sport of professional tennis.

Since this suit is still pending, I cannot talk about it in much detail. However, the point I want to make has to do with the schizophrenia that sets in when lawyers do battle while business people are still doing business.

There are no fewer than *nine* entities seriously interested in this antitrust suit, and even as the legal war heats up, we are actively doing business on an ongoing basis with *seven* of them!

These entities include several national and international tennis federations, players' associations, and so forth, and lawsuit or no lawsuit, none of us can afford *not* to keep doing business with each other!

It would seem to be in everybody's best interest to be co-operative and flexible in working out their differences. But because there is a lawsuit, the lawyers are running the show instead.

One of the principals involved has *publicly* announced that since he has insurance that picks up all legal costs, why should he even *think* of settling?

He (and his lawyers) have a meal ticket for as long as the suit drags on, while most of the principals, I would guess, have reached the juncture where they would just as soon negotiate and get on with their lives.

If only the lawyers would let them.

STAYING ON TOP

Are there ways to avoid losing control in legal matters?

The answer is yes and no.

Since the system itself is skewed toward the lawyers' advan-

tage, there will always be situations in which snowballing complexity and ever-higher stakes will pull matters out of the principals'
control.

J. Paul Getty had lawsuits he couldn't settle. Howard Hughes
placed himself in situations where legal processes could not be
stopped. No one is rich enough or powerful enough to control
the machinery once a certain momentum has been established.

However, one can stay in control *most* of the time **by taking
firm and decisive steps *before* the momentum has reached that
threshold:**

1. Make it clear to your attorney early on—preferably in writing
   —that you intend to retain *sole and final discretion* as to when
   and whether the matter should be settled.

   If the attorney protests that this undercuts his chances of a
   fat contingent fee, either negotiate a provision whereby *a flat
   or hourly rate* will be paid in case of settlement—or get a
   different lawyer.

2. Do a calm and sober cost-benefit analysis to determine at
   which point(s) it might make sense for you to bail out. Remember: *In almost every instance, the longer a suit drags on,
   the higher the proportion of benefits accruing to the lawyers!*

   In real terms, settling for fifty cents on the dollar *early* in
   the game is very often a better deal than a higher figure down
   the road.

3. Always be skeptical when a lawyer tells you you're going to
   win, and keep in mind the following axiom:

McCormack's Axiom of Stubborn Hope
There is nothing likelier than excessive optimism to
pull you into a runaway suit that never ends!

THE CLIENT AS VILLAIN

In the preceding examples, the principals in legal actions have been portrayed as reasonable and rational, and it's the lawyers themselves who have been shown to be manipulative and self-aggrandizing.

But of course that's not always how it works.

In the typical instance, the lawyer just does the client's bidding—and *if the proceedings get nasty, it may be because the client's purpose is nasty to begin with.*

They don't teach it this way at law school, but the terrible truth is that **the law is a game**—full of paradoxes and of opportunities that exist on the fringe of fair play.

The same system, for example, that piously asserts that contracts are sacred offers myriad ways of breaking contracts.

And a big part of what clients ask their lawyers to do is to seek out the glitches and the loopholes: **to use the letter of the law to subvert the spirit of the law.**

That this can be done certainly constitutes a big flaw in our system. But then I have never heard of any system that can't be turned against itself somehow.

For practical purposes, the idea is **to understand how those twists and turns can be employed against you, and to deal with them as they occur.**

A KILLING ON KILLY

Consider the case in which Jean-Claude Killy was essentially *forced* to become a plaintiff against the giant conglomerate AMF, and in which he had to squander a considerable portion of his wealth in the process of claiming what was rightfully his.

Killy was one of our earliest clients. He was also, in the years following his unprecedented three gold medals in alpine skiing in the 1968 Olympics at Grenoble, one of the most sought-after personalities in sport.

Killy was handsome, he was charming, and he was undisputed champion of a pastime that was becoming synonymous with cosmopolitan glamour and sophistication. The ski industry was absolutely booming in those years, and its demographics were a dream.

Those were also the years when wooden skis were giving place to plastic and fiberglass, and the Head Ski Company found itself lagging behind some of its more adventurous competitors in the transition. It was becoming clear that fiberglass skis were the wave of the future, and Head needed to make up for lost time by entering that field with a lot of visibility.

What better way to do it than with skis autographed by Jean-Claude Killy?

We negotiated a contract which provided that Killy would get certain minimum guarantees against a royalty on sales of all nonwooden skis.

What happened, of course, was that from year to year, a higher and higher percentage of skis were nonwooden, and Killy's earnings moved up accordingly. Head soon became a leader in the high-tech ski business, Killy was making several hundred thousand dollars a year from his endorsement, and everybody was happy.

Then Head was bought out by AMF.

It took the new regime about a year to go through its existing contracts. When they finally did so, AMF apparently decided that Killy was costing them too much money.

The company itself was doing fabulously well, but, as so often happens, the new management came to resent the deal made by the old; they wanted to build monuments of their own, not be burdened with those of the old regime.

Besides, their fiberglass ski business was well established by now, and AMF could reach the smug conclusion that it simply didn't need Killy anymore.

AMF's tactics for getting out of its contract were simple, cynical, and eventually effective: it would just stop paying Killy, force him to sue, defend these actions on whatever grounds came to hand, and simply wear down the skier in terms of time, trouble, and expense.

Killy had no option except to fall in with the script.

He sued. To do so, he had to hire American lawyers and pay them out of pocket. He also had to fly himself and his representatives back and forth from Switzerland, where he lived, to the United States for an endless series of depositions.

With the expected trial still a year or two away, the skier had shelled out around $350,000 in fees and expenses. Additionally, he had been subjected to various annoyances, embarrassments, and invasions of privacy.

AMF, ironically enough, had decided to defend its unconscionable reneging on *moral* grounds. It claimed that Killy was leading a life of decadence that was reflecting badly on the products of the Head Ski Company.

Could anything be more ridiculous?

Sponsors had originally flocked to Killy precisely because his image of the carefree bachelor—an image exaggerated and to some degree *created* by the media and the sponsors themselves—was part of their scheme for selling the "skiing life-style" (or fantasy thereof).

Now AMF was trying to free itself of a corporate expense on grounds that Killy liked champagne and was living with a woman to whom he was not married (and subsequently did marry).

But the sad truth is that **one doesn't have to be reasonable to get what one wants out of a lawsuit.**

AMF, after all, could afford its lawyers a lot more easily than Killy could afford *his*.

Additionally, the corporation had the home-court advantage of U.S. jurisdiction.

And it had the commercial benefit of Killy's name on a huge inventory of skis even as it was giving Killy a hard time.

If all that sounds unfair, it was. And it suggests a central paradox about the law as it is actually practiced:

> While the scales of justice, in theory, start off level, much of what passes for "legal expertise" consists of cleverness in tipping them—by whatever means. When there's money on the table, most people lose their gusto for a fair fight.

Eventually, Killy had to settle for a fixed-fee payment from AMF and a termination of his arrangement with Head. He was clearly in the right, but he had no choice but to give up.

The fight had simply gotten too expensive—as AMF knew it would.

This was not law as justice, but law as a battle of attrition.

THE PROBLEM OF INJUSTICE

Stories like the above, I realize only too well, leave a bad taste.

Unfairness rankles.

The feeling of helplessness breeds rage.

How, then, should people deal with injustice—not just in practical terms, but *emotionally*?

How do you handle it when you know, to put it bluntly, that you have been screwed?

Clearly, this is a highly individual question, and people deal with it in various ways, from getting ulcers to having a couple more martinis.

Here's how I deal with it:

1. I remind myself that legal battles are almost always schematic —that is, it's player A against player B, with little or nothing *personal* involved.

   Remembering this doesn't help with the *practical* loss, but it eases the anger by making me realize it wasn't the *flesh-and-blood me* that was under attack.

2. I tell myself that while a result may be unjust in any given

case, the total of *all* results will probably even out. As in other games, with law you win some and you lose some.

3. I comfort myself with the patient hope that I may have a chance to get even somewhere down the road.

The *first* legal system, after all, was "an eye for an eye and a tooth for a tooth"—and don't ever let anyone tell you that people don't look forward to revenge.

9

A FEW
GOOD REASONS NOT
TO SUE

Yes, revenge can be sweet.

Furthermore, seeking revenge *through the courts* has become so much a part of our national customs that we sue each other almost by reflex.

We sue each other so often, and *with such unquestioning assurance that that's how things are done,* that some legal scholars have dubbed us "the litigious society."

The litigious society is based on a few assumptions that we take so much for granted that it hardly occurs to us to question them:

1. We assume that whenever someone suffers an injury or a loss, there's a *someone else* who's responsible.

   This assumption has two corollaries:

   It seeks to do away with the concept of plain bad luck.

It suggests that if ten thousand people step around a hole in the sidewalk and *you* fall in, you're not a klutz for doing so; it's someone else's fault.

2. We assume that every wrong has a remedy, and that the remedy can be provided by human mandate.

This obviously is not the way it happened during most of human history. When God caused Job's crops to fail, Job did not seek damages. When the barbarians sacked Rome, the Romans did not expect to have their losses made good.

3. We assume that *going to court* is the best if not the only way to seek redress.

Like bickering siblings, we look to the court as to an all-wise parent, **too often losing sight of the fact that the court is subject to the same prejudices, lapses in judgment, and blind spots as *we* are.**

THE DOWNSIDE

Those are our assumptions. We cling to them so fervently that we tend to overlook all the things that are *wrong* with litigation:

1. It costs too much.

2. It takes too long.

3. It benefits the lawyers too much and the clients too little.

4. It opens the gates to a flood of complications that take time and energy away from productive pursuits.

THE COSTS

Much has already been said in these pages about the steep and, in some cases, unconscionable charges that are rung up in connection with legal matters. For the present, however, I would just like to mention the concept of *threshold amounts*.

Pursuing litigation is so expensive that most companies have a policy, stated or otherwise, of not bothering to sue for amounts under the threshold of *half a million dollars*.

That seems to be about the point at which the benefits start to outweigh the costs. Since corporations routinely sue each other for much more than that amount, the threshold is reasonable.

But what about individuals?

Typically, suits between individuals are for smaller amounts. But a funny thing happens to fees and expenses in lawsuits:

They always go up when the stakes get higher, but they hardly ever come down when the stakes are lower.

In other words, *the smaller the suit, the higher the proportion of expenses.*

And the higher the proportion of expenses, the smaller the chance of coming out *meaningfully* ahead.

THE LAW'S DELAY

If the expense were the only drawback, I would say go ahead and buy your day in court; you'll feel better for it.

No one, however, feels good about the law's delay.

According to no less an authority than William Shakespeare, the slowness of legal procedures—the wall of molasses—is one of the "slings and arrows" that might well drive a man to despair or even suicide.

In Hamlet's famous "To be, or not to be" soliloquy, "the law's delay" ranks right up there with "the oppressor's wrong" and "the pangs of dispriz'd love" among the irritations "that make calamity of so long life."

There are times when *any* result, even a bad result, gets to seem preferable to the endless waiting, the endless review, the endless string of correspondence, of appearances, of hopes raised and hopes dashed.

THE WHY OF IT

Why do legal matters, and especially litigation, take so long?

Ironically, many and perhaps most legal delays have to do with the so-called "protections" built into the system.

At law school, students are taught that these "protections" allow both sides fair access to information and pertinent sources, due process for appeal, and so forth.

Like so many well-intentioned elements of our laws, however, the "protections" usually backfire.

They don't protect anybody—or at least not the people who *should* be protected.

In effect, what the "protections" do is **to set up an elaborate game in which stalling tactics figure prominently, and in which, since time is money, the side with the bigger war chest has a definite edge,** irrespective of the merits of the case.

Although it's not a phrase that people learn in law school, and it's not a strategy that the American Bar Association officially endorses, the tactic of choice in many cases is simply "to spend the other side to death."

This lends fresh meaning to the old cliché about "buying time."

THE FORTUNE 500 V. ME

Let me tell you a strange and rather complicated story that persuasively illustrates the law's delay in action—or, I should say, inaction.

This story begins in 1974—when Gerald Ford was president and "China" still meant Taiwan—and, as of this writing, the case is yet to be resolved.

Dollar one has yet to change hands—except of course between clients and attorneys, where many, many dollars have new owners.

Back in 1974 I made an agreement with Russ Meyer, who was then the chief executive officer of Grumman Aircraft Corporation. Meyer and I had known each other for years—ever since we worked together at Arter, Hadden. Meyer is a unique and versatile man who eventually left Arter, Hadden to become CEO of American Aviation, subsequently acquired by Grumman.

Now, in 1974 Russ and I had a talk about Grumman's efforts to sell private or corporate jets to very wealthy individuals. At this level of the market, the great difficulty was entree. How did you get the ear of the decision maker? How did you arrange for an appropriate introduction that might lead to a sale?

As it happened, I knew someone who I thought might be interested in buying a jet, and mentioned this to Russ. Russ asked where this individual lived, and when I answered Europe, Russ confidently told me that Grumman already knew of every prospective buyer on the Continent.

I then proposed an arrangement: I would tell Russ the name of the man I had in mind. If he was already listed in Grumman's files, then that would be the end of it.

If he wasn't known to Grumman, I would set up an introduction, and in the event that the introduction led to a sale, I would receive a finder's fee. We agreed that reasonable value for my services would be $50,000, based on an anticipated purchase price of $3.75 million for the plane.

Sure enough, the prospective buyer was not listed in Grumman's files; and off we went to Switzerland to meet the gentleman in question.

This, to repeat, was 1974. Nothing at all happened till 1978; then two things occurred almost simultaneously.

The man to whom I had introduced the Grumman executives

finally went ahead and bought a plane—not for $3.75 million, as had been projected four years earlier, but for $7.5 million. That was the good news.

The bad news was that Russ Meyer left Grumman to become chairman and CEO of Cessna.

Russ Meyer's personal behavior throughout had been totally honorable, as I hope is clear. He told me of his impending move and informed me that, as part of his wrapping-up process at the company, he had reminded his number two man, *both verbally and in a written memo,* of the valid commitment that the company had had to me since 1974, and still had.

Nevertheless, when the sale of the aircraft was completed, and I informed Grumman's new management of the money they owed me, they reneged.

I had no choice but to sue for $100,000—keeping my commission in proportion to the price of the aircraft.

Thus began an adventure in the courts of the state of New York that has featured both high drama and low comedy, that has resulted in both sides' lawyers being reprimanded by the bar association, and that has been *a veritable sourcebook on the stalling tactics that can be used by a company with virtually limitless resources and with plenty of in-house counsel looking for things to do.*

Round 1:

Grumman's first ploy was to try to have the case thrown out by way of a "summary judgment."

The company claimed, in brief, that there had never been a real agreement between Grumman and me, and that Russ Meyer had given me a "sweetheart deal" on his departure from the corporation.

In other words, the 1974 conversation had never taken place, and Meyer and I were supposedly in collusion to rip Grumman off.

This allegation, aside from being ludicrous, was insulting to both Russ Meyer and me, and ironically, in a context other than a court of law, might very well have constituted slander.

The motion for summary judgment was denied—since Grumman's own internal memoranda recorded the existence of the deal!

In any event, this opening gambit took six months.

Round 2:

It also set the down-and-dirty, no-holds-barred tone for much of what was to follow.

Still, it didn't suggest the rather bizarre confrontation that would occur during the *second* drawn-out phase of the case—the taking of depositions.

Having lost its attempt at disclaiming the deal outright, Grumman now changed tactics and decided it would base its argument on the contention that the airplane had been sold *not* to the person whom I had introduced to the company, but to his *unincorporated business.*

Technically, this was true—but meaningless.

How many people buy a $7.5 million airplane and *don't* put the transaction in the name of a business?

The point was that *this buyer had made the purchase decision,* and, further, that *the plane was mainly for his own use.*

Grumman denied this altogether and claimed, in fact, that it had had *no direct contact whatsoever* with the individual involved.

Now, there is a phase in a lawsuit known as "discovery." In principle, discovery is intended to let each side solicit pertinent documents and records from the other so that, in theory, the case can be argued from the fullest possible complement of facts.

Discovery tends to be an unspeakably tedious chore (see, for example, *Geffine* v. *Doyle!*), and can itself be used as a stalling device. But it can also be a powerful weapon for an attorney who is diligent at doing it.

As it happened, my attorney did it *very* diligently. *So* diligently, in fact, that at a pretrial deposition during which Grumman's attorney was maintaining the no-personal-contact stance, my lawyer produced a memo *from Grumman's files*—obtained through normal discovery procedures—in which the person I'd introduced made it very clear, above his own signature, that he bought the plane, he used the plane, and in fact he had complaints about the performance of the plane!

To put it mildly, it did not make Grumman's lawyer look good to be informed of the existence of this document by the other side.

And when my attorney began—as was perfectly proper—to read the letter into the record, the other lawyer became totally flustered. He shouted, he protested; he said, groundlessly, that he would not allow the letter to be read.

The two attorneys were sitting side by side, and my lawyer finally had no choice but to turn his back on his blustering colleague so that the court reporter could hear his recital of the letter.

Grumman's lawyer seems to have panicked at this point, and he actually reached over my attorney's shoulder, presumably trying to snatch away the document! In so doing, he—we presume inadvertently—hit my attorney on the side of the head and jostled loose his glasses.

Now, my lawyer is about five feet five, and past the age of sixty. He is an urbane, charming, and nonviolent man. However, he had been on his college boxing squad many years before, and some reflexes stay with you always. If you are hit, you hit back. Which is what he did.

Fortunately, there was a witness present who was thirty years younger and a head taller than either of the battling elders, and he separated them before anyone was hurt.

The upshot was that both attorneys had to respond to the bar association for that incident—and Grumman's *second* attempt at a defense had been discredited

Round 3:

No matter. By the time the trial—the *first* trial—rolled around, the resourceful attorneys for the defense had another tack to try.

They now acknowledged that the man in question had in fact bought the plane, and they acknowledged that Russ Meyer had in fact written a memo confirming our agreement.

They claimed, however, that Meyer's memo was a legal nullity, as he had written it after the board had accepted his resignation.

Forget that the memo merely *reconfirmed* a deal that had been made years earlier. Grumman now maintained that Meyer, at the time he actually wrote the memo, did not have the authority legally to commit Grumman to anything.

To our surprise, Grumman won this round.

Round 4:

But we appealed this ruling, and won a reversal from a panel of five judges who better understood the business realities of Meyer's postresignation position.

As was clear at the trial, Meyer had been given *explicit, written instructions by Grumman's board to leave memoranda on all pending matters.*

Having been issued those instructions, he was still functioning as a bona fide officer of the company during the time of the sale; ergo, the memo was back to being binding.

Now *we'd* won.

This, by the way, brings us to 1983—five years after the initial action!

Round 5:

However, the panel that heard our appeal was empowered only to decide the matter in principle; the judges were not authorized to assess a judgment.

So now we had to go back for a *second* trial.

And guess what?

Grumman pulled *yet another* gambit out of its apparently bottomless bag of defenses!

Simple common sense would tell you that if someone needs to try out five different arguments, he is probably grasping at straws; **if an argument has merit, you need only one.**

Part of the reason for the law's delay, then, is that **lawyers are allowed to concoct a different story for every stage of a battle.**

As ridiculous as one ploy is, you can wipe the slate clean and try another; *there's no real penalty* for trying people's credulity or patience, or even for proposing *mutually contradictory defenses at various stages.*

This time around, Grumman argued that it hadn't really sold a plane to the fellow I had introduced *nor* to his corporation!

Rather, the company had sold a plane to the Italian film producer Dino de Laurentiis—and if you're surprised to have a new character introduced at this point in the tale, imagine how *we* felt.

The story was that de Laurentiis had ordered the plane, then, for some reason, had decided not to take delivery.

Grumman, now acting *not* as an airplane manufacturer, but only as an agent for the film producer, arranged the transfer of that very plane to my contact.

Thus, the sale was between my client and the movie mogul; Grumman, which received only a $200,000 commission on the sale, contended that my fee—twelve years later—should be around 1½ percent of *that*!

Round 6:

However, if Grumman was arguing that the amount the commission would be based on should be *reduced*, I found I had grounds to claim it should be radically *increased:* My contact had bought two more airplanes from Grumman, bringing the total amount of his business with the company to around $22 *million*.

Why shouldn't my finder's fee be reckoned on the basis of the whole ledger?

Round 7 . . . and Counting:

So where has all this argumentation and legal ingenuity taken us?

Well, Grumman's contention that it was only an "agent" was discredited by the existence of a slightly embarrassing bill of sale between the company and the man I had introduced.

My contention that I should now receive a commission on the sale of all three aircraft was disallowed because Russ Meyer's memo was worded in such a way as to stipulate "the sale of *an* airplane."

The bottom line is that *I have yet to see a single cent from a claim that began in 1978.*

I was awarded a judgment which, counting interest, was within a few thousand dollars of what I asked for to begin with.

Did that get me any money? Well, not quite.

Grumman made *another* appeal, *still* claiming it didn't really *sell* the plane and arguing that the record of the sale was just a bookkeeping convenience. To keep things symmetrical, I *also* appealed, taking a shot at an increase in the amount of the judgment.

And what do you suppose? The appellate court *did* increase the amount of my judgment! Perhaps there was one appeal too many.

But, there are still appellate courts left in the procedure that Grumman hasn't used yet.

Check with me in the year 2000.

THE COMMON THREAD

In all the ingenious tactics the lawyers employed in dragging out the Grumman case, a common theme exists: **They all use the law to defeat the law.**

And every client, in deciding whether a given matter is worth pursuing, should be aware that **any skilled lawyer can use these techniques to prolong a case almost indefinitely.**

The terrible truth is that **the longer a case goes on, the less it is worth, except to the lawyers.**

By now Grumman has certainly paid more in fees than it would have cost to give me what I had coming.

This is inexplicable except in terms of *the unproductive stubbornness and obsessiveness that lawsuits tend to breed.*

THE ELECTRONIC COTTAGE GONE BERSERK

Before leaving this subject of legal stalling, I would just like to mention one recent practical development that ironically was *intended* to make all of us more efficient, but which, in practice, has made it *unprecedentedly easy to become strangled in red tape.*

I'm talking about electronic word processing.

Not long ago I heard a story about a businessman who made some stupid moves, and found himself with a half million dollars of personally guaranteed debt that he could not afford to pay.

He went to an attorney of great cleverness but limited con science and described his problem. The lawyer said to him: "Give me five thousand dollars up front, and I will lay such a burden of discovery on these people that you won't have to shell out another penny for at least five years."

There was no mention of right or wrong, guilt or innocence.

The soul and essence of the transaction was that five thousand dollars would buy five years.

How was this attorney able to offer such a bargain?

Simply by cranking up his word processor, hitting a few buttons, and demanding that the other side hand over *thousands* of documents—letters, memos, invoices—that *might possibly* have some bearing on the case.

These demands are legal, according to the rules of discovery. The problem is that *demanding* documents and records has become diabolically easy, while *producing* those documents and records has remained as tedious and time consuming as ever.

The papers still have to be scanned by human eyes.

Their significance still has to be appraised by human judgment.

Depending on the nature of the case, it can take one hundred or one thousand or ten thousand times as long to *furnish* documents as to demand that they be furnished.

The kicker is that **there is no way to know in advance what sort of research burdens will pertain in a given case.**

The lawyers' discretion is just too broad to be able to predict it.

This is one more good reason to consider letting the other side win by default sometimes.

THE PANDORA SYNDROME

So much for the question of time.

Now let's look at the issue of control of one's own destiny.

In theory, people sue to stay in control, or to regain control, of their lives: **to assert the fact that they won't be pushed around.**

In actuality, however, **lawsuits tend to make one vulnerable to so many complications that they usually *reduce* the amount of control one has and make it *easier* to be pushed around.**

This happens because of a phenomenon that can be described in terms of another axiom.

McCormack's Pandora Axiom
Once you open the lid on conflicts and complications,
those conflicts and complications generally multiply.

You find yourself in violation of clauses you never knew existed.

You find yourself confronted by regulations you never realized might pertain.

You find yourself fighting phantom opponents who weren't even part of the original disagreement!

And you come to realize that **normal business life is possible only because, most of the time, people ignore the kind of technicalities and nit-picking that** *nobody* **ignores once the lawyers have been brought in.**

LAVER V. CONNORS V. FCC V. EVERYBODY

Let me give you an example of the Pandora Syndrome at its most bedeviling.

Back in 1974, we conceived a tennis program that became known as the CBS Heavyweight Championship of Tennis. Our idea, essentially, was to do away with the early rounds of a regular tournament, and just arrange a "finals" between two top pros. Each player was to be paid a substantial guarantee, with an additional purse going to the winner.

The first match was played in 1975, at Caesar's Palace in Las Vegas, and pitted Rod Laver, who was managed by us, against Jimmy Connors, who was represented by a man named Bill Riordan.

Riordan and IMG co-promoted the match pursuant to a written agreement between us, and IMG's Barry Frank sold the television rights to CBS.

The match was a financial and artistic success. Connors won, so he would be a part of the following year's event.

That night, as Barry was leaving Caesar's Palace, he ran into Riordan in the casino. Barry congratulated Riordan on his client's win—and also congratulated Connors himself.

Barry suggested that next year's installment should match Connors against John Newcombe; Riordan agreed that would be a good idea.

Barry then remarked that IMG was close to Newcombe, who at the time was not a client, and would bring him in, in exchange for continuing the existing co-promotion deal.

Riordan agreed and the two men shook hands.

Now, **that conversation constituted a contract.**

Among lay people, the concept of a verbal agreement seems to cause a fair amount of confusion. In fact, the definition is very precise. A verbal contract, like any contract, consists of:

1. an offer made;

2. that offer accepted; and

3. agreement as to a consideration, monetary or otherwise, to pass between the parties.

What happened, however, is that Bill Riordan, upon reflection, decided he didn't need us to get to Newcombe or to handle television.

He cut us out of the deal, and we sued him.

We had Barry Frank, Barry Frank's wife, and Jimmy Connors himself as witnesses to a conversation that Riordan was now claiming had never taken place.

So up to this point, what we're talking about has been a straightforward, two-party dispute.

But now, skipping ahead three years, the Pandora Syndrome kicks in.

Connors beat Newcombe in Heavyweight Championship match

number two, and beat Guillermo Vilas in match number three. Match number four, against Manuel Orantes, was set up.

The suit between us and Riordan had become public knowledge, and it had a fair degree of gossip value among the press. So, for better or worse, the media were paying more attention to the Heavyweight series than they might otherwise have done.

By coincidence, Barry Frank at this time left our company and went to work as head of CBS Sports.

By coincidence again, Barry was sitting in a hotel room watching this *fourth* Heavyweight installment between Connors and Orantes when he heard commentator Pat Summerall describe the match as a "winner-take-all" event.

Well, Barry Frank knew damn well it wasn't a winner-take-all event.

It had started as a guarantee-plus-purse arrangement, and, in fact, the format had been changed from the original so that it was now a winner-take-*nothing* event. Both players got guarantees, and that was it.

So Barry—who'd had nothing to do with contracting for this match—dutifully got on the phone, managed to get hooked up with the remote unit that was stationed at the event, and told the on-site people that they'd got their information very wrong and they'd been misrepresenting the event.

Now, here's Pandora at work:

Word of Barry's call to the TV truck soon became fairly common knowledge (Pat Summerall was particularly upset that he had been duped) and eventually leaked to the press.

And a reporter from The New York Times *went on to tell the whole world that CBS was lying about the match being winner-take-all!*

This led to an FCC complaint, which led, in turn, to considerable acrimony between CBS and Bill Riordan, who'd been producing the events for as long as Connors had kept winning. Had Riordan been lying to the network about the format or had the network itself got its information wrong?

Now, since we were involved in a fight with Riordan, you

might think we were pleased that Pandora was making his life miserable.

But not so fast . . .

The FCC, once it opened its investigation, looked very closely at *all* the programs in the series, including the first one, which *we'd* produced.

And they found that, in the first installment, Caesar's Palace had been given about fifty-seven plugs, both audio and video, and *there'd been no concluding acknowledgment that the casino had paid a promotional fee for the exposure.* (You know that standard line: "A promotional fee has been paid by . . .")

So the FCC told CBS that the network was in violation of section 317 of the Federal Communications Code, which requires that all such promotional arrangements be revealed on the air—and now CBS was mad at *us*. To make matters even worse, the FCC was, at that time, reviewing the renewal of the license of CBS's station in Los Angeles, KCBS, which was valued at $300,000,000!

To cover themselves, the people from the network claimed they'd never been *told* that Caesar's Palace was paying a promotional fee—which meant that *we*, as producers, were in violation of Section 508, which stipulates that the providers of programming must inform the broadcaster of all promotional deals.

We claimed—and could document—that we *had* informed CBS of the Caesar's deal. This got *us* off the hook with the feds, but it didn't get the *network* off; they were the ones who now appeared to be guilty of an FCC violation.

So CBS agreed to investigate itself, and guess what: it found itself innocent of any malicious wrongdoing. Eventually, the FCC let the matter pass and the whole issue blew over. However, a new era of "awareness" was created, and the networks became much more cautious about what was said on their air and about the manner in which they promoted their events. And "winner take all" became a dirty phrase in television sports.

One other side effect was that Barry Frank had gotten so fed up with the politics of the "network game" that he resigned from CBS and rejoined IMG, where he eventually helped to collect $80,000 from the original suit against Bill Riordan!

And so a complicated chapter in the network television business ended with almost everyone happy and maybe even a bit wiser.

THE GYPSY'S CURSE

One final reason to think long and hard before initiating what might be thought of as a "discretionary lawsuit" is suggested by an old gypsy curse of truly devilish insightfulness: "May you be involved in a lawsuit in which you are in the right."

The evil of this malediction, of course, is contained in the idea of being the innocent party.

If you're in the *wrong*, after all, what have you got to lose? The *worst* that can happen is that justice will be done.

Anything short of justice and the bad guy is ahead while the good guy comes up short.

But who's "ahead" as long as the result is still pending?

It seems clear that **the side that has committed the injury maintains an unfair advantage through all the months or years it takes to get a lawsuit settled.**

The party that has been wronged is *still* being wronged, is still *aggrieved* about the wrong, and is still spending time and money to have the wrong undone.

Viewed in this light, stalling tactics are not just a way of suspending the action, but of *compounding* the injury.

And the person who brings suit, by opening himself to the sort of delays and complications we have discussed, *allows* the injury to be compounded.

True, he may recoup his losses and have his sweet revenge eventually.

But *eventually* can be an awfully long time coming. And I will testify from personal experience that there are times when long-awaited victories seem oddly hollow when they finally occur.

For all those reasons, I would urge that every potential suitor ask himself three questions:

Can I afford to lose?

Can I afford to wait perhaps a decade or more for a resolution?

Could I perhaps more easily afford—both financially and emotionally—to swallow my losses, dust off my dignity, and get on with my life?

10

SOMETHING'S GOTTA GIVE

Remember the famous *Pennzoil* v. *Texaco* case?

In that monumental litigation of 1986, Pennzoil claimed that Texaco had unfairly bought Getty Oil out from under them, and was awarded an epoch-making judgment of $10.5 billion!

Now, this is not the place to mull over the merits of the case, or do more than wonder about the possible justification for such a gargantuan award.

Still, there is a point I would like to make about *Pennzoil* v. *Texaco*.

The stock market is supposedly an accurate and efficient mechanism for separating winners and losers, and for keeping score in the matter of national wealth. In a head-to-head battle between two companies, then, you would expect that one corporation's loss would equal the other's gain.

But in fact after the *Pennzoil* v. *Texaco* decision, the total value of Texaco's stock shrank considerably more than the worth of Pennzoil's stock increased. The *net* loss was around $2.1 billion!

Where did that $2 billion go?

Legal fees, quipped one Wall Street pundit.

The remark, of course, is not literally true. Not even oil giants pay *that* much to their attorneys.

What is painfully true, however, as dramatically illustrated by *Pennzoil* v. *Texaco*, is that **litigation is nearly always a drain on wealth.**

It is an economic as well as an emotional depressant.

Further, this is true whether gigantic corporations are battling it out for billions, or whether the estranged Mr. and Mrs. Jones are fighting to see who keeps the beach house. The terrible truth is that **the net result is virtually always a loss.**

No new riches are created by a lawsuit. Lawsuits don't drill oil wells or build bungalows. Lawsuits don't bring products to consumers or buoy up the economies of summer communities.

All that lawsuits accomplish—sometimes—is transferring money from party A to party B.

In the process of being forked over, however, a portion of that money sticks to the fingers of the lawyers—who are *outside* the circle of the original conflict.

Therefore, the net result almost invariably is that wealth is taken *out* of a given system—whether the system is U.S. industry or the domestic economy of the Joneses.

And, as anyone with the slightest bit of common sense will realize, you can't take wealth out of a system forever, without making the system go broke. Which is why something's gotta give with legal practice, American-style.

WHERE WILL IT ALL END?

ITEM:

More than twelve million lawsuits are filed each year in the United States. Given that there are at least two parties to a suit, that works out roughly to one action for every dozen men, women, and children in the country.

ITEM:

Everyone talks about the debilitating effects of the U.S. trade imbalance and budget deficits. But no one seems to be aware that the federal government has a liability burden that runs to similar amounts. At this writing, there are roughly forty thousand civil actions pending against the government, and their total damage claims add up to an unbelievable $139 billion.

At least, for our trade deficit, we get in exchange cars, steel, and television sets!

ITEM:

Lloyd's of London, perhaps the world's most famous risk takers —a company that has written life insurance for wing-walkers and climbers of Mount Everest—recently dropped out of the American liability reinsurance game.

Their reasoning? The U.S. market is no longer just risky; it's simply a no-win proposition.

LAWSUITS NOBODY WANTS

The above items make plain what most of us already know: We have too damn many lawsuits on our hands, and most of them don't do anyone, except the lawyers, much good.

How did this sorry state of affairs come about in the first place?

Part of the answer lies in the old quip about the peaceful little town that didn't have enough business to support a lawyer— but had more than enough to support *two*.

Lawyers don't just *service* legal business; they *create* it.

Like any other successful group with a product it would like to sell, *attorneys don't just feed a need, they breed a need.*

Their mere presence inclines people to think in terms of settling differences legalistically. And contemporary America has more lawyers around than any society has ever produced in the history of the world.

As of 1987, there are around 800,000 attorneys in the United States, and the million-lawyer mark is due to be passed by the middle of the nineties.

By way of reference, consider that the number of American lawyers has more than doubled in the past twenty years, while the overall population has grown by only 20 percent. Consider, too, that the United States has *fifteen times* more lawyers per capita than does Japan!

WHERE THE BUCK STOPS

The temptation, then, is to say that we have too many lawsuits because we have too many lawyers.

But that's too easy.

A lawyer doesn't sue unless he has a client.

More specifically, a lawyer doesn't sue unless he has a client who *wants* to sue.

The word "wants," however, is a tricky one. What a client "wants" is partly conditioned by the prestige and power of the lawyers.

A client may "want" to sue because a lawyer persuades him that he *should* sue. An opportunistic attorney may dangle dollar signs in front of a prospective plaintiff's eyes. A shrewd practitioner may imply that a client is a wimp if he "takes this lying down."

Lawyers, like the rest of us, are salesmen.

Ultimately, though, it is the client's choice to buy or not to buy what the lawyer is selling. **Ultimately, it is the client's decision whether a given conflict goes as far as litigation.**

But that decision is a weighty one, and causes a lot of anxiety.

Because of the anxiety, *the decision is too often made not on the basis of positive action, but of passivity.*

What do I mean by that?

Let's say, for example, that one of our line executives had negotiated a contract that eventually is broken by the other side. Our legal department contacts the executive to learn more about the history of the deal and to get his input on how to proceed. But now the executive is busy with other things. Or he can no longer remember all the details. Or he doesn't *want* to remember all the details. So he tells Legal to handle it as they see fit.

Like Pilate washing his hands, the executive *should know* the likely course of events: Left to themselves, the lawyers will probably sue; *that's what they assume their job to be.* And the executive has *passively* made the decision to go ahead with the suit.

Every time a business person tells a lawyer, "I'm too busy; you handle it," he is asking for a lawsuit.

Every time an aggrieved individual tells an attorney, "I get too upset to deal with it; do what you think best," he is opening himself to having his life taken over by the courts.

The bottom line is that, while we may all moan about lawsuits none of us wants, ultimately it's usually our own fault when, by inattention, poor judgment, or the inability to say no, we find ourselves embroiled in legal squabbles.

WHEN IS DELEGATING MORE THAN DELEGATING?

I'm only too aware of this dynamic because I have gotten caught up in it myself on more than one occasion, usually just by stretching myself too thin.

It is a congenital defect of deal makers that they would rather pay attention to the next deal than to the last one.

It is also true that life is very complicated and it's impossible to take care of everything at once.

So, for example, if I'm negotiating a deal in Sydney, and a licensing arrangement goes sour in Paris, the Paris problem isn't going to get very much of my personal attention. I will delegate someone else to take care of it; or someone else will do it *automatically*, in keeping with the standard practices of our organization.

This, however, leads to the following axiom:

McCormack's Axiom of Delegating Versus More-than-Delegating:

Delegating authority to another executive is one thing; delegating authority to a lawyer is quite another.

Why?

Because something done by a lower-ranking executive can nearly always be *undone* if necessary. Usually there are mechanisms by which someone can be gone over or got around without a loss of face or employment. And in extreme cases, an executive faux pas can almost always be erased by firing the executive; there is an unwritten rule among business people that firing the wrongdoer eliminates the wrong, and we can all be friends again once X has gotten the ax.

With lawyers, matters are very different. You can't blithely call in a more senior lawyer to unsay the nasty things a more junior lawyer has said in a civil complaint. You can't make a lawsuit vanish just by firing the attorney who launched it.

In a very real way, **when you pass matters on to an attorney, you're not just delegating authority, you're surrendering it.**

TO SPITE YOUR FACE

Let me give you an example of the kinds of things that happen when executives take a see-no-evil, hear-no-evil approach to problems and passively let the lawyers do things their own way.

A number of years ago, a disagreement sprang up between our client Bjorn Borg, at the time the undisputed number one tennis player in the world, and Lamar Hunt, one of the world's wealthiest men and the promoter of World Championship Tennis tournaments. To put a rather complex matter simply, Hunt and Borg disagreed about whether Borg would play WCT tournaments and on what basis.

IMG executives didn't monitor this situation as closely as they might have. Neither, apparently, did Lamar Hunt himself. Probably neither side imagined that the other would be stupid enough to let this skirmish escalate into a war.

So the matter was handed over to the attorneys to resolve, and next thing we knew Hunt and Borg were suing each other!

If ever there was a case of two parties cutting off their respective noses, this was it. The world's best tennis player and the world's biggest tennis promoter were at an impasse at the precise historical moment when tennis's growth curve was at its steepest!

Hunt and Borg were natural allies in a hugely profitable enterprise—what did either have to gain by fighting? With or without Borg, Hunt would be vastly wealthy and tremendously powerful; with or without Hunt, Borg would still be the star of the tennis circuit. No way did Borg have the leverage to lord it over Hunt, nor could Hunt coerce Borg into *performing*, as opposed to just showing up, at his tournaments.

Hunt and Borg together, on almost *any* basis, made a more potent and profitable entity than Hunt and Borg at odds.

The lawyers, however, didn't see it that way. Hunt's attorneys, who were all on staff in any case, seemed inclined to pursue the action to the bitter end. Borg's lawyers—who had been hired *ad hoc* and were costing Bjorn a fortune—were equally belligerent.

Neither side apparently conceived that the purpose was to *resolve* the matter. Each saw itself as *winning*—irrespective of the fact that there was essentially nothing to be won!

There had to be a better way of dealing with the matter, and I decided to hop a plane to Texas and talk to Lamar Hunt directly.

Hunt greeted me with an "aw shucks" manner that seemed at odds with his wealth and influence until you realized that the informality was coupled with an incredibly keen attentiveness; he kept things homey, the better to observe what was *really* going on.

After a few minutes of talking around the problem, Hunt told me, in effect, that he didn't have much stomach for this battle, but he just plain didn't like a man who welshed on his obligations.

Now, Bjorn Borg never welshed on an obligation in his life; that wasn't what was going on now, and I told Hunt that.

In the same moment, Hunt and I both realized what *had* been going on: *His* lawyers had been portraying Borg as trying to weasel out of the commitment he had made to the WCT; *Borg's* lawyers had been portraying Hunt as bullheaded and inaccessible to compromise. Neither side was right.

It's not that the lawyers were *lying*, but they were looking at the problem through what might be called *the lens of litigiousness*, and that is what they saw.

Hunt and I looked at the problem differently: through a *business* lens.

Within an hour we were able to work out the framework of an agreement that put the lawsuit to an end and got the Hunt-Borg relationship back on track.

The thing I want to stress, however, is that the settlement I was able to strike with Lamar Hunt *did not* have to do with any negotiating razzle-dazzle.

There were no trump cards, no new factors, nothing mysterious.

The success of our meeting, in fact, probably had less to do with substantive issues than with *the spirit in which it was entered into.*

We were intent on being cooperative, not adversarial. We were determined to be gracious, not belligerent. As businessmen, we settled the matter in terms of costs and benefits, not egos, actions, and billable hours.

This is not to say that business people are intrinsically more reasonable than lawyers. Clearly, there are two sides to *that* argument!

The difference, rather, is one of context:

The lawyer's natural context is one of conflict.
The business person's natural context is one of mutual advantage.

Letting matters drift from the latter view to the former is asking for ill will.

A BRIEF CRUSADE

Throughout this book, I have tried my damnedest to stay off the soapbox. I have been at constant pains to keep the focus on real, immediate problems with real, practical solutions, and to steer clear of flights of theory, utopian visions, and just plain howling in frustration that the legal system doesn't work better than it does.

But I would be shirking a responsibility if I didn't say at least a little bit about possible reforms in legal practice.

The word "reform," I realize, is a loaded one—it carries all sorts of ideological baggage and it tends to make conservatives rush to the barricades.

But the kinds of reform I'm talking about have nothing to do with ideology, and everything to do with practical results:

I would like to see lawyers *expedite* the conduct of business, rather than slow it down.

I would like to see lawyers settle disputes in such a way that profits are enhanced, rather than drained.

I would like to see the courts regain their dignity as places where *actual* wrongs are *fairly* redressed, not where seven-figure handouts are thrown around in an atmosphere like that of a TV game show.

As I hope this book has managed to convey, **the system, in its current state, serves the lawyers better than it serves the rest of us.**

For that reason, the bar has a clear vested interest in maintaining the status quo, and they guard that interest with a passion. Anyone who has ever imagined trying to take a nice meaty bone away from a pack of Dobermans will have an idea of the difficulty of getting lawyers to accede to meaningful reform.

Still, change begins with awareness, and awareness comes about by people speaking up. So here goes.

THE WORST OF ALL POSSIBLE WORLDS

As things currently stand, lawyers get paid according to two ways of reckoning, and both of them are bad.

Either they get paid for time, which encourages inefficiency, stalling, needless confrontations, over-lawyering, and contentiousness.

Or they get paid on contingency, which encourages frivolous suits, dubious tactics, appeals to emotion rather than to reason, and sheer runaway greed.

Not only are these compensation methods suspect in themselves, but the way in which they are applied sometimes strikes me as backward.

Typically, of course, plaintiffs' lawyers work on contingency, and defendants' lawyers work on time.

The theory behind this—worthy enough—is that no one should be prevented from prosecuting a meritorious claim because of a lack of funds.

In practice, however, truly needy plaintiffs tend to be excluded *anyway*, for a couple of reasons.

First of all, there are almost always *some* up-front costs to be borne; second, suing entails at least a certain degree of power, and it's the indigent who are most likely to be lacking the requisite knowledge and resources.

So the plaintiff-contingency system doesn't truly help those who *can't* afford legal help; it just gives a free ride to those who *can*.

Now look at it from the other side:

By forcing defendants to pay their lawyers on a time basis, the system *presumes* that defendants have deep pockets. Further, although the plaintiff bears the burden of demonstrating that a wrong has been done—this is the civil-law equivalent of being "innocent till proven guilty"—the defendant is effectively being penalized from the first tick of the legal meter.

OUR OWN GRAY PANTHER

Let me give you a brief example of this lopsided logic in action.

A few years ago, IMG was sued by a former employee who claimed that she had been fired because of age discrimination —she was fifty-five. In fact, she was fired because, within a few months of being hired, it became clear that she had lied about her skills and experience.

Nevertheless, the woman was aggrieved, and she went out and got herself a lawyer. The lawyer no doubt felt he had a highly marketable client on his hands—a sweet, well-spoken, silver-haired woman who was bound to make a hit with a jury.

The lawyer informed us that we were being sued for $3 million!

Why not? Under our legal system, **it costs no more to file a moonshot claim than a reasonable one.**

A small proportion of the amount was based on income the woman *would have earned,* had she worked till sixty-five. The rest was punitive damages, on grounds that we had put a black mark on her record, or hurt her feelings, or something equally vague.

Now, at IMG, as at most companies, we have a procedure that we follow when we get sued. The procedure is complicated, time consuming, and it takes our in-house lawyers away from work that *makes* money, but we can't afford not to follow it.

We review the claim. We research our own files and talk to people within the company to ascertain, first of all, if we are actually at fault, and second, how strong a case could be made against us. Then we decide how to proceed. If the case seems likely to go to trial, we hire outside counsel to litigate.

In the present instance, we were sure we were blameless, and confident that we could not convincingly be portrayed as otherwise. Accordingly, our legal department wrote a letter to the other side, suggesting that this matter did not warrant litigation, and urging that our ex-employee's lawyer submit the case to labor arbitration instead.

But the lawyer was adamant. He knew that with this likable woman, whose feelings were hurt and whose self-esteem had been shaken, his best chance—his *only* chance—lay in pulling the heartstrings of a jury.

So the suit went ahead and, to make a long story short, we eventually "won." Our so-called victory cost us $50,000 in fees and expenses.

For better or worse, however, we weren't the only party to come out behind. The woman lost, too, since she had put in all that time and trouble for nothing. Even her lawyer lost, since he had no moonshot payday at the end. The only *real* winners were *our* outside lawyers, who made their hourly rate no matter what.

It seems to me there's something wrong with a system that takes three losers to add up to one winner.

PUTTING THE COMMON SENSE
BACK IN COMMON LAW

How might the situation be improved?

At least a few ideas can be had from going back to the source of much of our legal logic, English common law—which in turn derived from everyday, sensible practices that were already established by the time the law was codified.

Common law, then, is not a product of lawyers' self-serving ingenuity, but of *people trying their best to get along.*

Under common law, for example, *punitive damages were assessed only in cases where an injury was intentional; in other sorts of liability actions, the "negligent" party would pay the doctor bills, and that was pretty much all there was to it.*

In other words, *wrongs were redressed in a spirit of justice, not of revenge, opportunism, and misguided attempts to redistribute wealth.*

For better or worse, our culture has come to take very seriously such hazy concepts as "mental distress" and "pain and suffering." The belief in those concepts, coupled with the feeling that an injured party is *entitled* to a payoff, makes it unrealistic to return to medical-expenses-only judgments.

But clearly **a cap can and should be placed on awards for nonphysical or noneconomic damages.**

Laws to this effect have already been passed in several states, with $250,000—not a small amount—being a typical ceiling for "pain and suffering" awards. I would urge that these ceilings be universally adopted.

Needless to say, lawyers are fighting them to the bitter end.

FIGHTING FAIR

Another element of common law that we would do well to resurrect (it's still in force in England) is that **losers in civil actions should pay the legal costs of the winners.**

This, if you think about it, would only be fair, whether the suit is ultimately decided in favor of the plaintiff or the defendant.

Looking at it from the defendant's perspective, no one *asks* to be sued, and the mere fact of having to participate in a lawsuit is already a species of punishment. If the lawsuit turns out to be frivolous or groundless, should one have to pay legal fees as well?

Common sense cries out a resounding no. Under the English system, defendants at least have the comfort of knowing they won't go broke in the process of demonstrating their innocence.

Conversely, plaintiffs are discouraged from lodging unmeritorious claims because there's no such thing as a free ride if they lose.

Both sides are at risk in an English civil action—which is another way of saying it's a fair fight.

If the plaintiff *does* win, the English system still makes perfect sense. The defendant is ordered to pay the plaintiff's legal fees *separately* from the judgment.

Thus there is no ambiguity about what the size of the award really is, and no confusion about who is benefiting from it and to what degree. The process is clean, explicit, and fair.

THE FLY IN THE OINTMENT

These provisions are so clearly equitable and workable that the only mystery is why they *haven't* been enacted in the United States.

The answer, I strongly suspect, has to do with *another* practice in the English courts, corollary to the above.

Under the English system, legal fees are typically determined by the judges, and are assessed not on the basis of how much stalling, complicating, and wheel spinning the lawyers have managed to do, but *on what the job was actually worth,* in the expert and advised opinion of the court.

The fees assessed by English courts, it should be understood, are far from stingy, and no one needs to take up a collection on behalf of British barristers.

Still, English practitioners are not generally awarded quite the princely sums that American attorneys routinely chalk up for themselves, on their own recognizance and at their own discretion.

The terrible truth, apparently, is that the American legal profession has no inclination to adopt a system that would better serve the public, in place of one that so admirably serves itself.

SOME GLIMMERS OF HOPE

Still, even though full-fledged legal reform is probably too much to hope for in the near future, there seem to be certain positive stirrings among the many executives and lawyers I have occasion to deal with.

These stirrings have to do not with changes in statutes, but in changes in *attitude.*

There is an East Coast clothier whose motto is An Educated Consumer Is Our Best Customer.

Well, *legal* customers, too, are becoming better educated these days, and as they do, they are becoming more adept at steering clear of the worst horrors of the system.

They become better versed, as it were, in *guerrilla tactics* that enable them to achieve legal objectives without the grinding, plodding "conventional warfare" of litigation.

What are these guerrilla tactics?

PREVENTIVE LAWYERING

"Preventive lawyering" is really what Abraham Lincoln was talking about in one of the quotations that serve as the epigraphs of this book.

Honest Abe exhorted his fellow attorneys to "discourage litigation" and implement conciliation, pointing out that a lawyer's "superior opportunity" lay not in waging surrogate battles, but in serving as a "peacemaker."

Well, that's wonderful advice, but there's a basic problem with it: It flies in the face of how many Western lawyers have traditionally made their money.

Under the American and most European systems, those attorneys grow wealthy by taking conflicts to the hilt rather than by avoiding conflicts. It's worth remembering, however, that there *are* other ways to set things up.

Consider this analogy with medicine. Western societies pay doctors essentially on the same basis that they pay lawyers: for dealing with the "disease" once something has gone wrong.

In Eastern societies, however, doctors are paid *not* for curing someone when he's sick, *but for keeping him healthy in the first place*. In traditional China, for example, if you got sick, your doctor treated you for free, on the supposition that if he had been doing his job well, you wouldn't have become ill. You paid him if you stayed healthy—*there was a direct correlation between the charge and the benefit.*

Westerners do things backward! We pay nothing for the benefits of "health"—medical or legal—and we pay like crazy for the "privilege" of being sick or being sued!

Since that's the quality of "logic" we are stuck with, I suppose it follows "logically" that Western attorneys conduct themselves less like statesmen and peacemakers than like bodyguards and *agents provocateurs.*

Increasingly, however, companies and individuals are finding that **legal help can be a worthwhile investment** *before* **something goes wrong.**

Corporations are looking to lawyers to *steer them clear* of things like environmental violations or product-liability suits, rather than to *defend* them afterward.

Small businessmen are becoming savvier in using lawyers *early* to avoid later problems with taxes or partnerships that go sour.

Increasing numbers of couples are hiring lawyers to write prenuptial agreements to avoid ugly and expensive battles in case of divorce.

The growth of preventive lawyering, of course, will have everything to do with the *demand* for preventive lawyering. And that demand, in turn, can come only from an increasingly sophisticated clientele.

Once you know how much it costs to end up in court, you realize what a bargain it can be to pay someone to keep you *out* **of court.**

ALTERNATIVE DISPUTE RESOLUTION

Not long ago I had occasion to hear the words of a man named Peter Kaskell, formerly the general counsel of the Olin Corporation, and now senior vice-president of a public-service organization called the Center for Public Resources.

CPR is probably the nation's most prestigious promoter of alternatives to litigation, boasting on its judicial panel such august figures as Watergate prosecutor Archibald Cox, former Attorney General Griffin Bell, and former Health, Education, and Welfare Secretary Joseph Califano.

Kaskell quoted some facts and figures that I found astonishing:

As of late 1986, *more than half* the companies that comprise the Fortune 500 had signed a pledge saying that they would try to use less expensive, less time-consuming alternatives to litigation in conflicts with each other.

More than twenty-five major insurance companies had signed a similar commitment.

In all, companies accountinig for more than one quarter of the entire GNP had promised to take all reasonable steps to stay out of court against each other.

Given that conflicts among these companies are inevitable, how will they manage to avoid full-blown litigation? By turning instead to such forms of settlement as mediation, arbitration, "mini-trials," "private" trials, and other pragmatic techniques that have not traditionally been taught in law schools and that come under the umbrella of "alternative dispute resolution," or ADR.

Why are the general counsels of Fortune 500 companies so high on these techniques for staying out of court? Because they know a few things that most of us *don't*:

They know that many an expensive and bitter lawsuit comes about *not* because of substantive issues, but simply because two people with some power have gotten mad at each other!

They know that too many executives *think* they have had a "negotiation," when in fact all they have done is yell at each other over the telephone, getting worked up enough to throw the file disgustedly into the legal department's lap.

They know that, once the *principals* in a conflict stop talking, the chances of settling become radically slimmer.

They know that arbitration or a "mini-trial" will cost their companies about one tenth as much as litigation.

All of which says, they understand the *psychology* of conflicts, and how to use that psychology to *save* money and time rather than squander them.

It's beyond the scope of this book to talk about all the different forms of ADR, but let me pass along one anecdote that summarizes the dynamics that are typically involved.

Back before the 1984 Winter Olympics at Sarajevo, Yugoslavia, IMG was doing everything possible to cement our relationships with contacts in Yugoslavia. Obviously, we wanted to enhance our connections so as to secure as big a slice as possible of the promotional and TV-production pie.

Around this time, we were approached by an individual with whom we had done some business before. He was a very well-traveled adventurer, sometime journalist, and entrepreneur. He had lived for a time in Eastern Europe, and made a very impressive pitch about the sort of entree he could provide for us in Yugoslavia.

His pitch was *so* impressive that we arranged to have him accompany one of our executives to Europe, and we agreed to give him a 10 percent cut of any commissions we received from the Sarajevo event.

Well, it turned out that this fellow's star contact hadn't even *been* in Yugoslavia for fifteen years! His other connections and expertise turned out to be only slightly less worthless.

In the meantime, through our executives' own diligence and ingenuity, we ended up doing very well in Sarajevo and the Winter Olympics were quite profitable for us.

So we decided to give our "envoy" $25,000 for his (limited) time and (limited) trouble—and frankly I thought we were being damn generous under the circumstances.

Far from being too embarrassed to cash the check, however, the fellow informed us that he wanted the entire 10 percent, and that if we didn't pay up, he would sue us!

Now, an odd and perverse thing happens when litigation looms that I call:

McCormack's Axiom of Sudden Virtue
In the face of a court battle, both sides become almost instantly convinced that they are not just right, but *righteous*, and flexibility vanishes.

To prevent this happening, we suggested submitting the conflict to a "mini-trial." A mini-trial is a procedure whereby the parties to a disagreement, usually but not necessarily accompanied by their lawyers, sit down to present their case to a neutral "judge"—usually an attorney, though it could be anyone skilled in the art of mediation. The "judge" hears the presentations, then renders a "verdict"—i.e., gives his advised opinion of how the case *would* turn out if it did go to court.

The results of mini-trials are nonbinding. However, in the overwhelming majority of instances, they lead to speedy settlements *because they undo the Axiom of Stubbornness*. Opinions coming from *a neutral source* are acceptable when *those same opinions*, coming from an adversary, would be scorned.

In the present instance, the "judge" said essentially, "McCormack, you cut yourself a dumb deal this time because the agreement was pegged to *results*, and not to *means*, and therefore you'd probably lose. However, a jury would probably realize that this fellow hasn't earned anything like the full commission, and I suggest you settle on a figure somewhere in between."

In the end, we gave him $40,000.

No one likes to give away that much money, but look at it this way: If we had gone to court, forty thousand *might* have covered our legal fees. On top of that, a jury might have awarded the full amount—who knows? Finally, this fellow and I would have been mad at each other that much longer.

Business people, by and large, don't like to hold grudges; it's not in their interest. And **one of the worst things about lawsuits is that they make conflict a habit.**

CONCLUSION:
HOW TO THINK LIKE
A LAWYER
(WITHOUT HATING YOURSELF
IN THE MORNING)

Every honest book, whatever its apparent subject, is really a book about human nature.

This volume is no exception. And my intuitions about human nature lead me to suspect that, even though most of what I have said about lawyers has been less than complimentary, what many people will want to carry away from these pages is a sense of how they can be more *like* lawyers.

Lawyers, for all the criticisms that I and countless other observers have leveled against them, still feel pretty darn good about being members of the bar. They tend also to be oddly proud about being generally disliked and avoided like the plague.

And a fair proportion of nonlawyers continue to be more than a little intrigued and envious, not to say impressed or even awed, by attorneys.

Why?

In a word, because lawyers—skilled ones—are *effective*.

In their own way, they get things done—and in fact what looks from the outside like stalling or inaction is often the most efficacious playing out of *the lawyer's own agenda*.

Skilled lawyers can be brilliant at defining the rules of the game and making other people play within their boundaries. So, in accordance with another axiom:

McCormack's Axiom of Ground Rules

If you can be the one to establish the terms of play, you have already gone a long way toward winning.

Winning is what people admire, albeit grudgingly, about attorneys.

When possible, attorneys win on behalf of their clients; come what may, however, they almost always win on behalf of *themselves*.

And this capacity to turn almost any situation to advantage is what so many nonlawyers would like to be able to emulate. So how can they?

THE FOUR CORNERSTONES

To begin answering that question, let's come back to the four basic lawyering skills—Interviewing, Counseling, Negotiating, and Drafting.

As we said earlier, these four abilities form the bedrock on which lawyers really operate, and yet **they aren't generally taught in law school!**

Which means, among other things, that attorneys haven't got a lock or even necessarily a meaningful headstart on the learning and application of these abilities.

These skills are partly intuitive and partly gathered from real-life experience—whether it comes from legal practice or business practice or, for that matter, almost any arena where a premium is placed on:

listening carefully;

reading people accurately;

thinking logically;

writing clearly; and

being open to creative and sometimes oblique solutions.

INTERVIEWING

A journalist friend once told me that the most exhausting aspect of his job was not writing, but interviewing the subjects of his stories. A two-hour interview, he said, left him wrung out—and made him realize that, by contrast, people barely pay attention to each other in the course of normal conversation.

In everyday chitchat, nuances go unnoticed, points are ignored, threads get lost.

Opportunities to zero in on ideas are wasted for want of concentration.

Chances for clarification go by the board because people's "conversational reflexes" aren't quick enough to seize them.

What interviewing *is*—whether done by a reporter on the trail of a story, a lawyer in the service of a client, or a business person in pursuit of a deal—is **a highly specialized, highly energized, and highly active mode of listening.**

Interviewing, done right, *is* exhausting because it calls into play a number of faculties at once.

Hearing what someone says is only part of it.

There is also a sort of "listening" that one does with the eyes.

What statements, for example, does your opposite number feel strongly enough about to reinforce with emphatic gestures? At what junctures does he try for eye contact, and when does he look away? Does he lean forward aggressively while making his points, or does he settle back against his chair?

If he is taking notes, what are the sorts of things he seems to be writing down? Does he appear to be most interested in numbers or ideas? On what topics does his attention seem most crisply focused, and when does it become diffuse?

What makes him squirm?

All these various observations need to be filtered through the mill of intuition, and synthesized into *a responsive awareness of what the other party really wants from you*—whether the interview is between a lawyer and a client, or between a vendor and a potential customer in a business situation.

That may sound obvious, but in fact it isn't obvious at all **because what the other party *seems* to want from you, and what he or she *really* wants, are often two different things.**

Let me illustrate this point by way of an example. A few years ago, I was approached by a very well-known sports broadcaster who was interested in having IMG represent him, and I suggested we get together for a talk.

This announcer had previously been represented by another agent with whom he had become disenchanted. Having had representation before, however, he was quite sophisticated, knew all the jargon, and was savvy and articulate enough to ask all the right questions.

If I went *only* by his words, I would have concluded that he was a highly businesslike person who wanted an agent to make him the best deals and make him the most money, period.

His posture and gestures, however, told a somewhat different story.

During almost the whole conversation, this individual leaned forward across my desk, made gestures across the space between us, and at moments seemed almost as if he wanted to tug at my cuff while making a point.

It didn't take a Doctor Freud to realize that, while the ostensible subject of our cnat was contracts and money, its *subtext* was this announcer's need to feel personal concern and warmth coming from his agent, to feel that he would get emotional as well as business support from the person who represented him.

This, I stress, would not have been remotely evident from a transcript of our talk; it had everything to do with the *visual* side of listening.

By paying attention to what this fellow was *showing* me as well as what he was telling me, I was able to address what he *really* wanted from me.

Sure, he wanted the best business advice he could find; the emotional side in no way negated that, but just added another element. By responding to his unstated as well as his stated needs, I was able to forge a relationship that still continues.

COUNSELING

We all know the old quip about free advice being worth exactly what you pay for it.

For all that, most of us still love to give advice—first of all, because it's flattering to be consulted, and second, because it's generally less unpleasant to think about someone else's dilemmas than about one's own.

Similarly, most of us probably find ourselves *asking* for advice (whether or not we have the faintest intention of following it!), if for no other reason than that life is sometimes so mystifying that it can't hurt to have a second opinion.

Lawyers make their living, in large part, from the giving of advice, or counseling. They are thus in the enviable position of being very handsomely paid for an activity that most of us jump at the chance to do gratis.

Therefore, one should keep in mind this rule.

McCormack's Axiom of Expert Opinion

The notion that free advice is worth nothing does not suggest that expensive advice is necessarily worth a lot. It depends on who's giving the advice, not on the amount of money being shelled out for the privilege of receiving it.

Whether or not someone is paid to give advice *next* time has a lot to do with what that person's advice turned out to be worth *last* time.

Attorneys are paid for counseling because of the things they *do* learn in law school. They are privy to a body of knowledge on which they are uniquely qualified to have opinions.

But the *psychology* of counseling is the common property of everyone—agents, salespeople, brokers, managers—for whom giving sound advice is part of doing business.

What, then, are the essential components of effective counseling?

First of all, **effective interviewing.** As we will see, each of the four basic skills delineated here feeds on all the others, and you obviously can't give someone sound advice unless you have listened carefully to what his problem really is.

The next step in effective counseling is **separating the other party's best interests from your own.**

In some situations, of course, both parties' interests are perfectly aligned; that is a best-case scenario that makes advice giving and decision making blessedly simple.

Usually, however, situations aren't quite so cut-and-dried.

Let's say I am approached by a manufacturer, with whom I have not done business before, who would like to retain one of IMG's clients as an endorser of his product.

Clearly, this is of benefit both to the client and to the company. We will both make money in the short run. And in the long run, the company will presumably benefit from starting a new relationship that might bring in other business in the future.

But what if this deal isn't *absolutely the best* we could get for the client? What if we could get even *marginally* better terms from a competing manufacturer with whom we already worked —in which case IMG would sacrifice the additional benefit of opening up new territory?

What would I counsel my client to do?

Well, it so happens that agents have an explicit ethical and legal responsibility to play a fiduciary role, so the decision would be clear: I would counsel the choice that was best for the client, and mourn *my* lost opportunity in private.

However, what if I were operating in a domain where there was no such well-defined fiduciary role?

What if, say, I were an air-conditioner salesman who would make *x* dollars in commission if I sold a customer the unit he really needed, or 2*x* dollars if I could get him to take the next model up? What would I counsel the customer then?

There are two issues here, one moral and one pragmatic.

The moral issue comes down to whether you want to do business on the basis of let-the-buyer-beware, or whether you believe in the ethic of service. Personally, I have always felt that **good service and good salesmanship go together.**

Purely practically, the decision comes down to whether one is more interested in the quick score or in repeat business.

It is a quirk of human nature, I believe, that many of us spout off advice rather lightly, *but we* receive *advice with the utmost seriousness: We remember where the advice came from, and if it turns out to be bad, we remember whom to blame!*

Advice, in other words, carries with it *accountability*, and advice that in the long run is shown to have been self-serving is one of the surest ways to breed ill will.

On the other hand, one of the surest ways to breed *good*will and to cement loyalty is to do the sort of counseling that makes it clear that one is putting the other party's best interests ahead of one's own. There is no better or fairer way of making someone feel indebted.

I heard a story once which illustrates this point. A friend of mine was about to invest a substantial sum of money through a broker with whom he had done only a small amount of business before.

Between the time the investment was decided upon, however, and the time it was actually executed, the expected yield on the investment dropped by *one quarter of 1 percent.*

The broker dutifully ran the new numbers, then called my friend to tell him that the investment was no longer his best bet, and counseled him instead to make a move that entailed *a far smaller sales charge.*

My friend was momentarily flabbergasted. And if you don't think he'll bring that broker a lot more business in the future, then you haven't been paying attention either to this book or to real-life human beings!

NEGOTIATING

In a broad sense, every page of this book has been about the art of negotiating.

Whether the issue has been getting Gary Player the most advantageous endorsement deal on golf clubs, or putting Bjorn Borg and WCT back on track, or freeing the Royal Perth Yacht Club from interference in exploiting its ownership of the America's Cup—all these situations have entailed **the mediation between competing interests, with an eye toward a mutually profitable, face-saving, and, whenever possible, relationship-preserving result.**

Human beings, whether they are aware of it or not, are negotiating all the time.

When you ask a waitress if you can substitute a second vegetable for a baked potato, that's a negotiation. When you suggest to your garage attendant that he can have the business of waxing your car if he gives you fast in-out service, that's a negotiation.

Leave it to lawyers, however, to take this natural, universal activity, and to formalize it with a lot of technical jargon and written or unwritten rules. While much of the jargon is utter nonsense, some of it happens to be useful.

Consider, for instance, the three categories into which attorneys divide negotiations: cooperative, adversarial, and hostile.

The first category is self-explanatory: A cooperative negotiation is one in which the two parties' interests are more or less aligned and it is a given that both sides want to come to terms. The haggling is over *emphasis and details*, rather than over basic issues.

It is the distinction between the other two categories, however, that is interesting, *and far too often overlooked—in business, in the press, and even in diplomacy.*

An adversarial negotiation and a hostile negotiation are two different things, and only bad feelings and splitting headaches can come from confusing the two.

Probably the classic instance of an adversarial negotiation that is misconstrued—*and therefore mishandled*—as hostile is the bargaining that goes on between labor and management at contract time.

Clearly, this is a case in which the two sides have widely differing agendas. Moreover, since the executives and the unions are essentially haggling over slices of the very same pie, they are involved in a zero-sum game, where one side's gain almost certainly comes at the expense of the other. This scenario makes for spirited debate, to put it mildly.

Still, it is a terrible mistake to think of the two sides as enemies. Each side—though it might cringe to admit this—*needs* the other.

Neither can afford to *alienate* the other.

The bottom line is that they will be doing business again. **And while their short-term interests are in conflict, their long-term interests are inextricably linked.**

If one side is made to lose face, both sides will eventually suffer.

If the negotiations conclude in a spirit of waiting for revenge and not in conciliation, nothing will have been accomplished.

A classic case of this labor-management snafu can be seen in the handling of the 1982 major-league baseball strike. Without rehashing all the details of that unfortunate episode, suffice it to say that it was conducted and concluded in an atmosphere of unproductive mistrust and lingering ill will. The "settlement" wasn't truly a settlement at all, but just a temporary expedient for getting the players back on the field. The issues weren't really resolved and the wounds, far from being healed, were left to fester.

So it isn't surprising that the owners have been trying to take back most of what they conceded at that time, nor is it surprising that *another* strike has remained a constant possibility and could happen anytime. With due respect to the parties involved, the terrible truth is that that was a terrible negotiation.

Terrible—but not atypical.

In my business career, I have seen far too many negotiators *imagine* that they are being toughminded, when in fact they are merely being pigheaded.

They seem to think they're being "strong" if they refuse to give ground, and "weak" if they make accommodation. This, as I would hope is clear to any civilized person, is nonsense.

Insofar as the don't-give-an-inch mentality is *ever* appropriate, it is appropriate only in situations where negotiations are out-and-out hostile.

And those situations, in turn, are very few. To my mind, they occur *only* when one party's rights have clearly been violated before negotiations have begun.

If someone seizes hostages, then wants to talk, that's a hostile negotiation.

If one party to a contract reneges unconscionably, *then* wants to discuss the matter, that's a hostile negotiation.

Short of that, negotiations may be adversarial but still friendly, and should be approached on that basis.

You *don't* want to leave the other side bleeding on the floor.

You *do* want to leave the other side feeling that they've cut a good deal—while you have the quiet satisfaction of feeling that you've cut a better one!

I like to think that the anecdotes throughout this book have presented a versatile repertoire of tactics for achieving that result, so I won't belabor the point further. However, by way of summing up, I would like to drive home just a few basic principles:

—Talk Issues, Not Egos

Everyone likes to feel important, and one of the great negotiating pitfalls is to go in thinking that one's own brilliance, clout, and resourcefulness are the true subject of the proceedings.

Well, they're not.

The subject is a contract, or a renewal, or whatever: It is something *external*.

In a negotiation *everyone* is an agent, someone standing as spokesperson for a certain point of view. That's what I mean when I say that arguments are *schematic*.

Keep that in mind, and you won't trip over your own self-importance.

—Don't Grandstand

A trial lawyer banging his fist on the table and raising his voice to a shriek may be good theater, but it's bad negotiation.

Don't play to an audience—either a third party or other members of your own team.

Just talk to your opposite number. Make yourself understood, not by extravagant gestures but by logical argument.

The more theatrical you become, the more the other side feels obliged to respond in kind. The danger, then, is that, instead of a negotiation, you end up with a spectacle that features all the chest thumping and ham acting of pro wrestling—and accomplishes about as much.

—Be Open to Oblique Solutions

I say a hundred; you say fifty; we settle at seventy-five.

This is the simplest sort of compromise. It is also stupendously dull and breathtakingly unoriginal.

Still, it is the basic dynamic by which most negotiations are settled—*not because it's the best way, but because people look no further.*

Maybe there's a way to do a deal so that I come away with the effective value of a hundred, *and* you get off with the effective cost of fifty.

Maybe, for that matter, we're better off talking *less* about the numbers, and *more* about the intangible benefits *both* of us can get from the arrangement.

Rather than getting fixated on the concept of "middle ground," maybe there's a way in which both of us can have *most* of what we want.

In savvy negotiations, two plus two sometimes *can* add up to five.

This is called synergy. It's also called the effective way of doing business.

DRAFTING

One of my first assignments as an associate with Arter, Hadden was to assist in drawing up a rate-increase application on behalf of the Ohio Bell Telephone Company.

My colleagues and I spent hours and hours struggling to word the document *concisely, consistently, and simply.* We tried to turn four pages into one, four paragraphs into one, four phrases into one.

Ironically, my legal education both helped and hindered me in this process.

It had given me the basic tools to use the language effectively.

But on the other hand, it had made me so relentlessly sensitive to loopholes, formalities, and what-ifs that to say *anything* simply became a real challenge. At every comma I was in danger of falling into the deadly trap of legalese.

The exercise made me aware of the double challenge in composing any sort of document: **Keep it simple, but make it complete.**

The tension between those two goals is not always easy to resolve. And sometimes it makes for the plodding, cliché-ridden tripe that is representative not only of bad legal writing, but of bad business writing, too.

Bad business writing, it must be said, is epidemic in America. This is a shame, because **written communication can and should do more than merely convey information; it should help to forge a relationship.**

In college I had an English professor who drummed into us the notion that **all writing is rhetoric**—that is, writing is *always meant to persuade.*

I don't mean persuasion in the narrow sense of talking someone into something. Rather, I mean persuasion as *winning someone over to a certain way of looking at things, charming someone with incisiveness of thought and fluency of expression.*

To put the matter kindly, the terrible truth is that business writing usually falls far short of that.

Why?

For one thing, business people, chronically pressed for time, dash things off without sufficient regard for *what's at stake* whenever they put something on paper.

In this, executives would be wise to take a lesson from attorneys.

True, we all complain about how long it takes for lawyers to draft even a simple document; however, we don't always appreciate the care that goes into the drafting.

Lawyers are taught early on that a document does more than record facts; **it also reflects the quality of the mind of the person who wrote it.**

This goes for *any* sort of writing, and I believe it is the real reason why so many people find writing so terrifying.

A spoken comment can always be modified, conveniently misremembered, or disclaimed altogether. A written document is *there*. It can be referred to, examined, criticized.

It isn't just on the record, it *is* the record.

For that reason, I would urge all business people to take a cue from lawyers, and spend a little extra time to make damn sure that *every* piece of correspondence says what you want it to say, in a manner that represents you accurately.

Remember: If *you* don't think it sounds like you, it's going to sound insincere to the person who receives it.

And few things are more embarrassing than having to explain what you *meant* to say, to someone who has what you *did* say in his files!

"GRACE UNDER PRESSURE"

Ernest Hemingway liked lawyers less than he liked bullfighters, fishing-boat captains or bartenders.

So maybe he would wince at having his famous definition of "guts" applied to attorneys.

Still, there is no denying that *grace under pressure* is part of every successful lawyer's makeup, and emulating that grace is perhaps something that nonlawyers would most like to be able to do.

So how do attorneys do it?

How do litigators remain composed and logical in the face of needling from the other side and occasional browbeating from the bench?

How do professional negotiators remain focused on the minutiae of contracts long after most of us would have lost our tempers or made disadvantageous trades?

How do lawyers, in the face of raised voices, raised blood pressure, and pounding temples, see an argument through to its conclusion?

Partly, it's their training—those hard-learned law school lessons that **for every argument there is a counterargument,** and that, come what may, **one should never be at a loss for words.**

But I would suggest that, aside from and prior to that training, there is an intuitive skill—*attainable in varying degrees by all of us*—that allows people to be graceful under the pressure of professional conflict.

This is the final point I would like to make, and I believe it is so crucial that if the reader of this book carries away nothing except this single observation, it will still have been worthwhile:

> **What allows skilled lawyers—and can allow all of us— to function well under great duress is** *the ability to strike a balance between commitment and detachment.*

The effective professional—lawyer, executive, salesman— should be *wholly concentrated on and committed to* the fulfillment of his professional role.

All the while, however, he should be aware that he has a self *beyond* that role.

Attack me in a negotiation, and you are not really attacking *me;* you are attacking the point of view that I, with all my attention and even passion, am representing.

Still, I am removed enough to be able to answer you calmly.

The balance between commitment and detachment is what allows for the quality we call poise.

And poise is something we instinctively admire: in athletes, in executives, in professionals.

A lawyer who has achieved true poise will never want for clients.

And business people who attain true poise will deal effectively with lawyers when they need to; better still, they will be able to minimize those occasions when they *have* to.

But poise, it should be said, is not really an end in itself.

It's a stepping-stone to a higher good: dignity.

Dignity is what poise *grows into* when it becomes second nature. And dignity—an *effective* dignity that lets us get things done not just with flair but with peace of mind—is really the ultimate object of the exercise.

When he's not revealing the terrible truth about lawyers, Mark McCormack writes about business street smarts in *Mark McCormack's Success Secrets*, a monthly eight-page newsletter for managers, entrepreneurs, and sales executives. The newsletter is available to readers of this book at the special rate of $48 a year (a full 20 percent off the regular $60 rate).

To subscribe to the newsletter, call toll-free 1-800-257-7600. For a free sample issue, send a self-addressed stamped envelope to SUCCESS SECRETS, One Erieview Plaza, Suite 1300, Cleveland, OH 44114.

Mark McCormack graduated from Yale Law School and is the founder and chairman of International Management Group, the world's leading sports management and marketing organization. He is the author of the best-selling *What They Don't Teach You at Harvard Business School.*

When he got back from making the purchases, the No. 1 wife told him to sweep the courtyard. The master and the first and second wives in the Yang family dressed themselves up very handsomely when they went out, but their rooms and the courtyard were all as dirty as garbage heaps. The yard made Happy Boy sick to look at it, so there was nothing for it but he should clean it up, forgetting that a rickshaw boy is not also a house coolie. When it was spick and span the No. 2 wife told him to clean up the rooms also. Happy Boy didn't argue, but the thing that surprised him was, considering how good-looking and smart-appearing the two women were, how their rooms could be such a dirty mess you couldn't put your foot down in them.

The rooms were hardly straightened out when the No. 2 wife handed a sticky little devil of a one-year-old to him to hold. There was nothing he could do. Any kind of work where you sold your strength was in his line, but he'd never held a baby before. He held this little master in both hands: if he didn't hold him firmly enough he was afraid he might drop him; if he held him tight, he was afraid he might hurt him. Sweat came out all over Happy Boy. He wanted to hand this little jewel over to the amah Chang, a big-footed woman from north of the Yangtze, but when he found her, she only cursed him.

The Yang family generally changed its servants every three or four days, and both the master and his wives regarded them as personal slaves. If they didn't work the poor people to death they didn't feel that they'd got their money's worth. Only the amah Chang could stay with them, and she'd been around for five or six years. The first reason for that was that she dared curse them all out. It didn't matter whether it was the master or one of the wives; if they got on her nerves, they got a cursing. With the poisonous sharpness of the master's tongue, the power of the first wife's Tientsin drawl, and the fluency of the second wife's Soochow singsong, the three together had never before met their match, but when they ran into the amah Chang's toughness, they felt as if they had found someone who could return their compliments: it was like a brave man meeting another of great courage. For that reason they appreciated her and made her a sort of bodyguard.

Happy Boy was born in a northern village where the one thing most avoided was this casual cursing. However, he didn't dare strike Chang Ma, because a true son of Han never lifts his hand against a woman. Nor did he want to answer her: he only glared at her, and Chang Ma didn't utter another sound, as if she could sense the danger.

Just then the first wife called to Happy Boy to go fetch the children back from school, and in great haste he delivered the dirty little brat in his arms back to the second wife. That lady thought he was purposely making a show of contempt for her, and as quickly as she could get her mouth open she started cursing him to a many-colored melon.

But to begin with, the first wife had not been content to see Happy Boy holding the second wife's baby, and when she heard her cursing him, she too opened her highly polished throat to curse, and the person she was cursing was also Happy Boy. He had become a target for everybody's cursing. In the greatest haste he got between the shafts of his rickshaw and started off: it was as if he had even forgotten to be angry. Because he had never experienced anything like this before, now that suddenly it had hit him in the head, he was, to put it bluntly, a little dizzy.

One by one he brought the children all back to the house. The courtyard was more noisy than a market place. With three women cursing at the top of their lungs and a mob of children wailing, it was more confused than Theatre Street at night when all the plays were over; and besides, it was a confusion without any reason.

Fortunately Happy Boy still had to go get Mr. Yang, so he

could run out again right away. The cries of people and the whinnying of horses on the street seemed easier to bear than the commotion inside the house.

He kept running back and forth right up till midnight before he found a moment to catch his breath. Not only did he feel completely worn out, with a buzzing noise in his head, but he could still hear the master and his two wives cursing him, as if he had three separate and different victrolas all playing crazily at the same time inside his heart, making him terribly uneasy, although in reality the whole Yang family, old and young, had already gone to sleep. He had no time to think of anything but sleep. But no sooner had he entered this narrow little room of his than his heart grew cold, and he was no longer sleepy.

It was the room next to the front gate, and had been divided into two by a panel in the middle. Chang Ma slept on one side and he slept on the other. There was no light except that which by good fortune came in through a little two-foot window from the street lamp outside. The room was damp and foul, with a layer of dust as thick as a copper penny on the floor. A board lay across trestles next to the wall, and there was nothing else. Feeling the board, Happy Boy discovered that if he put his head down he would have to lie with his feet propped up on the wall; and if he put his feet down he'd have to sleep in a half-sitting posture. He wouldn't be able to sleep curved like a bent bow, so after thinking a long time he finally arranged the board crosswise of the room. That way, with his feet in one corner of the room and his head in the other, he could put his head down, though his feet hung out over the end of the board. But he'd have to put up with that for the night.

He brought his bedding in and, spreading it out any old way over the board, lay down. He couldn't get used to his feet hanging out in the air, and he couldn't go to sleep. Forcing himself to close his eyes, he tried to console himself. "Go to sleep—tomorrow you've got to get up early. You've suffered everything, why should you not accept this? Don't think of the fact that the food is bad and the work too hard. Maybe they are always inviting guests to play mahchiang, and go out to dinner a lot. What did you come out for? Wasn't it for money? If only the money comes in, you'll have to be able to put up with anything."

These thoughts made his heart much more comfortable, and the room no longer seemed to have so strong a stench. Slowly he drifted off into a dream. In it he felt confusedly that there was a stinkbug nearby which he couldn't be bothered with trying to catch.

By the time two or three more days had passed, Happy Boy's heart was as cold as it could become. But on the fourth day there were women guests and Chang Ma hurried to set up the card tables. It was as if a spring breeze had blown across a little lake that had been frozen solid.

66

When the two wives started playing mahchiang, they handed all their children over to the servants. Since Chang Ma had to serve the guests with cigarettes, tea, and hot napkins, the whole crowd of little monkeys were all turned over to Happy Boy's guardianship. He detested these animals, but when he stole a glance into the room where the grownups were playing, it looked to him that the first wife was being very conscientious about putting aside a part of the winnings after each hand for the "head money" to be given the servants. In his heart he thought, "You mustn't take notice of the old lady's toughness: maybe she's not dumb at all, and knows how to take advantage of an opportunity like this to give her servants a chance to make a little extra money." He was especially patient with the little monkeys; on account of this "head money" it was up to him to treat this bunch of bastards like little masters and young ladies.

When the mahchiang was over, the first wife asked him to haul the guests back to their homes. The two wanted to leave at once, so they had to hire another rickshaw. Happy Boy called one over. The first wife felt around her girdle hunting for money to pay the fare for her guest. The guest politely refused several times, but the first wife cried out as if her life were at stake: "What's this? Sister! You come to my house and won't even let me pay for the rickshaw home! Take the rickshaw, please!"

It was only then that she managed to find a ten-cent piece. When she handed over the ten cents, Happy Boy could see very clearly that her hand shook a little.

When he had come back from taking the guests home, and was helping Chang Ma put away the card tables and straighten things up, he took a look at the first wife. She told Chang Ma to go out and get her some hot water for tea, and when the amah had left the room she took out a ten-cent piece and handed it to Happy Boy.

"Take this, and stop glaring at me."

Happy Boy's face suddenly went purple. He stood up so

straight it seemed as if his head would strike the ceiling, and threw the ten cents in her face.

"Give me my four days' wages!"

"What's the matter?" she asked, looking at Happy Boy. Then without saying anything more she gave him his wages. He had hardly got out of the front gate with his bedding in his rickshaw when he heard a new string of curses breaking out behind him . . .

6

ON the early autumn night the starlight was so bright that the leaves that had not fallen threw shadows on the ground; a faint breeze came and then went away and then came again. Happy Boy raised his head to look at the Heavenly River, high and far away. He sighed. The evening was so cool and refreshing, his chest was so broad, yet he felt as if there were not enough air, as if he were being smothered by the sadness in his breast. He wanted to sit down and weep bitterly. With his stature, his patient disposition, his desire to better himself, he could still have people treating him like a pig or a dog and he could still be unable to hold a job. He did not stop at hating that whole pack in the Yang household: his bitterness aroused in him a vague and pervasive feeling of hopelessness, a fear that he would never in his whole life come to anything. The further he walked, pulling his bedding roll along after him, the slower his pace became. It was as if he had ceased to be the Happy Boy who could pick up his feet and run eight or ten li at a stretch.

When he reached the avenue there were only a few passers-by and the brightness of the street lights on this deserted thoroughfare made him feel even more completely swallowed up in his desolation.

He did not know where best to go. Where should he go? Naturally he could go back to the Human Harmony Shed. But that would be hard to do, and the thought made his heart unhappy. As meekly and submissively as he had tried to carry on his work, and as much self-respect as he had already sacrificed in the hope of being able to buy a rickshaw, it hurt his heart to think that in the end he had held this job only three days and a half. Was he no different from one of those slippery old weasels who as a matter of habit avoids holding any job for longer than three days on end? It was almost as if he felt that he did not have the face to go back to the Human Harmony Shed to give the crowd there a chance to laugh at him and say, "Look at that. Happy Boy blows up in only three days! Heng!"

But if he didn't go back to the Human Harmony Shed, where else could he go? To avoid thinking of the matter any more, he walked straight out toward the great road of the Gate of Western Peace, in the direction of the shed.

It was a one-story structure three store frontages in width. The middle section of the three served as the office; rickshaw boys were permitted to enter it only to settle their accounts or to discuss some business. They were definitely forbidden to walk back and forth through it whenever they pleased, the reason being that the rooms forming the frontages on the east and west of the office were the bedrooms of the father and the daughter of the Liu family.

Next to the west room there was a rickshaw entrance with big double swinging doors lacquered in green. Above the entrance way to which these doors formed the portal there was stretched a heavy iron wire; from it was suspended a very bright electric bulb, naked of any shade or covering. Beneath the light, and also suspended on wires, was a horizontal metal plaque with the legend "Human Harmony Rickshaw Shed" engraved on it in gold lettering. This was the entrance which all the rickshaw boys used in taking out their rickshaws or bringing them back, as well as in their casual comings and goings. The lacquer on the leaves of the door was a deep green, according well with the gold lettering on the plaque above, and both the sign and the doors glittered in the light of the naked bulb that shone so brightly on them. And the rickshaws that came in and out of those swinging doors were all sleek and glossy too; whether they were lacquered in yellow or in black, they were all alike polished until they shone, their cushion covers as white as snow. And the men, too, all dressed more neatly and bore themselves with more pride than did others of their calling, as if they regarded themselves as the aristocrats among rickshaw boys.

You had to go through this main entrance way and follow around behind the west room before you came upon a large square-shaped enclosure in the center of which stood a large tree —a locust of the yellow flowers. The rooms to the east and west of this yard both opened upon it and served as the sheds in which the rickshaws were kept. The hall on the south side of the yard, called the "south room," together with the little rooms in back of it that were built around a second and smaller courtyard, were the sleeping quarters for the rickshaw men.

It was probably after 11 o'clock when Happy Boy arrived at the very bright but strangely solitary lamp at the door of the Human Harmony Shed. There was no light in either the office or the east room, but the west room was still alight. He knew that Tiger Girl had not yet gone to bed, and thought to go in stealthily; it would not do to have her see him. Precisely because ordinarily she held him in high regard, he did not want her to be the first witness of his failure. He had hardly got his rickshaw in through the doorway and under her window when she came out from within the entrance.

70

"Yo, Happy Boy? What . . ." She was on the point of completing her question but when she saw how crestfallen he looked, and that he had his bedding roll in his rickshaw, she swallowed the rest of her sentence.

If you fear something, it's bound to happen. All the mortification and depression in Happy Boy's heart froze into one hard ball, and forthwith he came to a dead stop, standing there as if stupefied. Unable to say anything, he just gaped at Tiger Girl.

She was different tonight. He didn't know whether it was the strong light or whether she had powdered her face, but it was much whiter now than usual, and the new whiteness veiled away much of her evil manner. It was certain, too, that she had rubbed rouge on her lips: it had given her an almost seductive air. When Happy Boy became aware of this, he felt it to be very strange indeed, and his heart became more mixed up than ever. Because in his day-to-day meetings with her he had never looked upon her as a woman, suddenly now seeing her red lips, he felt as suddenly a tinge of shame in his heart. On the upper part of her body she wore a short silk jacket of a very light soft green color, and on the lower a pair of tissue-thin silk crepe trousers that were very full in the legs and at the feet.

Under the glare of the lamp the green jacket bore a soft yielding sheen that carried beneath its bright surface the slightest suggestion of sadness. Because it was so small and short, the jacket revealed beneath its hem some of the white waistband at the top of the trousers, so that its green color seemed for that contrast even the more simple and pure. The wide black silk trousers clothing the lower part of her body rippled a little in the evening breeze, as if they were moved and made restless by some sinister spirit come out of the teeming darkness and wanting now to escape the glaring brightness and lose themselves in the night.

Happy Boy did not dare to keep on looking, and hastily lowered his head, but even when his eyes could no longer see it, there was still in his heart the little green jacket. As far back as he had known her, he could not remember her having got herself up this way before. From the standpoint of the Liu family's means, she could full well wear silks and satins every day of her life. But she spent her whole day every day meeting and dealing with rickshaw men, and always wore a cotton jacket and cotton trousers. If they sometimes were gaily colored, there yet had never been anything about them to attract the eye. Happy Boy felt as if he were seeing something extraordinarily new and strange that was at the same time very familiar: it was a startling and inexplicable difference where there should be none that confused his heart and raised in it an uneasy suspicion that he had got on the wrong street and come to the wrong door.

To begin with, his heart had been sick with its distress, and on top of that he had met this new strangeness, this living person who was standing in front of him. What should he do now? He could think of no plan, and stood witness before her. Since in his own indecision he was unwilling to stir from where he was, he hoped she would quickly go back into her room, or perhaps order him to do some little thing that would take him out of her sight. He simply could not bear this strain, this added affliction that wasn't like any other feeling he had ever known, but was still terribly painful and embarrassing.

"Hai!" She thrust herself a step forward toward him, and said in a low voice: "Don't stand there like a block of wood! Go put your rickshaw up and hurry back as quickly as you can; there's something I want to talk to you about. See you in my room."

He had long grown accustomed to helping Tiger Girl in the work about the shed, and the only thing he could do was to obey her. But tonight she wasn't the same as she usually was, and he wanted very much to be able to think a little about the matter. For a moment he stood there with a vacant look pondering her request, but the trance-like emptiness of his mind only flurried him more.

72

Unable to think of anything else, he picked up the shafts of his rickshaw and pulled it back into the shed. Looking at the south room, he saw that there was no light in it; probably they were all asleep, or perhaps some of them had not yet brought in their rickshaws. When he had pushed his own into its place, he turned and walked back, defeated, to her door. Suddenly his heart started to pound violently.

"Come in! I want to tell you something." Tiger Girl stuck her head out of the portal and spoke half smilingly, half playfully.

He went slowly in. On the table there were some small white pears that were not altogether ripe, their skins still dark green, and a wine pot with three white porcelain wine cups. In a large dish of the finest glaze there was set out half a chicken, cooked in soy sauce, together with some smoked liver, broiled tripe and other things to eat.

"You see," said Tiger Girl, waving him to a chair and watching him sit down, "you see, I'm giving myself a little treat tonight to pay myself back for the hard work I do in the daytime. You eat some too!"

As she finished the sentence she poured him a cup of wine: it was bygar, a white wine made of kaoliang, and its pungent acrid fumes, blended with the odor of the soy sauce, seemed to envelop his nostrils in a heavy fog.

"Go ahead and drink it. And eat the chicken. I've already finished eating, so you needn't wait for me. A little while ago I told my own fortune with dominoes, and I could tell for certain you were coming back. Isn't that uncanny?"

"I don't drink!" Happy Boy stared at the wine cup in his hand, his mind lost in the empty desert of his thoughts.

"If you're not going to drink, then wriggle on out of here. For a kind heart and a good intent, how can you turn the gift away? You stupid camel, you! The wine is not so bitter that it will kill you. Even I can drink three or four cups of it. If you

73

don't believe me, just watch!" She took the cup from his hand and poured more than half of its contents into her mouth. Closing her eyes, she gulped once, blew her breath out sharply, and then held the cup up to him.

"You drink the rest! If you don't I'll grab you by the ear and pour it down your throat."

Happy Boy's stomach was heavy with resentment at the wrongs he had suffered, and there was nowhere he could go to give vent to his anger. To be confronted now with this woman who was bent on making fun of him truly enraged him: he wanted more than anything else just to glare at her, to stare her down. But he knew that in the past Tiger Girl had treated him well and was well-disposed toward him. Moreover, she acted with the same breeziness and freedom toward everybody, and it was not proper for him to offend her. Since he was unwilling to offend her, the next thought that occurred to him was, why not just go to her in all openness and tell her the things that had hurt him? Heretofore he had not been one who wanted very much to talk, but tonight it seemed as if there were a thousand words and ten thousand sentences pent up in the sadness of his heart, and he could never be happy again until he had said them all.

Thinking of it in that light, he no longer felt that Tiger Girl was trying to make a fool of him, but rather that she had no other thought than openly and frankly to love and protect him. He took the wine cup from her hand and drained it.

Slowly, surely, powerfully the stream of pungent spirit coursed down within him. He stretched out his neck, threw back his chest, and belched a couple of times, not altogether comfortably.

Tiger Girl started to laugh. It had not been an easy operation at all for him to get that wine shifted from the cup to his stomach, and at the sound of her laughter he looked quickly across in the direction of the east room.

74

"No one over there," she said, checking her laughter, but still with a smile on her face. "The old man has gone to take part in his sister's birthday celebrations, and he'll be tied up for at least two or three days. My aunt lives in Nan Yuan." As she spoke she filled up his wine cup again.

When he heard this, Happy Boy's heart turned a corner, and he felt that somewhere there was a little something wrong in all this. At the same time he could not bear to get up and leave. Her face was so close to his, her clothes so clean and shiny, her lips so red; all of these things together produced in him a new kind of excitement, stimulated him in a way he had never been stimulated before. She was still as ugly as ever, but she had now a fresh vivacity, as if some added part of her had just this evening come alive, or as if she had suddenly become another person. She was still herself—but somehow more than herself.

He did not dare investigate too closely what this new part of her was, and at the same time he was afraid to accept it from her in any offhand manner. But neither could he bear the idea of rejecting it. His face got redder and redder with this further confusion. While he sat there, Tiger Girl poured herself another cup of wine, and, as if to pluck up her courage, drained it at one swallow.

A little while before Happy Boy had been thinking of telling her his troubles, but at this moment he could not recall what they were. For no special reason, he turned his red face to look at her more closely; the more he looked, the more confused his heart became: this new part of her that he did not understand was coming forth more and more clearly in her, and its hot pungent power was trying more and more to communicate itself to him, was coming closer and closer to him. Gradually she was becoming some overpowering abstraction of herself, some sea of scalding lava that demanded his immersal in it, that would draw out all the strength in his body and return it to the shore a dry and withered thing.

75

He tried to arouse himself, to warn himself that he must now at all costs be careful, but he wanted, too, to be brave. There was one way to do that: he drank three cups of wine, one right after the other, and forgot all about whatever it is that is called "being careful." He looked at her with a muddled grin on his face; he did not know just why he felt so extraordinarily happy and bold. He was overflowing with courage, and wanted instantly to grab a firm hold on a new experience. Ordinarily he was a little bit afraid of Tiger Girl; now there wasn't the slightest thing about her to be afraid of; on the contrary, he himself had become transformed, and realized suddenly how awe-inspiring and strong he really was. In comparison, the vaunted Tiger Girl was like a soft little kitten whose smooth fur he was stroking.

The taunt, the edge of sarcasm, the mean disdain had gone out of her now, and he could feel only the hot admiration she had for his strength and the submissiveness with which she sought his comfort.

76

He had not known how much the glare of the light had bothered him until she turned it out, nor how tightly he had rolled and knotted the stomach band at the top of his trousers until she had untied it for him. It seemed natural, too, that in the darkness she should have no need of silk or rippling crepe; he could be freer still. Ages ago he had forgotten what she looked like: he could not see her face, but could only feel how avid her breath was as her hands showed him a place that was made for him. So it was that he came to pin down the thing that had been flaunted at him; all his strength now had a purpose, and even his anger had a way to spend itself.

The night outside had come into the room, and all the heavens were black. Suddenly a white planet pricked its way through the Silver River, painting a path across the darkness, carrying its tail of red fire floating softly, or sticking out hard and straight behind it, streaking directly down or cutting across the arc of the sky. Sometimes its trembling shivered the universe with brightness and heat, rending the darkness with sharp flashes of light; then all the stars in the firmament would fall in a final explosion that would shake the void of autumn night. Ten thousand flickering points would be caught in confusion, and then grow dim and dark and quiet, until after a long time a new planet would stab across the horizon, thrusting itself forward through ten thousand heavens in a fierce radiance of joy. But it, too, would come in the end to quiescence; the night would gather it in, and quietly, quietly, lazily, lazily, the multitude of stars found their own proper places, and the breeze of an autumn night smiled in its coolness. Outside there was now only an occasional firefly seeking a mate before the winter should end its time, and playing the while as well as it could at being itself a star . . .

The next morning Happy Boy got up very early and went out with his rickshaw. His head and throat ached a little: that was because it had been the first time he had taken wine, and

77

he didn't pay much attention to it. Seated by the roadway at the mouth of a little lane, with the light dawn wind blowing on his forehead, he knew that the pain would be gone before very long. But there was something else in his head that made him very sad, a matter that he could not be quit of so quickly. The affair of the night before made him suspicious, ashamed of himself, and built a barrier in his heart that was hard to get across. More than that, he sensed that it was very dangerous for him.

He did not understand what Tiger Girl was up to. That she had long before lost her virginity was a thing that Happy Boy had first discovered only a few hours previously. He had always had great respect for her, and he had moreover never heard anyone say there was anything wrong with her behavior. In spite of her free and easy manner toward everyone, no one had talked about her behind her back; if there had been any among the rickshaw men who spoke evil of her, it had only been to say she was a hard taskmaster; there had been no other ground of criticism. Then why had there been a performance like last night's?

Although it might seem stupid, Happy Boy had his doubts about last night's business. She knew he was not in the rickshaw shed. How could she just have been sitting there with no other thought than to wait for him? Suppose it did not matter which one of the men it had been: that anyone would have done as well? Happy Boy buried his head in his hands. He had come from the villages, and although he had up to now given no thought to the matter of taking a wife, still it was not at all that he did not have a plan. Assuming that he had his own rickshaw, that his circumstances were a little more comfortable, and that he wanted to take a wife, he would certainly go back to the country and select a maid who was young and strong, could stand a hard life, could wash clothes and do housework. What one among the youths of his own age and who, like himself, had no one to control them, did not steal out all the time to run among the "white houses"? At no time had Happy Boy ever been willing to follow along with them. In the first place, he regarded himself as a person who wanted to better himself, and he could not spend his money on the bodies of women who sold themselves to anyone with the price. In the second place, he had seen with his own eyes the fools who paid this miserable rental—some of them not more than eighteen or nineteen years old—standing in the toilet wrenching their necks until their heads hit the ceiling and still unable to urinate. And, lastly, he had to behave himself or he would not be able to face his wife. Because if one day he did take a bride, he would certainly want her to be the purest of virgins when she came to him. Therefore he should be the same way himself.

But now, now . . . Thinking of Tiger Girl, supposing you looked at her as a friend, it was a fact that she was all right. But from the standpoint of being your wife, she was very ugly, old, sharp-tempered, and had no regard for her own face or anybody else's. He could think even of the soldiers who had stolen his beautiful rickshaw and very nearly taken his life without as much hatred and disgust as he felt when he thought of Tiger Girl. She had destroyed completely the clear fresh spirit that he had brought from the villages, and made him into a man who takes women by stealth.

And another thing: what if this affair got bruited about and Fourth Master Liu came to know of it? Did he know that his daughter was a broken package, a piece of spoiled goods? Suppose he didn't know, wouldn't that leave him, Happy Boy, to carry alone the whole weight of that black pot sooty with shame? Suppose, on the other hand, that the Old Man had known all along but just didn't want to try to control his daughter, what kind of crawling things would that make both father and daughter? And what kind of a thing was he himself, to get mixed up with people like that? Even if father and daughter both desired it, he could not take such a woman to be his wife, and he didn't care whether Old Man Liu had six rickshaws or sixty, or six hundred, or six thousand.

He would have to get away from the Human Harmony Shed at once, and with one stroke of the knife cut all connection with both of them. Happy Boy had Happy Boy's own resources, his own kind of ability, and he would depend upon that to buy himself a rickshaw and to get himself a wife. Only if he did that could he feel that he was an upright person worthy of his own respect. When he had thought to this point, he lifted up his head again, and felt once more that he was a real fellow after all; there was nothing to fear, nothing to worry about. All he had to do was to work really hard and he would be sure to succeed.

But no matter how much he hated her, how much he despised her, Tiger Girl seemed always to have her claws in his heart; the more he wanted to stop thinking of her, the more likely she was suddenly to leap up from his heart, all naked and bare, to bring to him at one time all her ugliness and whatever beauty and good there was in her, to give it all to him.

It was like buying a pile of broken scrap: in the midst of the old copper and rusted iron you would find one or two bright and colorful little things that would make you unwilling to pass them by. He had never before shared this kind of intimacy with any living soul; and although he had been taken by surprise, had been swindled and seduced, still in the end that kind of relationship could not be forgotten at will. Even if you thought to put it to one side, it might naturally and of itself wave and bend about in your heart, as if it had taken root there. For him it was not only an experience, it was a vague something indescribably disturbing, leaving him no longer sure of what it was best to do. He had no way to manage his relations with her, with himself, or with his future: he was like a little bug caught in a spider web; however much he struggled, it was too late.

Absent-mindedly he carried a succession of several fares. Even while he was running along with the rickshaw behind him, his heart had not forgotten this affair. Not that it arose in his thoughts in any clear form so that he knew where it began and where it left off: rather, it came to him constantly in the guise of some idea, or perhaps of some slightly remembered taste or odor, or again of some fragment of feeling, always vague and indistinct but at the same time very close and real. He wanted very much to go some place alone and drink, drink until he was too drunk to recognize anyone or remember anything; perhaps then he could be a little happier. He could not bear this affliction any longer.

But he did not dare go get drunk. He could not on account of this affair destroy himself. Once more he thought of buying a rickshaw. Now, though, he could not keep his whole mind on that alone: there was always something obstructing his thinking. He would no sooner get before his eyes the picture of the rickshaw he would some day buy than this other thing would slip stealthily out and take possession of his heart, like a black cloud blanketing the sun and cutting off the rays of light.

When evening came, and it was time to put away his rickshaw, he was unhappier still. He had to go back to the rickshaw shed, but in truth he was afraid to. What would he do if he met her? He pulled his empty rickshaw up one street and down another, taking the long way round. Two or three times he was not far from the shed, and each time he wheeled back again and walked in some other direction, very much like a child who has for the first time played hooky from school and does not dare go home.

The strange thing was, the more he thought of avoiding her, the more he thought at the same time of meeting her. And the darker it got, the sharper this thought became. Gradually a confused purpose that he clearly knew was wrong, a brash desire to try something again, got hold of his heart. It was just like this when as a little boy he used to take a long stick and go poke it in a hornet's nest: he would be afraid, but his heart would be pounding in anticipation of the attempt, as if some evil thing outside himself were pushing him on. Obscurely he felt the strength of a force stronger than himself that was kneading him into a soft round ball and that would shortly cast him into the flames. He had no means of checking his own progression.

Again he turned back toward the Gate of the Western Peace. This time he had no more thought of delay. He wanted to go right straight to the office and hunt her out. She wasn't any very special personage, she was only a woman. His whole body got hot at the thought of it. Just as he reached the Gate and was turning down the road toward the shed, a man of forty-odd years walked under the street light. Happy Boy seemed to recognize this man's face and bearing, but he did not dare speak to him. Almost instinctively he asked instead, "You want a rickshaw?"

The man stopped and stared at him. "Happy Boy?"

"Yes, it's me." Happy Boy grinned broadly. "Mr. Ts'ao?"

Mr. Ts'ao smiled a little and nodded his head. "I say, Happy Boy, if you haven't got a family to work for, why don't you come back to my place? The man I'm using now is too lazy, he never polishes the rickshaw, although he's a strong runner for all of that. Will you come?"

"Do you think I could refuse, sir?" It was as if Happy Boy had even forgotten how to smile. He kept wiping his face and forehead with a little towel. "When do I come to work, Master?"

"That doesn't matter." Mr. Ts'ao thought a while. "Day after tomorrow."

"Yes, Master." Happy Boy thought a moment himself. "Master, may I take you back home now?"

"There's no need. You recall I went to Shanghai for a while, don't you? When I came back I didn't live any more at the old place. Now I live on Long North Street and every evening I come out for a walk. See you day after tomorrow." Mr. Ts'ao told Happy Boy the street number of his house, and then added, "I'd prefer that we use my own rickshaw."

Happy Boy was so overjoyed that he wanted to take wings and fly. The worry and vexation of these last days were now suddenly cut clean and clear away, as a great rain might flush off the dust and dirt from the white stones of a marble avenue. Mr. Ts'ao was his old master, and although they had not been together for many days, still the feeling between them was excellent. Mr. Ts'ao was a very amiable and agreeable person; moreover, there weren't many people in his family, only his wife and their little boy.

Happy Boy raced his rickshaw straight to the Human Harmony Shed. There was still a light burning in Tiger Girl's room. When he saw the light he stopped dead, suddenly become wooden. After he had stood there for what seemed a long time, he made up his mind to go in to see her. He would tell her that he had found another job working by the month, turn over to her his earnings for these last two days, and ask to be given back the money he had saved up. From then on he would sever all connection with her, as with a single stroke of a sharp knife you might cut one rope into two separate ropes, neither any longer being connected by even a slender strand to the other. Naturally it would not be convenient to say this clearly, in so many words. She would certainly understand.

He went into the shed, first wheeling his rickshaw back into its proper place, and then he came back and, plucking up his courage, called her name.

"Come in!" He pushed open her door. She was lying across her bed, wearing her ordinary clothes and without shoes. Without changing her position, she asked, "What is it? Has the little boy come back to eat some more of my honey? Has he discovered how good it tastes?"

Happy Boy's face got as red as one of the dyed eggs that you

83

give as a present to a mother who has just borne her child. He stood helplessly for a while, and then slowly and hesitatingly he managed to say: "I've found a job again, I go to work day after tomorrow. The family has its own rickshaw."

She heard him and sat upright on the bed. "You little brat, you! You don't know when you're well off!" Half smiling, half teasing, she pointed her finger at him. "Here there's food for you, there are clothes for you to wear. Is it that you never get enough of the stench of your own sweat? The old man can't control me, and I can't go on being a widow for the rest of my life. Suppose he does make his neck as stiff as a bull, I've still got enough change in the palms of my hands to keep the two of us. The two of us could get two or three rickshaws and rent them out. We'd make eighty cents or a dollar a day—wouldn't that be better than your running all over the streets the whole day long until your feet swell with weariness? What's wrong with me? Except that I'm a little older than you—but I can't be so much older. And I can protect you, and love you, and take care of you, and anticipate the things you want."

"I want to be a rickshaw puller." Happy Boy could think of no other argument with which to meet what she was saying.

"You've certainly got a head like a dough-cake! Sit down for a while. I can't bite you!" As she finished speaking she smiled, exposing two wolfish teeth.

Happy Boy bounced down in a chair with the stiff awkwardness that tense young muscles gave him. "How about that little bit of money of mine?"

"The Old Man has it. It can't get lost—you needn't be afraid. You better not ask him for it. You know his temper. When it's enough to buy a rickshaw with, then ask him and he'll give every copper of it back to you. If you asked for it now, he'd give you such a cursing it'd be a wonder if your soul and body stayed together. He thinks well of you. You won't lose your money, and for every dollar that it's short I'll give you two.

You've got the mind of a villager—don't make me get sarcastic and hurt your feelings."

Again Happy Boy could think of nothing to say, and sat with his head down for a long while, digging in his pocket. Finally he found the rental money for the last two days and, getting up, put it on the table.

"That's for two days." Then he remembered. Backing out of the room, he said, "I'm turning the rickshaw in today. Tomorrow I'm going to rest for a day." In his heart he had not the slightest desire to take a day off, but this way he felt that the break was a cleaner one. From today on he would not come back again to the Human Harmony Shed.

Tiger Girl crossed the room, picked up the money from the table, put it back in his pocket. "For these last two days you've had both me and the rickshaw absolutely free—there's no charge for either. That's good luck for you, little boy. Just so you're not ungrateful."

When she had finished speaking she swung about and locked the door behind her.

7

HAPPY BOY went to live and work in the Ts'ao household. Toward Tiger Girl he felt a certain sense of shame. But since the affair had come out of her seduction of him, and since moreover he did not covet her money, he felt that to cut off all connection with her from this time on would still not wrong her so much that he would be unable to look her in the face with a good conscience. The thing that he was not easy in his mind about was the money Fourth Master was holding for him. If he went at once to ask for it, it was to be feared that the old man would be suspicious. If from now on he never went back again to see either father or daughter, it would not unlikely happen that once Tiger Girl got angry, she would make a few slanderous remarks about him to the old man and his money would be fried in bean sauce. If he went right on entrusting his savings to the old man, he would have to meet her every time he went to the Human Harmony Shed and that would put him in a very difficult position. He could not think out any proper method of handling the matter, and the longer he was without a method the more uneasy he became.

He wanted very much to ask Mr. Ts'ao to advise him as to what he had better do, but how could he explain it to him? That part about Tiger Girl and himself he would never be able to tell anybody. When he reached this point in his thinking he began to understand what it is really to regret something you have done, and for the first time, too, he began to see clearly that he could not cut himself completely from what he had done as you would cut a rope with a knife. You could never wash yourself clean of an affair like that—it was like a black scar deep in the flesh. Without any reason he had lost his rickshaw, and now without any reason he was caught in this entanglement. He felt that his whole life would probably come to no more than this in the end; no matter how much he wanted to better himself, it was a vain excursion, a useless detour that could only bring him back at its close to the point from which he had started at its beginning.

He thought up one avenue and down the next, and he could make out only one thing: in all probability he would ultimately have to give up every last shred of his self-respect and ask for Tiger Girl in marriage; if not on her own account, would it not have to be on account of those two or three rickshaws? If you choose the part of a turtle you have to take warmed-over food: the man whose wife has had other men eats from a dirty dish. He could not bear even the thought of it, but he realized that when the time came it still might be a question of this or nothing. The best thing to do was to go ahead working hard. He would do as well as he could and await what evil might come; no longer did he dare have the confidence in himself that he used to have. His height, his strength, his broad chest, all counted together did not amount to anything. His life was his own, but he had let someone else get control of it, a someone who was as mean and cheap and dark a she-dog as could be found.

According to the rules of reason, he should be very happy, because of all the households with which he had ever been mixed up the Ts'ao family was the most to be loved. It was not that the pay was better than in other places: except for the bonus at each of the three festivals, there was not very much extra money, but both Mr. and Mrs. Ts'ao were so exceptionally friendly and sympathetic and agreeable. Every man, whoever it might be, they treated as a human being. Happy Boy wanted to earn more money, was putting his very life into earning more money, but at the same time he wanted a place to sleep that looked like a room, and he wanted to be able to eat enough so that he would not be hungry. Everywhere in the Ts'ao household it was very clean, even the servants' quarters. The food they ate was wholesome and there was enough of it; moreover, they would never give the servants something that stunk with rottenness while they themselves ate well. He had a wide spacious room for himself, and he could eat three quiet and leisurely meals. When you added to that the fact that the master was so affable, Happy Boy—even Happy Boy—was unwilling to think only of the money involved.

Moreover, when your food and lodging both suit your taste perfectly, your work does not weary you; you lose nothing by taking an opportunity like that to get your body back into its best shape. If he himself had had to dig up the money to buy food for himself, he would never have eaten as well as this. Now, since his meals were all made ready for him, and since he would not have to break his back in bitter toil to partake of them, why shouldn't he eat his fill? This was an item of which he had kept a very clear account: food cost money to buy. To eat well, sleep well, and to keep oneself clean and neat were all things it was not easy to find a chance to do.

Furthermore, although the Ts'ao family did not play mah-chiang, and did not often have guests, so that there was no side-money, yet any time that he did some special little job of work he might get ten or twenty cents for it. For instance, if the mistress of the house asked him to go buy some pills for the little boy, she would be sure to give him an extra ten-cent piece, telling him to go by rickshaw, although she well understood that he could run faster than any rickshaw man. A little bit of money like that doesn't count for much, but it made him aware of a genuine human feeling for him, the kind of sympathy that made you know they were thinking of you and remembering how they would feel if they were in your place. It was this that opened his heart and let the sunlight in.

The masters whom Happy Boy had met up with could not be counted as few in number, and of them nine out of ten would pay you your wages one day late if they could, just to make it clear to you that they would much rather not pay them at all—that it would be better to use your services free, servants being no better than cats or dogs, perhaps not so good.

The Ts'ao family did not follow that pattern; that was why he liked it here. He would go straighten up the yard, water the flowers, and do the other necessary little things, all without waiting to be told. And whenever they saw him busy with things like that they would be certain to say something to him that would be nice to hear, and they would even take advantage of such occasions to hunt out some torn old garments and give them to him, telling him to exchange them for a few boxes of matches. In spite of what they said, the things would be sure to be usable, and he would simply keep them himself, as they intended he should. It was in actions like these that Happy Boy could taste the flavor of human kindness.

In Happy Boy's eyes, Fourth Master Liu could be counted as taking the part of the Tyrant of the Yellow Turbans, the famous leader of that famous band of rebels at the close of the Eastern Han Dynasty, nobody knew how many ages ago. The storytellers told about him in the teashops, and every child had heard about him—about how, for all he was so dangerous and hard, he would still not cost you face, would still consider the proprieties, call things by their right names. Never could he be black on one side and white on the other.

And aside from the Tyrant of the Yellow Turbans there was only one other worthy who had a place of respect in Happy Boy's heart, and that was the Sacred Sage, Confucius. When you got right down to it, Happy Boy was in a fog as to what kind of a person this Sacred Sage had been, except that everybody said he had known how to write a great many words and was excessively reasonable about everything. In the households that Happy Boy had been mixed up with there had been men of the literary type and of the martial type. Of the martial type there was not a one who came close to Fourth Master Liu. Of the literary kind, although there had been college professors and workers in government offices among them, who naturally could read a great many printed characters, yet he had never met one who was reasonable. And if the master of the household should happen to be somewhat inclined to be reasonable, the mistress and her daughters would be sure to be very harsh and demanding and unreasonable and hard to please.

Only Mr. Ts'ao could read and was reasonable too. Moreover, Mrs. Ts'ao was so quiet and modest that she won your heart. Therefore Mr. Ts'ao must take the role of the Sacred Sage; when Happy Boy couldn't quite recall what Confucius looked like, he just had to think of Mr. Ts'ao: that was what Confucius looked like, whether the Sage was agreeable to that arrangement or not.

As a matter of actual fact Mr. Ts'ao was not a man of such high attainments. He was simply a man of ordinary talents who occasionally acted as a tutor and for the rest did other work of one kind or another. He regarded himself as a socialist and as something of an aesthete at the same time. A little chance reading that he had done in the works of an English writer named William Morris had considerably influenced him. He did not have profound views on either government or art, but he did have one slight advantage: the little that he did believe was all capable of being carried into practice in the small acts of his

90

everyday life. It was as if he himself recognized that he did not have personal force or ability of a kind that would startle anyone, or that would make it possible for him to perform feats that would surprise the heavens and shake the earth, and he had therefore decided to follow out his theories in ordering his own life and his own household. Although this course did not bring aid to the social order, it at least made it possible to keep his words and his actions in accord with one another, and kept him from hypocrisy. Because of this, he was very attentive even to the smallest things, as much as to say that if he could bring that one little household into perfect order, society could do whatever it wished for all of him. Sometimes these thoughts made him ashamed of himself, at others they made him happy with himself. His home was a little island of green foliage in the midst of a sea of sand; it could only supply water and sustenance to those who chanced upon it, and had no larger mission.

By sheer good luck Happy Boy had come to this green island; after having wandered for so many days in the desert it seemed a miracle to him. Never before had he met a man like Mr. Ts'ao, so it was natural that he should take him to be the Sage. Perhaps this was because he lacked experience, or perhaps because even men of Mr. Ts'ao's calibre are rarely seen in the world. When you took him out in a rickshaw his clothes were so quiet and refined, the man himself was so full of animation and good spirits, his manner was so large and generous-minded, and you too were so clean and smart-looking, so stalwart and strong, that just to pull the rickshaw made your spirits extraordinarily high: you felt that only you were fit to be the rickshaw puller for a man as fine as the master.

In the home there was nowhere anything sullied or unclean, and it was always so tranquil that it gave Happy Boy a feeling of comfort and security. During the time when he had lived in the villages he had often seen old men sitting in autumn evenings or through the long winter days silently sucking their pipes and

91

never saying a word. Although he was too young to copy these old men, he loved to watch them sit in their serene silence. It must be, he would ponder as a child, that they find some special flavor in it. Now, although he was in the city, the quiet peacefulness of the Ts'ao household was enough to make him think again of the villages: he had a very real desire to find himself a pipe and sit somewhere smoking it, drawing out of its stem the last little essence of a fine flavor.

But unhappily that Tiger Girl and the dab of money made it impossible for him to be really at peace. His heart was like a green leaf that a caterpillar has wrapped round and round with the thin silk web of its thread, making ready its cocoon. Because of the Liu family affair, he could not be at ease with himself, and in his dealings with other people, sometimes even with his master, he would become so lost in abstraction that the answers he gave were unrelated to the things that had been asked him. This made him terribly unhappy. The Ts'ao family went to bed very early; by nine o'clock in the evening he would be through with his work, and he would sit alone in his room or in the yard thinking back and forth, back and forth, always of these two problems.

Sometimes he would even be of a mind to get married right away. That would certainly be sufficient to put an end to Tiger Girl's desires. But how could he raise a family on his earnings as a rickshaw man? He knew how it was with his bitter brothers in the tenements. The man pulled a rickshaw, the woman worked at odd jobs mending for people almost as poor as herself, on the streets the children rummaged in ash heaps collecting occasional kernels of unburnt coal. In the summer they gnawed on watermelon rinds off garbage dumps, and in the winter they all went together to stand in line at one of those sheds where the rice gruel is doled out free to the starving poor. Happy Boy could not stand anything like that.

And besides, supposing he took a wife, he would certainly

not be able to get back the money Fourth Master Liu was holding for him; how could Tiger Girl so lightly forgive him? He just could not bear the idea of giving up that money: it had almost been the price of his very life.

It had been a year ago, at the beginning of autumn, that he had bought his first rickshaw. Over a year had passed, and now he had nothing at all, nothing but thirty-odd dollars that he could not get back, and a sickening entanglement to boot. The more he thought, the glummer he got about it.

It was ten days or more after the Autumn Festival, and the weather was gradually getting colder. He calculated that he would need two extra pieces of clothing. That would take money too! When he spent his money to buy clothes he could not at the same time save it, and his hope of buying a rickshaw—to come right to the point about it, he didn't dare even to go on hoping! And supposing he was to continue on this month-to-month basis, what would his whole life come to in the end?

One evening Mr. Ts'ao was coming back a little late from the East Gate. As a precaution, Happy Boy brought him through the Gate of Heavenly Peace, along the wide avenues, to avoid the pitfalls of narrow lanes. The road stretched out spacious and level, free of pedestrians. There was the faintest stirring of a cold wind, the quiet softness of the street lights. He began to thrill with the feel of the thing and to run with more strength. His heart had been melancholy for many days, and now for a while he could forget about it. Listening to the regular fall of his feet on the roadway and to the soft sound of the springs of the rickshaw behind him, he forgot everything. Unbuttoning his jacket, he let the cold piercing wind blow against his chest and was happy. He could run on like this forever, right straight down this broad avenue into the evening, into some land that he did not know. And the death of the runner would be a clear thing, crisp and fine.

The longer he ran the faster he went. At one time there was

another rickshaw in front of him, but he called to it and it made way for him. In no time at all they were through the Gate of Heavenly Peace. It was as if he had steel springs in his feet: no sooner would one of them touch the earth than it would shoot back up; the wheels of the rickshaw behind him were already turning so rapidly that one could not see the spokes, and the rubber tires looked as if they had left the ground entirely. The puller and the passenger and the rickshaw itself all looked as if the sudden force of a very urgent wind had lifted them up into the air. Happy Boy had found his running legs again, and in his heart he thought vaguely that if he could just sweat once all over his body, so that his clothes would be wet with it, then tonight he could sleep soundly and would not be likely to lie awake brooding over anything.

They were already not very far from Long North Street when they passed into a stretch of the roadway the northern side of which was shadowed into blackness by a forest of locust trees beyond the wall. Happy Boy was just thinking of slowing down his pace when his foot hit something sticking up in the road. When his foot reached it the wheels of the rickshaw reached it too. He was pitched forward head-long to the gravel of the street, and as he fell he could hear the snap of one of the rickshaw shafts breaking in two.

"What is it?" Mr. Ts'ao's question had hardly got past his teeth when he followed it out of the rickshaw and into the street. Happy Boy uttered no sound, but picked himself up. Mr. Ts'ao also drew himself up quickly to a sitting position. "What happened?"

Before them both was the pile of newly unloaded rocks for repairing the road; the workmen had not put a red light on it.

"Are you badly hurt?" Happy Boy asked.

"No. I'll walk back. You bring the rickshaw." Mr. Ts'ao was still completely composed, and was feeling around among the rocks to see if he had dropped anything.

Happy Boy felt the broken rickshaw shaft. "It's not badly broken—I can still pull the rickshaw and Master can ride back!" As he spoke he dragged the vehicle out from among the rocks. "Master, please sit in it!"

Mr. Ts'ao did not want to ride back but he could hear the sound of a sob in Happy Boy's voice and decided that the best thing to do would be to get in. When they came beneath the electric street lights at the mouth of Long North Street, Mr. Ts'ao saw that a piece of skin had been rubbed off his left hand.

"Stop a minute, Happy Boy." Happy Boy turned his head to look over his shoulder. His face was covered with blood.

Mr. Ts'ao was so startled that he didn't know what to say. "Quick, quick!"

Happy Boy could not figure out what his master was talking about, and thought that he was probably telling him to run faster. He set himself and in one breath ran all the way home.

When he put the rickshaw down, he saw the blood on Mr. Ts'ao's hand and ran in great haste into the courtyard, thinking to get some medicine for it from the mistress of the house.

"Don't worry about me," Mr. Ts'ao said, hurrying in. "Take care of yourself first!"

Happy Boy looked at himself and for the first time felt the pain. Both of his knees and his left elbow were scraped raw; the wetness on his face, that he had thought was sweat, was blood. Without caring what he did or what he thought, he sat down on the stone step in the entrance of the gate house, staring stupidly at the rickshaw with its broken shaft. You take a new rickshaw all covered with sheer black lacquer, and when you break the front of it off, so that the white splinters stick out bare and shattered, there's something terribly wrong about it: it's a terribly hard thing to bring yourself to look at it. It's like one of the paper men they carry in funeral processions, when you've got him all beautifully pasted together but haven't yet put on his feet. Only the splintered ends of the millet stalks stick out from

95

under the gown where his legs should be, and it makes you shiver as you do at the sight of some horrible deformity. Stupidly Happy Boy stared at the shattered ends of the rickshaw shaft.

"Happy Boy!" The woman servant of the Ts'ao household, Kao Ma by name, was calling him in her loud clear voice. "Happy Boy, where are you?"

He kept on sitting there without moving, his eyes fixed unerringly on the broken shaft.

"What kind of an odd splinter are you? Not uttering a sound, hiding here: you see how you frightened me! The master is calling you."

Kao Ma's speech always mixed up the thing she wanted to say with her feelings about it: the result was at once moving and a little confusing. She was a widow thirty-two or three years old, clean, brisk and of good spirits, energetic in everything she did and careful at the same time. There might in other places have been people who regarded her as too boastful and expansive, too full of ideas, and always describing the eyebrows of the spirits and the laws that the devils follow. But in the Ts'ao family they liked clean shining people, and didn't pay very much attention to all the little shortcomings, so that she had already been with them two or three years, and when the whole family moved they took her along with them.

"The master's calling you!" she said again. When Happy Boy stood up, and she caught sight of the blood on his face, she cried out: "My mother's! You frightened me to death! What's been going on here? And you were just going to sit there, without moving or saying a word. Suppose you caught cold on top of all this, then what could be done for you? Hurry in there—the master's got some medicine there."

Happy Boy walked in front, with Kao Ma following along behind him and keeping up a steady flow of scolding. Together they went into the library. Mrs. Ts'ao was also there. She was in the act of putting some medicine on her husband's hand and wrapping the bandage around it. When she saw Happy Boy walk in, she exclaimed involuntarily, "Ai!"

"Ma'am, this time he cut himself up plenty to look at!" Kao Ma was afraid her mistress wouldn't notice the blood all over Happy Boy. In a great hurry she poured cold water into a washbasin, and in an even greater hurry kept on talking. "I knew it, I knew it all along. When he starts running he doesn't care whether he's alive or dead, and I could have told you that sooner or later he'd run right into a fork in the road. And you still aren't in a hurry to wash your face? When you finish we can put some medicine on you. It's the truth!"

Happy Boy gripped his left elbow, but did not move. The library was so clean and elegantly beautiful. It was the ultimate in unseemliness that a great big fellow like himself, his face covered with blood and his clothes torn, should be standing in the center of it. It was as if they all felt the wrongness of it, and even Kao Ma could think of nothing to say.

"Master," Happy Boy hung his head and the sound of his voice was low but full of strength, "Master must find another rickshaw boy. This month's wages you keep to pay for the repair of the rickshaw. One shaft is broken and the glass is gone from the lamp on the left hand side. It's in good shape everywhere else."

"First wash your face and put some medicine on it, and then you can talk about this other business." Mr. Ts'ao was looking at his own hand as he spoke. His wife was slowly wrapping a bandage around it.

"First get washed up." Kao Ma had by now thought of this original contribution to make to the conversation. "The master hasn't said anything, and you mustn't rush out and smash the tile just because you're afraid someone else might possibly smash it."

Happy Boy still did not move. "It's no use to wash—it'll be

all right in a little while. When a rickshaw man that you hire by the month throws his employer out into the street and smashes up the rickshaw, he hasn't the face to . . ." His words were not sufficient to be of real aid to him in fully expressing his idea, but the emotion in his heart was laid out bare before them, and one only waited for the sound of the sob in his throat. Giving up his job and waiving his pay were in Happy Boy's eyes not very different from killing himself. But it seemed to him that at a time like this his responsibility, his self-respect were even more important than continuing to live.

That was because it had not been some other person that he had thrown to the roadway but it was Master Ts'ao himself. If, for instance, he had spilled that principal wife of the Yang family into the mud, a spilling would be a spilling, and she'd have been well served. Toward the Yang woman he could bear himself in the sharp tough manner of the streets because she had never treated him as a person capable of anything else. It would not have been easy for him to be polite to such a person; the money was everything, and no question of face or self-respect could arise at all. What would be called "acting correctly" in that kind of a situation?

Mr. Ts'ao was in his very origins a different type of person, and Happy Boy could not but sacrifice all thought of money in order to protect his self-respect. He could not spend time being resentful at anyone or hating anyone: he could only hate his own destiny. He was on the point of deciding that from the time he left the Ts'ao household he would never again pull another rickshaw. Since his own life was worth nothing, he could smash it against a wall if he chose, but what of the life of some other person? Suppose he had thrown a living soul to its death, what then?

Before now he had never thought of these things, but because this time it had been Master Ts'ao whom he had dumped out and injured, he had been brought suddenly to a realization of the principles and ideas involved. All right, then, he could give up his month's wages, and henceforward he would change his calling and never again work at this task in which he had to carry the lives of others on his back. Rickshaw-pulling was the profession he had always thought of following, and to give it up was to give up all his aspirations. He felt that he could do nothing more than shuffle confusedly through what would be left of his life, like a blind man groping his way through a cavern and walking always farther from the light. There was no use thinking now even of becoming a good rickshaw man. In vain had he grown so tall!

When he had worked out on the streets picking up individual fares, he had chased after prospective customers without any consideration for the other fellow, and had stood on no ceremony in competing for business with his fellows. He had been soundly cursed out by them for that practice, but when he sacrificed face in such a fashion it was actually because he wanted to better himself, wanted to buy a rickshaw of his own. He could forgive himself for that, but to be pulling a rickshaw in a private household and bring an evil like this upon himself—what could he say now in his defense? If people found out that Happy Boy had spilled somebody, and had broken up his rickshaw, what kind of a joke would that make of his reputation as a puller?

There was no road out for Happy Boy. He could not wait for Mr. Ts'ao to discharge him. The best he could do was to crawl out of there before he was told to go.

"Happy Boy, you wash yourself," Mr. Ts'ao said. "You don't have to talk right off about resigning your job. It was not your fault. When they dumped that pile of stones in the roadway they ought to have put a red light on it. Let's just count the matter closed. Wash up and put some medicine on yourself."

"Yes, of course, Master"—Kao Ma had once more thought of something to say—"Happy Boy just can't get around the idea of his having accidentally injured Master like this. But," turning to Happy Boy, "since Master says it was not your fault, there's no use in your continuing to be difficult about it." And then to the room in general: "Look at him! A great big fellow, and not lacking in strength, and still he acts like a little boy. It's a fact—he's in a terrible stew. Mistress Ts'ao, you say a word to him, to make him easier in his heart." Kao Ma's talk was like a victrola record: it went round and round and took in everybody in the room, without there being the slightest mark on it to show you where it began, or how it had been developed, or at what place it had turned from one point of view to the opposite, or from one subject to another.

"Quickly, wash yourself, you frighten me," Mrs. Ts'ao managed to say.

Happy Boy's heart was terribly confused, and now finally when he heard the mistress say she was afraid of blood, he found a simple little thing to do to comfort her: he carried the washbasin outside and at the door of the library took a try or two at washing his face. Kao Ma waited for him inside the door with the bottle of medicine in her hand.

She daubed the stuff on his face and neck. "How about your arms and legs?" she asked.

Happy Boy shook his head. "Not necessary."

The master and mistress went in to rest. Kao Ma, with the bottle of medicine in her hand, followed Happy Boy out. She put the bottle down in his room and stood at his door.

"After a little while you rub some of it on yourself. It's my idea that you don't need to eat your heart out, as you are doing, about a little thing like this. In the beginning, during the days when my old man was alive, I was always quitting my job too. The first reason for that was, I was out working, wearing myself out, while he had no ambition at all, and that made me very angry. The second thing was that when I was younger and more coarse in spirit, if a single phrase was spoken which didn't suit me, I'd quit. I'd say: 'I'm selling my strength to make money, and I'm not a slave; you can keep your stinking money. If I were made of mud, I'd still have the qualities of dirt. Nobody could wait on an old woman like you.' I'd say that to one mistress after another. But I'm much better now. When my old man died, I didn't have anything more to worry about, and my disposition improved a little. Here in this house—well, I've been here for a little less than three years now; that's right, I came to work here on the ninth of September. The extra money in tips that you get here is too little, but they treat you well. What we're selling is our strength, and we're doing it for money, and it's no help if all you get out of it is a few nice words. But there's more that must be said: there's an advantage in seeing the thing from the long view. If every two or three days you quit your job, in one year you will have been six months out of work. You don't make money out of that. It'd be better, when you meet up with a good-natured master, to put up if you can with staying longer on the one job even if the outside money is too little, and depend on the length of the period you work to save a little money.

"In that business today, since the master didn't say anything, I'd just count it done. Why not? It isn't that I'm trying to presume on my age, but you're still a little brother, and it's easy for you to catch on fire. There's no need for it at all. You can't make a brittle temper do instead of rice to eat. As honest and hard-working and well-disposed as you are, you better just prepare to stay on here a while. That will certainly be better than flying all over heaven trying to catch a fish. And I'm not telling you this on their account: I'm thinking of you, and how fine it would be for the two of us to go on working here together."

She caught her breath quickly, and then added: "All right. See you tomorrow. Don't dig your hoofs in the ground like a stubborn bull. There's only one eye in my heart, and it isn't a shifty one. When there's anything I have to say, I say it right out."

Happy Boy's left elbow hurt him very much, and for half the night he couldn't sleep. Figuring the thing out from beginning to end, and counting all the sevens for sevens and all the eights for eights, he felt that Kao Ma had sound reason in what she said. Everything was false, and only money was true. He would save money to buy a rickshaw: he could not put the heat of his anger in a bowl and eat it for rice. When he had thought it all out that far, there came to him the spirit of a little peaceful sleep.

8

MR. TS'AO had the rickshaw repaired, and didn't take the cost out of Happy Boy's wages. Mrs. Ts'ao gave him two pills of "Triple Yellow Precious Wax," which will cure practically anything, but he didn't swallow them. He didn't say anything more about the matter of resigning. Kao Ma's advice gained the ultimate victory in his mind, although for many days he could not get away from the uneasy feeling that he had not done quite right about it. After a few weeks had passed, however, his life slipped back into its old groove, and very gradually he forgot the whole affair.

All his old hopes began to put out their little buds again. During the times when he was free to sit alone in his room, his eyes would grow bright with the mental calculations he was making about the ways in which he would save money, and how he'd buy himself a rickshaw; his lips would be pursed with his muttering, like a person with some slight sickness in his mind. His method of calculating was neither illustrious nor profound, but on his lips and in the center of his heart there was this constant refrain: "Six times six makes thirty-six." These figures had no connection whatever with the sum of his money: it was only that this was the phrase of his ritual, and he repeated it over and over again. It was as if his heart could feel more replete because of it, or as if he were actually settling some account that someone had with him.

For Kao Ma he had a proper respect, feeling that this woman had more pathways in her mind and more strength and ability than most men. In the things she said she tried to get right down to the roots of the matters of which she spoke. He didn't dare hunt her out to pass the time of day, but if he met her in the courtyard or at the doorway, and if she had the leisure to say a sentence or two, he was delighted to listen to her. He felt that even her least formal lectures were worth mulling over for half a day, so that whenever he ran into her he would smile his broad foolish smile to make her understand his respect for her wisdom. She, too, would be tickled by the happen-chance of their meeting and by his obvious regard for her, and even if she did not have the leisure to talk she would manage to get in a few words.

But there was this to be said: when it came to plans for the management of money, he did not dare to smash recklessly forward following the principles she outlined for him. Her plan was one which from his point of view could not be regarded as bad, but it meant running a risk, however great or however small the risk might prove. He liked very much to hear her describe it, because it gave him a chance to get used to the mention of large sums of money: it opened up his heart and made it spacious, so that he felt like a wealthy man. On the question of putting her scheme into actual practice, he was still a follower of his old principle: never lightly loosen your grip on money, no matter how small the sum may be.

There was no mistake about it: Kao Ma did in all truth have a plan. From the time she had become a widow, she had taken the little bit of money she could save each month and lent it out; if it was a dollar, she loaned a dollar, and if it was two dollars, she loaned two dollars. She loaned it to other servants or policemen of the second or third grade in rank or people who had small businesses. The rate of interest was at least three per cent for a month or less. People of that type were often so worried for the need of a single dollar that their eyes ground round and round like grindstones in their heads to find some way to get hold of it. If someone offered them that dollar with the demand that they promise to pay back two dollars instead of one, they would still be forced to reach out their hands and receive it. Except through means like these, they would never know what money looked like. All the money that they saw was covered with poison; they knew that if they accepted it, the very blood in their veins would be sucked dry, but they still had to take it. Anything that made it possible for them to draw just one more breath, they would have the courage to take. Their whole lives were no more than the desperate postponement from one short gasp to the next of that hour when even the strength to gasp would be gone. For them the evils of the day were sufficient; tomorrow would be time enough to think of tomorrow's troubles.

Kao Ma herself, when her husband was alive, had suffered from the effects of this same kind of poison. Her husband would no sooner get drunk than he would come looking for her, and insist that he would not leave until she had given him a dollar. If she had no money, she would stand outside the gate of the house in which she happened to be employed, crying and cursing and making a drunken row until she had no other way out. No matter how much interest she had to pay, she had to borrow the dollar right away. From experiences like these she had learned this plan of hers. It was not that she sought revenge but rather that she accepted what had been done to her as proper and right, and saw no reason why she herself should not do the same things to others. Since it meant the saving of many people from extremities of immediate need, it was almost to be considered a work of charity. When you had on one hand a person who had money and was willing to lend it, and on the other a person whose need for money wouldn't wait, it was like Chou Yü and Hwang Kai in the story of "The Three Kingdoms." Chou struck his friend Hwang to prove to an enemy general that they were no longer friends; one was happy to strike and the other to be struck, so what could be wrong with it, whatever the bystanders thought?

Being thus without any scruples of conscience so far as the principle of the thing went, Kao Ma could be a little sharp in its actual practice. She could not throw money into a stream just to see if it would float; when she said something she meant it. For a plan like this you had to have good eyes, you had to be resourceful, and you had to taste bitter where you spilled over or you would find yourself only feeding the falcons that the swindlers had flown, and be done out of every penny.

She spent as much of her heart's blood in weighing the chances as did the manager of a bank, because she had to be even more cautious and prudent than a banker. Whether the capital is large or small, the principle is the same, and because ours is a capitalist society, it is like a tremendous sieve with the very finest netting: little by little the money drains from the top down; and the farther down it gets the less there is. At the same time the principle of the thing comes down too, but it is the same at the bottom as it is at the top, because it is a disembodied thing that is not like money, and does not have to fear the smallness of the holes in the sieve; it slips through anyway.

Everybody said that Kao Ma was sharp and hard. She admitted it herself. Her hardness and her sharpness had come from the long hammering and grinding of deep poverty. Whenever she thought of the distress she had known, and how even her own husband had been so lacking in either reason or affection toward her, she would only clench her teeth the more grimly. She could be very affable and kind, and she could be very sharp and bitter. She knew that that was the only way in which she could survive in this crooked world of ours.

She urged Happy Boy to lend out his money too. Entirely out of the best intention toward him did she give him this advice, and if he were willing to follow it she would help him.

"I tell you, Happy Boy, as long as you keep it in your pocket, a penny is forever only a single penny. If you will let go of it, money will grow more money. There's no mistake about it. What are our eyes made for? You can take a good look to be sure of the borrower before you let any money out of your hand. Naturally you can't get a grip on the tail feathers of an eagle that's already shorn. But take a policeman, for instance. If when the time comes he doesn't pay the interest due on his money, or doesn't pay back the principal when he should, you just hunt up his police captain. One word and his job is finished. Do you think he'd dare! Find out clearly on what day they are paid, and then block all escape from the nest while you reach in to take out the eggs. Not return your money? That would be a new one. We can compare one to the ten that have gone before, and we need lend money only when we have some security for doing so. Just passing it out to anybody, and then feeling all over the ocean bottom to find a lost pot, what good would that be? You just listen to me, and I guarantee you won't go wrong."

Happy Boy had no need of saying anything; his whole manner and attitude amply expressed his vast admiration of Kao Ma and the things she said. But when he got off to himself and figured it all out, he still felt that to have the money in your hand was better than any other system. It was right to say that your money was dead, and had no way to multiply itself, but it was also true that you couldn't lose it. He took the few dollars he had managed to save in the last few months—it was all in cash —into his fingers, and lightly and lovingly turned it about in his

106

hands, putting it all first in one hand and then in the other, as softly as if he were afraid of the sounds the coins made striking against each other. They were so bright and shining, these silver coins, so full and rich and real, so worthy of regard: he felt more than ever that not for ten thousand urgings could he be got to release them, except only to buy himself a rickshaw. Each man has his own methods, and it was not necessarily fitting or advantageous that he should follow those which were proper for Kao the amah.

At one time he had worked in the household of a family by the name of Fang. The master himself and the whole family, from the biggest to the littlest, even including the servants, all had, each of them, one of the folding passbooks of the Postal Savings put out at the Post Office. The First Wife Fang had also exhorted Happy Boy:

"It only takes a dollar to open a passbook. Why don't you get one? The proverb speaks well which says, 'If always when there is sunlight you will think of the day when there may be no sun, you will never wish there was still time when the time is past.' You are so young now, and yet you will not take advantage of your youth and the fullness of your strength to save a few coppers? There are three hundred and sixty days in the year, and they cannot every one of them be bright and fair and with a big sun in the sky. This doesn't take any trouble, it's very trustworthy, and moreover you get interest. At any time that you're pinched for money, you can draw a little out to use. How could it be more convenient than that? You go now and get an application blank, and if you can't write I'll help you fill it out. And that's altogether out of the goodness of my heart!"

Happy Boy knew she was good-hearted, and he knew too that the cook, Wang the Sixth, together with the baby amah, Ch'in Mah, both had passbooks, and he thought very seriously about trying it himself. But one day the Eldest Daughter Fang told him to go deposit ten dollars to her account. On the way there and back he studied the passbook very carefully. On the face of it were some characters and a little red seal. Heng! it wasn't much heavier than a handful of toilet paper. When he handed the money in, they just made a few more figures in the passbook and stamped another little seal mark opposite them. He felt that if this wasn't a swindle, it just had to be a swindle anyway. You took new white coins, as bright as fresh flowers, and turned them in through the gratings, and the only thing you got to show for them were the three strokes and five lines that some stranger with an easy pen slapped into a folding passbook, and that was the end of the transaction!

Happy Boy wasn't going to get caught in a cheat like that. He suspected that the Fang family and the Post Office had gone into this business together. He had felt all the time that the Post Office was just a commercial concern that had branches everywhere. Probably its firm name was very old, at least as old as the Auspicious Water Beetle or the Sign of the Wild Swan. The Fangs no doubt had a connection with this business, which explained why they were so enthusiastic in trying to drum up trade for it. And even if the actual facts were different from this, it was in the last analysis much better to have the cash in your hands than to have it in the passbook. Much better! The money in the passbook was no more than a few characters!

Of the big banks and smaller banking houses he knew only that they were good places to go to find fares. Supposing that the policeman on the beat didn't forbid his parking his rickshaw at the bank entrance, he would be sure to pick up a passenger there. As to what it was they were all busy about doing inside the bank, he could make no clear guess. There was no mistake about the money part of it; in a place like this there was certain to be a very great deal of money, but he couldn't understand why people should come particularly to just such a place to put in their own money or to juggle with what others had put there. In any case it would be no easy thing for him to become in any way connected with a bank, so why should he make his heart anxious thinking about it?

Within the four walls of the city there were many, many things that he did not understand. In the teahouses he would listen to his friends discussing them, but they would only confuse him the more, and make him feel more stupid than before. Because each one would say something different from anyone else, and none of them would seem to him to be bringing the talk home or to have got the real point of the problem. He didn't want to listen to any more of it or to think any more about it. He knew that if you were going to carry out a robbery, the very best place to rob would be a bank; and since he had no desire to become a robber, the best thing for him to do would be to keep his own money firmly in his own hands, and not to concern himself with any of the rest of it. He felt that this was after all the most dependable and correct method.

Kao Ma knew that Happy Boy's heart was red with his desire to buy a rickshaw and for that, too, she proposed a scheme.

"Happy Boy, I know you're not willing to let your money out at interest. But that would also be a way of buying your own rickshaw much sooner. If I were a man, and if I were a rickshaw puller, I would have to pull my own rickshaw. I would pull my own cart and sing my own song, and in the ten thousand things I would ask for aid from no one. If I could be that way, I wouldn't trade my place with the magistrate of the district. Pulling a rickshaw is a bitter business, but if I were a man and I had my share of strength, I would be determined to be a rickshaw puller, and I wouldn't go and be a policeman. For him it's always the same monotony, winter and summer; he must always stand there at his post in the street, and in a month he only makes a few dollars. He has no outside money and no freedom. Even if he decides on his own to grow himself a mustache, he gets fired for it. To tell you the straight truth, he hasn't the slightest chance of improving himself.

"What I started to say was—yes, that's right, if you want to buy yourself a rickshaw in a hurry, I'll tell you a good way of doing it. Start a club with ten or more people—twenty at the most—in it, each one to pay in two dollars a month. You could use the first month's collection—wouldn't you have almost forty dollars then right away? And no matter how little, you've already got some money saved up. By adding one thing to another, you'd be able to get yourself a rickshaw to pull. A clear-cut, smart move! Then, when you had the rickshaw in your hands, you could change the club into a lottery association and you wouldn't have to pay any interest; and besides, it would be a very respectable thing and certain to suit your own ideas. If you really want to form a club, I will come into it as one member. And I guarantee I'm not talking nonsense, either. How about it?"

In all truth this proposition made Happy Boy's heart beat faster. If he could really get together thirty or forty dollars, and add to that the thirty-odd dollars in Fourth Master Liu's hands, together with the few dollars that he had now himself, would he not then have a little less than eighty dollars? Although that wouldn't be enough to buy him a rickshaw that was ten parts new, he could certainly manage one that was eight parts. Furthermore, if he went at it this way, he could go to Fourth Master Liu and get his money back. That would save its just lying in the old man's hands, like nothing on earth. And eight parts new would be eight parts new; good or bad, he could pull the rickshaw until he had a surplus and could change it for another.

But where would he go to find these twenty people? And supposing he could collect them together, there was a matter of face involved. When he himself needed money he would form a club, but what of tomorrow when the other fellow needed money and came to ask him to join such a club? This business of forming clubs, in years and months as poor as these, could often as not slip away from you and fall apart, and your money would be gone. The good son of Han seeks no man's aid; it was clear-cut then; if he were destined to buy a rickshaw, he would buy it, and not ask for help.

Seeing that he was immovable, Kao Ma seriously thought of trying to whip him into action with sarcasm, but when she thought again of his simple and sincere and straightforward way, that had a kind of force of its own, she could not feel easy in her conscience about doing it.

"You're certainly something!" she said. "Why don't you herd pigs in the little side-lanes? You could go straight up and come straight back; that would be simple, too."

Happy Boy didn't say anything but waited until Kao Ma had gone off, and then he silently nodded his head to himself, as if in recognition of the fact that his own plan for keeping a dead grip on his money was the only one worthy of respect. In his heart he was strangely elated.

The weather was already that of the tenth lunar month, the first month of winter, and in the evening in the narrow lanes you could hear the hawkers calling out, "Selling chestnuts roasted in sugar," "Selling peanuts." There were other voices too, but they were lower and a little shamefaced and melancholy, as if they were only doing an unpleasant thing that had to be done, saying: "Selling night pots, selling night pots."

On the carrying poles of the night-pot sellers were also porcelain containers made like gourds with a small opening in the top. Happy Boy bought one of the largest size. It was the first sale the hawker had made and he couldn't find enough change. Happy Boy's heart turned quickly in accommodation of this lack: his eye had been caught by the cutest little night pot in green porcelain, its color broad and deep, and with a pouting little mouth. "Don't bother about the change, I'll take one of these instead."

When he had put away the porcelain gourd, he took the small green night pot into the inner rooms.

"Has Little Master gone to sleep yet? I bought you a small plaything."

They were all in the act of watching Little Elegance—the Ts'ao family's baby boy—being given a bath, and when they saw what the toy was that had just been given him they could not keep from smiling. Neither the mother nor father said anything. Probably they felt that although the gift itself was awkward, still Happy Boy's idea had been a kind one, and that they should accept it on that account. Therefore they both turned their faces to him with smiles to express their thanks.

But Kao Ma's mouth could not remain idle. "Now look! For a fact, Happy Boy! As big as you are, you're capable of thinking up a high-minded thing like this—what an unsightly thing that is!"

Little Elegance was delighted with his toy, and forthwith began scooping up the water in his bath into the little pot. "This little teapot big mouth," he observed, making his contribution to the proceedings.

Everybody laughed even harder at that. Happy Boy straightened himself up, and because when he was really pleased about something he never knew what to do with himself, he walked out. He was very jubilant. To have everybody in the room turning toward him with smiling faces, as if he were some very important personage, was something he had never experienced before. He smiled a little to himself and then again brought out his few dollars and very lightly, a dollar at a time, dropped them through the narrow lips of the porcelain gourd. In his heart he was saying: "This is more dependable than anything else! On the day when the sum is sufficient, on that day I'll throw this gourd against the wall and, pa ja! there'll be more dollars on the floor than there are tiles on the roof!"

He decided definitely that he would never ask anyone to help him again. Even with Fourth Master Liu, as trustworthy as he was, in the end there were times when it became annoying and irritating. In the Fourth Master's hands the money would not be lost, but he was still a little uneasy in his mind about it. This thing called money was like a ring, it was always better on your own finger. The decision he came to made him happy, and he felt as he did when he tightened his belt so that his broad chest would be even more impressive and firm.

Each day was colder now but Happy Boy did not seem to know it. In his heart he had a definite purpose, and on that account the things around him had become bright and clear, and in that bright clarity he could not feel the cold. For the first time there was ice to be seen on the ground, and even the dust in the side roads was hard and frozen. Everywhere there was manifest a dry solidity; the color of the black earth had taken on the slightest tinge of yellow, as if all the moisture in it had been exhausted. Especially in the early hours, when the dust that the big trucks raised was streaked with fine thin strands of frost. In a while the edges of the small winds of the morning would cut through the clouds and blow them away from the sky, exposing the highest, bluest and gayest of heavens. Happy Boy liked to take his rickshaw out for a run before the sun rose. The cold wind would blow up his sleeves, making him shiver all over as if he had taken a cold shower, and making him want to sing, as a shower did. Sometimes a mad wind would rise and lash at him so hard that no breath could come out of his mouth, but he would put his head down, grit his teeth, and weave his way forward, like some great fish swimming against the current. The stronger the force of the wind, the stronger was the force of his resistance: it was as if he and the wind were making war on one another to the death.

When a fierce gale laid hold of him and would not let him breathe, he would close his mouth for a long time and then belch as if he were a harpooned whale. But he would go forward as before, battling his way on; he was a giant that nothing could stop. There was not a muscle in his body that was not flexed and tense. He was like a green bug that the ants were attacking; his whole body shook with its resistance.

And the sweat that covered him! When he had put his rickshaw down, and had had a chance to blow out the air in his lungs and to wipe away the yellow dust from the corners of his mouth, he straightened himself up, proud in the belief that he had no equal anywhere. He watched the wind, carrying ashes and gravel along with it, sweep across before him, and gravely nodded his head. The wind bent the trees along the roadside until they looked like bows; it took the cloth shop signs with their red symbols showing what the store sold and tore them into shreds; it ripped all the handbills posted on the walls clean away; it covered the very face of the sun itself with clouds; it sang, it shouted, it moaned; it turned back upon itself in a vast

114

and reckless swirl, and then as suddenly charged straight forward like a disembodied spirit driven mad by fright that will rend the heavens and split the earth in the agony of its flight. Abruptly then it seemed to become confused and to be running amok in every direction at once; it was an evil demon seeking only to know how best to harm the most; recklessly it swept crosswise taking advantage of the unpreparedness against this flanking movement to attack everything on the ground, to twist off the branches of trees, to carry away the tiles from the roofs, and to snap the telephone wires in two.

But Happy Boy only stood there watching. He had just come from out of the wind, and it had been unable to do him any harm. The victor had been Happy Boy! And when he met with a favorable wind, he had to do nothing more than take a firm hold on the handles of his rickshaw, and he would not have to spend his strength in running; the wind itself was capable of turning the wheels around for him like a good friend.

Naturally he was not blind, and of necessity he had seen the old and feeble rickshaw men. A little breeze would go through the clothes they wore, and a real gust of wind could tear them apart. With torn clothing and feet wrapped up in God knows what odds and ends of cloth, they would stand shivering at the street entrances, their eyes watering like a thief's. If a person appeared on the street, no matter from where, they would scramble and fight to be the first to ask him, "Rickshaw?" When they got a fare they warmed up a little, and the sweat would show through their torn and thin clothing. Once they stopped, the perspiration would freeze on their backs. If they ran into a wind, they would be unable even to lift their feet, but they would try with all the life left in them to drag their rickshaw along behind them. When the wind smashed down on them they did their best to hide their heads in their chests; when it drove up from under them, their feet would be unable to find the ground. When it came directly at them, they could not hold out a hand lest their arm fly up like a kite; if it came from behind them, they no longer had any means of controlling either the rickshaw or themselves. But they would exhaust every possible way, use to its very last all the strength and breath in their bodies, drag along half dead and half alive, until finally they had got their fare to his address. It would be for a few coppers that they had done all this—for a few coppers that they had smashed and poured away their own lives.

In a trip like that, the dust and dirt blown into their faces would have been turned into mud by the sweat, and would cover them like paste, so that there would be only three holes in the mask—their eyes and mouth, all of them red with cold. The days of winter are so short and cold that there are not many people on the streets. They could follow this bitter road for a whole day and not be sure that at the end of it they would have earned enough even to buy one good meal. But the old in years would have an old woman and children at home; the young would have parents and brothers and sisters. In the winter time they were altogether and completely in a hell of their own. They were worse off than a ghost for the breath of life that they drew, and at the same time they lacked its leisure and freedom. A devil did not have to wear himself out as they did! Like the homeless cur that dies at the street corner, death brings them closer to comfort and nearer to peace than they have ever been before. And according to what people say, a poor devil who freezes to death dies with a smile on his face.

How could Happy Boy have failed to see people like that? But he didn't have the time to be anxious about them or to meditate on their fate. Their sin was his own, except that he was in the strongest years of his youth, and could stand hardship, was not afraid of the cold or the wind, had a clean place to sleep in the evening, a clean gown to wear during the day; but because of these differences he felt that he could not be mentioned in the same breath with the others. Although they and he were now together in bearing hardship, yet the degree of the hardship they bore was not precisely the same. He was suffering less now, and he hoped in the future to be able to escape their fate. He thought that when he himself was old, he would never be pulling a broken-down rickshaw, hungry and cold. He had faith that his present excellence was a guarantee of his future victory.

It was the same with him and those others as it was with the chauffeurs whom he occasionally met outside of hotels or private homes. They were unwilling to fall into conversation with him, because they felt that any intercourse they might have with a rickshaw man would be injurious to their station in life and their position in society. Their attitude toward rickshaw men had a good deal in common with Happy Boy's attitude toward these aged and broken-down soldiers of his craft. They were in the same inferno, but bore different grades in it. They would never have thought of joining together, but tried each to walk his own road alone, blinded by his hope and by the energy with which he sought to improve his own lot. Each thought that empty-handed he could set about establishing his family and setting up his trade. Each sought in the darkness to feel his own way. Happy Boy thought of no one else, and paid heed to no one else; he thought only of his own money and future success.

Slowly the streets took on the air of the year's ending. In clear bright weather, during the times that there was no wind, the roadways blossomed in color for all the dry cold of winter. New Year paintings, gauze lanterns, tall wax candles of red and white, colored flowers of silk for women to wear in their hair, big and little likenesses of the Heavenly Messenger who bears reports on earthly happenings to the Throne of God, with his lips smeared with honey so that he would say nothing but sweet things about the members of the household where his likeness was hung—all these were arrayed before the shop fronts, making the hearts of men happy.

117

But this feeling was mixed with not a little disquietude, for the reason that everyone, no matter who he was, looked forward to the few days of merrymaking at New Year's time, and yet for each of them there were bound to be difficulties, great or small. Happy Boy's eyes grew brighter at the sight of the New Year's goods along the street; he thought of the presents the Ts'ao family would be sure to make, and how for each one he delivered there would be a twenty or thirty cent tip for him. And the New Year's cumshaw was already set at two dollars. That was not much, but when people came to extend their New Year's greetings to his master, he would take them back in his rickshaw, and for each such trip he would again receive two or three dimes. Put all that together and it would be a sizeable sum. He wasn't afraid of small amounts so long as they kept coming into his hands. His porcelain gourd was not capable of cheating anyone. Late at night when his work was done he would sit with his soul in his eyes staring at this little clay friend of his, that could eat money but did not want to spit any of it out again, and in a low voice he would exhort it, "Eat more and more, fellow worker; eat more and more! On the day when you've had enough, I'll be all right too."

The time of the New Year's Festival grew closer and closer. In one short turn of the hours it was already the eighth day of the twelfth lunar month, the day on which the thin gruel is eaten. By the pleasures that they anticipated or the fears that crowded them, people were forced to make their plans and to put their affairs in order.

There were still twenty-four hours in every day, but these few days were not like those that had gone before it; they would not permit you to pass them in any way convenient to yourself, but required that you be busy with something, something which looked toward the coming of the New Year. It was as if Time had suddenly become conscious of himself, had acquired emotions, was forcing people to follow him in their thinking and

118

to follow him, as well, in all their flurried scurrying about. Happy Boy stood on the side of the delighted; the bustling life in the streets, the sound of the hawkers calling their wares, the anticipated cumshaw at festival time, the New Year's vacation, the image of all the good things he would have to eat, all these things made him as happy and as full of hope and anticipation as a little child.

He had it all thought out, how he would break out eighty cents or a dollar to buy some small New Year's gift for Fourth Master Liu and take it to him. "The present is a trifle, but the gesture of giving is freighted with love." He just had to take him a little something: in the first place, to make his amends for not having gone to see the old fellow in so many days, on account of his being so busy at the Ts'ao household; and, in the second place, because it would afford him an opportunity to collect the thirty-odd dollars that were being held for him. If by spending less than a dollar he could get back that sum of money, it would be well worth it. With this figured out, he picked up his gourd and shook it ever so lightly, trying to imagine how much more full and beautiful the sound would be when he had added the thirty-odd dollars. It was a fact: once he had gotten that money back, there would be nothing about which his heart need be uneasy.

On one such evening, just as he was lightly shaking his bowl that collected precious things, Kao Ma called out to him:

"Happy Boy, there's a girl at the gate looking for you. I just happened to run into her on the street as I was coming back, and she asked most particularly after you."

When Happy Boy came out Kao Ma added in a low voice: "She looks like a great black pagoda—she's enough to frighten anybody."

Happy Boy's face suddenly grew as red as if it were wrapped in flame. He knew now that the whole affair had spoiled and would turn rotten!

119

APPY BOY had hardly the strength to step across the threshold. His head swam with befuddlement and his feet had not yet managed to get over the raised boarding at the bottom of the outer door, but already he had seen Tiger Girl under the street lamp. She had probably powdered her face again; the light made her skin look gray-green, like a black and withered leaf coated with frost. In simple truth, Happy Boy was afraid to look her in the eye.

The expression on Tiger Girl's face was very complex: in her eyes there was something of the light of an ardent longing to see him; her lips, though, were parted a little, tracing a cold smile; her nose was raised up in wrinkles which enfolded within them the haughtiest suggestion that of course the whole thing involved a condescension that she well realized was hardly fitting for one in her high station. Her eyebrows stuck up at sharp angles, and through its fantastic coat of white powder her face revealed an almost evil seductiveness combined with a grim determination to accomplish her purpose, no matter how destructive it might prove.

When she saw Happy Boy coming out, her lips pouted a little and all the varied expressions of spirit and feeling in her face sought in vain for some adequate precipitant. She swallowed a mouthful of saliva, and, as if she had succeeded in reducing her complex feelings and emotions to order, she managed to assume something of the worldly and nonchalant air she had learned from the Fourth Master. Half teasing and half smiling, pretending the while that none of this mattered very much, she said jestingly:

"You're a good one, though! I take a roll of meat and beat the dog with it, and still he runs away from me and won't come back!" Her voice was shrill and loud, the same as it was when she was wrangling with the rickshaw men back at the shed. When she had finished speaking, the half-smile disappeared from her face, and suddenly she seemed to feel a kind of shame at her own cheapness. She bit her lip.

"Don't shout!" It was as if Happy Boy had brought all the strength of his body to his lips to explode these two words. They were low in sound but very strong.

"Heng! I should be afraid!" Her smile was evil, but involuntarily she lowered a little the tone of her voice. "No wonder you've been avoiding me—sure enough you've got a sweet little fairy-fox of an amah here. I knew a long time ago that you were no toy for a child to play with. You don't fool anybody looking like a big simpleton with your coarse black face. A Tartar dangling a pipe, pretending to be stupid when you're not stupid at all!" Her voice was growing loud again.

"Don't shout!" Happy Boy was only afraid that Kao Ma might be eavesdropping from behind the door. "Don't shout. Come over here!" As he spoke he walked over toward the road.

"It doesn't matter to me where I am, I'm not afraid. My voice is naturally loud and that's all there is to it." On her lips there was opposition, but she walked across after him.

When they had crossed the highway and had come a little way up the street to the east and were close to the red wall that surrounded the public park, Happy Boy—he had not forgotten the customs of the village—squatted down on his haunches.

"Why did you come?"

"Me? Heng! There's reason enough!" Her left hand was stuck in her waistband, over a stomach that curved out like a bow. Her head drooping a little, she looked at him out of one eye and thought a while, as if suddenly her heart felt compassion for him, pitied him. "Happy Boy, I came looking for you about a matter, an important matter."

The low gentle sound of the words "Happy Boy" dissipated much of his anger. He raised his head to look at her. There was still nothing about her that you could love, but the sound of that "Happy Boy" still echoed faintly in his heart with a soft intimacy, as if somewhere he had heard the words spoken in that tone before, as if they tugged at a bond of affection that he could not deny and would find hard to break however much he might wish to break it. His voice was still low but warmer and more friendly.

"What matter are you talking about?"

"Happy Boy," she said, pressing closer to him, "I've got—"

"You've got what?"

"This!" She pointed to her stomach. "Tell me what you want me to do about it."

He put his hands to his head, and made one sound—"Ah!" Suddenly he understood everything. Ten thousand things he had never thought of before all rushed in on his consciousness, coming in such numbers and with such haste and such confusion that in a violent upheaval of its own his heart became a block of white emptiness, like a moving picture screen when suddenly the film breaks in two. The street was extraordinarily quiet and deserted. In the heavens gray clouds covered the moon, and over the ground there moved from time to time a little breeze, shaking the dead branches and their withered leaves. From some place far away there came the sharp-edged sound of a cat wailing.

Happy Boy's heart had come from confusion to emptiness; he did not even hear these sounds around him. His chin in his hand, he sat stupidly staring at the ground before him, staring at it so hard that it seemed as if it were about to move. He could not think of anything and did not want to think of anything;

he only felt smaller and smaller, and yet he could not draw himself back entirely into the ground. His whole life stood now just on this one moment that was so hard to bear. Of anything beyond that there was nothing at all. It was not until now that he knew how cold it was: even his lips were trembling.

"Don't just squat there, say something! Get up!" She, too, seemed to have felt the cold and wanted to walk a few steps.

He could not stand the heavy sarcasm of her voice, and got up, following her as she walked off in a northerly direction. He could still find nothing to say. His whole body had suddenly turned numb, like a drunk who has just been frozen into soberness by the cold.

"You have no plan?" She let her glance run over Happy Boy, in her eyes an expression of her fondness for him.

There was nothing that he could say.

"When the twenty-seventh comes around, the old man will have a birthday. You pay us a visit."

"Too busy. That's just before New Year's." Even in the uttermost confusion in his heart, Happy Boy could not forget his own affairs.

"I know the kind of a little rascal you are—you'll take the hard but not the soft—talking nicely to you is just a waste of time." Her voice had got loud and shrill again, and the cold solitude of the street made the words that she was saying sound exceptionally clear. In Happy Boy's ears they were a maddening scream.

"You think I'm afraid or what?" she asked. "What do you think you're going to do? If you don't want to listen to what I'm telling you, I've got no leisure to spend wasting my spittle in playing about with you. If you want it that way, I'm perfectly capable of blocking the door of the house where you work and cursing you out for three days and three nights. Wherever you go I can find you. I'm not going to be stopped by any arguments about right or wrong or who was at fault to begin with."

"Could you do without shouting?" Happy Boy stepped away from her.

"If you were afraid of my making a noise, you shouldn't have come around trying to get something for nothing in the first place. You've got tired of the flavor, and you want me to carry the black pot all alone. Why don't you pull back the skin on your dead jeebah and take a look at me out of your one eye, take a look at who you're dealing with."

"Take your time, and say what you want to say. I'll listen." In the beginning, Happy Boy had felt very cold, but with Tiger Girl's imprecations he had suddenly become hot all over. The heat opened the pores on his skin that had been benumbed with cold, and his whole body began to itch. On his head, particularly, these stabbing little prickles that cried to be scratched were almost unbearable.

"This thing isn't going to end here, and there's no use making it any more uncomfortable for yourself than you have to." She parted her lips in what was meant to be a smile, showing the tiger fangs. "You mustn't be so darkly suspicious. I'm truly very fond of you. And don't forget what's good for you, either! You won't get any good out of making your neck stiff like a bull's, I'm telling you."

"There's no—" Happy Boy wanted to say, "There's no use slapping me once and then patting me three times," but he couldn't think of the whole phrase. When it came to the smart slang of Peking, he knew quite a bit of it, only he wasn't facile in speaking it. If somebody else used it, he could understand; it was just that he couldn't quite get it out himself.

"There's no what?" Tiger Girl demanded.

"You go ahead and say what you were going to."

"I'll tell you a scheme." Tiger Girl took a firm position directly in front of him, sticking her face into his. "See here. If you got a go-between to ask the old man to give me to you in the regular formal way like everybody else does, he would cer-

124

tainly refuse. He's an owner of rickshaws, and you're only a rickshaw puller, and he wouldn't be willing to go beneath his own social station to find a son-in-law. For myself, I don't care anything about that. I like you and that's good enough for me —why should I give a mother's for any of the rest of it?

"No matter who spoke for me it would be the same. When anybody comes to the old man to talk about my marriage, he thinks right away that they're calculating on getting hold of those several tens of rickshaws of his. He's turned down suitors higher in station than you are. So I made up my mind that this matter was one that I'd have to manage myself, and I picked you out. We went about it like the executioner who first cuts off the prisoner's head and then memorializes the throne asking for permission to sentence him to death. Anyhow, whatever way you look at it now, 'the joy is already in me,' and neither of us can run away from the other now.

"But it would still not do for us to walk right into the main hall of the house and say all this. The old man gets more and more stupid all the time. If he got wind of the two of us, he's perfectly capable of taking a young wife to himself and running me out. The old man is as strong as a staff—don't think that just because he's almost seventy he wouldn't do it. If he really took a wife, well, I don't dare say more than this: I guarantee he could manipulate two or three children out of her, believe it or not."

"Let's move along while we're talking." Happy Boy had noticed that the policeman on the beat had walked over toward them several times.

"We'll talk right here. Who can stop us?" Following Happy Boy's eyes, she too noticed the policeman. "You're not pulling your rickshaw—why should you be afraid of him? Do you think that without any reason or excuse at all he could still bite anybody's jeebah off? That would really show him up as a vicious actor. Let's go ahead with what we were saying and pay no attention to him.

"See here, this is what I think. When the twenty-seventh— that's the old man's birthday—comes around, you go and kowtow three times to him. Then when New Year's Day comes, you call on him again to wish him a happy new year. That will soften him, and when I see he's in good spirits, I'll bring on some wine and have him drink enough to make him happy. When he's seven or eight parts drunk, you can come right out and tell him that you take him to be your foster father.

"Then, after several days, I can gradually let him know that my body has this inconvenience. He's bound to question me very closely, and I'll act like the official of old who was brought as a prisoner into the camp of the great General Ts'ao. At first I will be unwilling to say anything at all. I'll wait until he gets in a real frenzy about it before I mention anyone's name. Then I'll tell him that it was Chiao Two, who just recently died—he was the manager of the coffin-storage room to the east of us. He didn't leave a single living relative, and they've already buried him in the potter's field outside the Straight East Gate. Where could the old man go to search out the truth of that?

"He won't know what to do, and we can gradually stir the breezes a little with the thought that the best thing would be to give me to you. To begin with, you would be his foster son, and from that to becoming his son-in-law wouldn't make a great difference. We could propel the boat along as the currents favored us, and so save a nasty situation for all of us. Tell me, have I thought the thing out well or not?"

Happy Boy said not a word.

Feeling that she had come to the end of the chapter in what she had been saying, Tiger Girl started walking away toward the north, her head lowered a little and seeming to be flavoring with a critic's appreciation the way she had spoken her part. It was also as if she were giving Happy Boy an opportunity to ponder the meaning of what she had told him.

Just then the winds blew open a little crack in the gray clouds, letting the moonlight through. The two of them had already reached the northern end of the street. The waters of the Grand Canal had early frozen over, and the shining gray ribbon of its course followed through the night the ancient battlements of the Forbidden City, offering them always its poised and sure support. There was not the slightest sound from within the city walls, and the gem-like watchtower rising above them, the gold and jade-stone archway, the great red portals, and the Pagoda on the Mountain of the Beautiful Vista all seemed to be waiting breathless in the bright moonlight to catch the echo of some heavenly voice that would never speak again. A little wind blew fragilely across the walls, moving ever so lightly through the halls and pavilions of the Forbidden City as if it thought to tell some tale of long ago that still should not be overheard.

Tiger Girl walked in a westerly direction, and Happy Boy followed along with her to the Jade Pillar surmounted by the Golden Turtle. On the marble bridge there were no passers-by, and the obscure clarity of the night's brightness made the wide stretches of ice on either side shimmer with a desolate coldness that told the wanderer how as long as he lived in the world he would always be alone. It made Happy Boy shiver, and he didn't want to go any farther.

Ordinarily when he pulled his rickshaw over this bridge, all his energy would be in his feet, for fear of slipping, and he would have paid no attention whatever to anything to the right or the left of him. Now he was free to look about him, but in the center of his heart he felt that there was something fearful about all this beauty: the ashen cold ice, the shadows of the trees that moved ever so slightly, the sad empty whiteness of the tall pagoda were all so intensely lonely that Happy Boy was terrified lest they should suddenly shriek at him or make some mad lunge toward him. Even the bridge on which he stood was extraordinarily remote and unreal in its whiteness; the street lamps at either end of it were mournful in their light. He did not want to go any further or look any more and of all things he wanted least to be with Tiger Girl. He knew what he truly wanted to do: he wanted to jump off the bridge, right now, head first, break through the ice, and be frozen into it, like some great dead fish.

Suddenly he swung around. "See you tomorrow," he said, walking rapidly away.

"Happy Boy! We'll do it that way—see you on the twenty-seventh!" She called it to his broad back. With the sentence said, she glanced up at the White Pagoda, sighed, and walked off in a westerly direction.

Happy Boy did not even turn his head. He felt as if there was a devil at his side, and as he stumbled confusedly down to the guard wall he almost ran into it. He had been there, wooden and motionless, for a while when he heard a voice calling to him from the bridge. "Happy Boy, Happy Boy, come here." It was Tiger Girl's voice again.

Very slowly he moved a couple of paces toward the bridge, and Tiger Girl came down to meet him, her body bent forward a little and her lips parted. "I say, Happy Boy, come here—I've something to give you." Before he could take two more steps she was standing in front of him. "I'm giving this to you—the thirty-odd dollars that you saved. There was some change too, but I've added enough to it to make it a round sum. Here it is. I'm not doing this for anything but to show you my heart. I think about you, and feel for you and try to protect you. There's no use saying the rest, only you mustn't forget favors that are done you, or turn your back on a good intent. Take it, and be careful of it. If you lose it you can't blame me."

Happy Boy took the money—a stack of bills—and stood there vacantly, unable to think of anything to say.

"Good enough. We'll meet on the twenty-seventh—if you don't meet me we'll still not part." She smiled at him. "It's you that's getting the best end of the bargain. You just calculate the whole thing carefully." She turned about and walked away.

He fumbled with the money and looked stupidly after her until the bridge hid her head from view. The moon was covered again by the gray clouds; the street lights were brighter than ever; and the bridge was abnormally white and empty and cold. He wheeled quickly away. It was as though it had frozen his mind: when he was already at his house gate, the shadow of that cold, sad, comfortless bridge was still just over his shoulder, as if by just blinking his eyes he would be back there again.

When he was back at last in his own room, he counted the bills. He counted them all over three times, and the perspiration from his hands was making the bills sticky, but still he could not get the same count twice. When finally the number came out right, he put the bills in his gourd and sat on the side of his bed staring at the little vessel of porcelain. He did not intend to try to think anything out; he had money now, and when you had money there was always a way. He had complete confidence that this little bank would solve all his problems. It wasn't necessary for him to fret himself trying to think any more. The Grand Canal, the Mountain of the Beautiful Vista, the White Pagoda, the bridge, Tiger Girl, her big stomach—they were all a dream; when he awoke from the dream, his china bank would have thirty-seven more dollars in it. That was real.

When he had looked long enough at the gourd he hid it away, and thought he would get a good long sleep. Your troubles might be as big as the heavens, and still you could sleep through them. Tomorrow would be time enough to speak of them again.

He lay down but couldn't close his eyes. The things that had happened were like a nest of hornets—you come out and I'll go in—and each one of them with a sting in its tail.

He was unwilling to think, and the awful truth was—there was nothing more to think about. Tiger Girl had blocked every road, and there was no way of escape left to him.

The very best way would be for him to pick up his feet and leave. But Happy Boy couldn't leave. Even if you told him that if he stayed he'd have to stand guard over the "Northern Sea" and the White Pagoda, he would still be happy to do that rather than go back to his village. Go to another city? He could not think of any place in the world that compared with Peking. He could not leave. He wanted to die in Peking.

Since he did not want to leave, there was no use wasting his energy thinking on the rest. If Tiger Girl told him he had to come, he had to come. If he did not follow her road, she was truly capable of making a terrible uproar about the whole thing. As long as he was in Peking, she could hunt him down. With her, to tell the truth, there was no use thinking of slipping out of anything. If you angered her, she might even bring Fourth Master Liu into it, and if he hired the services of a man or two

—there wasn't much use in dwelling on it—in any secluded spot they chose they could take Happy Boy's life.

Thinking over from the beginning to the end what the Tiger Girl had said, Happy Boy felt as though he had fallen into a trap, and that both his arms and legs had been pinned down by the steel spring of it, leaving him absolutely no chance of getting away. He lacked the ability to criticize her proposals one by one, and he could therefore find no crack in her armor. He could only see with sickly certainty that the net she spread was one which would be the end of himself and his line. A fish an inch long would never have been able to slip out of it.

Since he could not think minutely of each individual point in her plot against him, he had no way but to see it all as one large whole that pressed him down like a thousand pounds of stone piled on his back, or like a giant stone crusher coming down with immense force on the top of his head. Beat down by this oppression which he had no means to resist, Happy Boy felt that the fortunes of a rickshaw man throughout the span of his life could be completely expressed in two words—hard luck. A rickshaw man, just by reason of the fact that he was a rickshaw man, should think of nothing but pulling a rickshaw, and not do anything at all out of the way. He shouldn't even try putting a little glue into a woman: you do it once, and you've committed a crime as vast as the heavens. Fourth Master Liu relied on his ownership of a few tens of rickshaws, and the Tiger Girl on her possession of a stinking glue-snatcher, to swindle him, to cheat him out of everything that he really held close to himself.

There was no use thinking about it in detail. Suppose he decided to accept his fate; well then, he could go and knock his head on the ground and call Fourth Master his foster father, and afterwards wait for the time to receive in marriage that stinking monstrosity, that she-devil he hated and despised. If he did not accept this fate, then destiny would be ripped down the middle for him: he had to choose between accepting destruction or being destroyed.

When he had thought to this point, he put the Tiger Girl and the words she had spoken to one side. No, it was not that she was so hard and cruel but that this was the fate ordained for a rickshaw man. He was like a dog: of necessity it must expect to be beaten and abused. Even the little children around it would sometimes without any reason or cause at all beat it with sticks. A life-destiny like that, what was the use of it? Why should he try to keep it? If it was to crash, then let it crash.

He could not sleep, and with one foot he kicked away the covers and then sat up. He made up his mind to get some wine and drink until he was as drunk as he could be. Then all this whole affair, and whatever you call custom and the rules of behavior—your grandmother's! Get drunk! Sleep! The twenty-seventh? He wouldn't knock his head on the ground on the twenty-seventh or the twenty-eighth or any time at all for anybody at all. Then we'll see who thinks they can take Happy Boy and by what means.

Quickly he threw his gown around him, picked up the big bowl that he used as a tea cup, and ran out.

The wind was even higher than it had been, and the gray clouds that had covered the night were all blown aside. The moon was small and far away, indifferently shedding its bitter cold light. Happy Boy had just climbed out from his warm covers, and the chill made him draw his breath sharply. There wasn't a single pedestrian on the street, and there were only two or three rickshaws at the side of the road, their pullers standing close to them stamping their feet up and down and covering their ears with their hands to keep warm.

In one breath Happy Boy raced down to the little store on the south corner. To hold in the warm air, the store had already put up its shutters and barred its doors, but you could pay in your money and get what you wanted to buy through a tiny peek-hole window that the proprietor slid open to look out at you when you knocked. Happy Boy bought four catties of bygar and three big coppers' worth of peanuts. Carefully balancing the wine bowl, not daring to run, but slithering along rapidly without lifting his feet, like the men who carry a sedan chair, he got back once more to his room and hurried as fast as he could to get back under his covers. His teeth were chattering, and he didn't want to sit up again.

The wine on the table filled the room with a sharp pungent odor that he didn't like, and he didn't have it in his heart to touch even the peanuts. The few moments in the winter air had been like cold water thrown in his face to awaken him. He was reluctant to stretch out his arm from under the covers, nor was his heart any more so consumed with fire.

After he had been lying there for a long time his eye caught sight again of the bowl of wine on the table by the bedside. No, he could not destroy himself just because he had got a little tangled up in that other mess. He could not on that account break his resolution never to drink wine. The business was in all truth a hard one to handle but there was certain to be some little crack through which he could squirm. Even if it were true that there was absolutely no way of escaping, it was still not proper for him to take himself out beforehand and roll himself around in a mudhole. He must open his eyes and see as clearly as he could how it had been that he had after all allowed himself to be pushed down to where he was now.

He put out the light and pulled the covers up over his head. He figured that that way he could go to sleep. But still he could not sleep. Pulling the covers back, he looked out. The moonlight in the courtyard was turning dark on the paper panes of his window, as if it would soon be daylight. The tip of his nose felt the chill of his freezing room, the cold air bearing within it the faint odor of wine. Suddenly he sat up, reached out for the wine bowl, and drank it dry in one long gulp.

133

10

A FIGHTING cricket that has lost one of its big legs in combat still thinks to crawl on the little legs that are left it. Happy Boy was exactly like a cricket or any other living thing when it has been grievously wounded and knows there is nothing that can help it but still seeks with pitiful tenacity itself to mend the wound. He had no clear program but thought only of somehow getting slowly through one day after the other, of bearing as well as he could each period of pain the passing days brought to him. He would not hold before himself any distant objective but would be content to reach each day the stage to which this crawling pace would bring him. For him there could be no more thought of the strong leaping stride, of the fine far hop up into the air, than there could be for the legless cricket, once so brave.

There were still some ten days till the twenty-seventh but his whole attention was now completely concentrated on that one day. In his heart he thought of nothing else; his muttering lips endlessly formed the words; and all his dreams were about the twenty-seventh. It seemed that if he could just get through that one fatal day he would have a solution for his difficulties. But in this thought, too, he knew he was only cheating himself.

Sometimes his mind went out into the distances. Suppose he should take the few tens of dollars that he had in his hands and go to Tientsin? When he got there he might just strike it lucky and be able to change his trade and never have to pull a rickshaw again. Could Tiger Girl chase after him all the way to

Tientsin? In his heart it seemed that all places that you have to take a train to get to are of necessity very far away, and he knew that no matter what happened she would never be able to follow him that far.

He thought that was a fine idea, but to be honest with himself he had to admit that the scheme was only one which could be followed in a great extremity; if any chance remained of his staying in Peking he wanted to do so. In this manner he came again to think of the twenty-seventh; thinking only of the things immediately before you was still the simplest and easiest way. If he could just get somehow through this one narrow pass, he could probably plunge through the whole affair without having to make any change in the larger position. Even if it would not be possible by this method to make a clean sharp break and shed himself of the involvement, get clear of it entirely, still in the last analysis a stage passed was a stage over.

But how would he get through this stage? He had two plans. One was not to pay any attention to her business and simply not go there to visit the old man on his birthday. The other one was to do what she had told him to do. Although these two plans were not alike, they would in the end bring about the same result. If he did not go, she would certainly be incapable of allowing the thing to come to a good and generous ending, or of reaching some kind and gracious agreement about it; if he did go, she would still not pardon him from the punishment she had determined should be his.

He could still remember how, when he had first begun to pull a rickshaw, he had tried to copy the other pullers, and whenever he saw a narrow side street he would turn down into it in order to take every possible short cut. Once when he was doing this he got by mistake into the Lane of the Laid Trap; 'the more it twisted the further he was from where he wanted to go, and when finally he came to the end of it he was just where he had started from. Now he was back again in just such a narrow side street: whichever direction he turned, he came out in the end at the same place.

Lacking any other solution, he tried sometimes to look on the good side of things. Suppose he should make a clean-cut job of it and receive the girl as his wife? Why could he not do that? But, no matter from what point of view he approached it in his thinking, there was always that stifling feeling of repressed resentment that was like holding your breath when you were smothering. When he thought of her manner, the way she looked and the air about her, he could only shake his head. But leaving her looks out of it: think of her behavior—heng!

Just to consider himself, as ambitious as he was and as well-behaved, and then to think that he should take as his wife a piece of shopworn goods like that! He would never be able to look anybody in the eye again, and even after his death he could never face the spirits of his father and mother. Who could tell for sure whether the child in her belly was his? It was true she might bring with her as a dowry a few rickshaws; but was there any real guarantee of that? Fourth Master Liu was never a man whom it would pay to provoke. Even if everything went well, Happy Boy would still not be able to bear it.

Would he ever be able to get the best of Tiger Girl? All she had to do was to stretch out her little finger to keep him running until his head was dizzy and his eyes blurred and he could no longer tell east from west or south from north. He knew how mean and sharp she was. If he wanted to set up a family, there were the most basic reasons why he could not marry such a person as she was; there was just nothing else to be said about that. To take her would be to finish him, and he was no one to despise himself. There was no way.

With no means of putting her in her place, he turned about and hated himself. He longed to give himself a few sharp slaps in the face. But, to speak the truth, he had definitely not done anything wrong. The whole thing had been arranged by her, and had wanted nothing but for him to walk into the trap. It seemed as if his trouble had been that he was too simple and honest and well-disposed; the honest were bound to be cheated, and there was no reason or right to be spoken of.

The thing that made him the unhappiest of all was that there was no place he could go to unburden his heart of his wrongs. He had neither father nor mother nor elder nor younger brother, and he had no friends. Ordinarily he thought of himself as a real upstanding Son of Han, with head scraping the heavens and feet firmly planted on the earth, altogether free of any tie or hindrance. Only now did he understand, did he know enough to regret his mistake. No man can live independent and alone.

Especially did he feel toward the others of his calling that there was now something to be loved and cherished about them. Supposing that in ordinary times he had made friends with two or three of the others who were big strapping fellows like himself, he would still not be afraid even if there were two Tiger Girls. His friends would think up some way out for him, and they would even be willing to use their strength for him in pulling the thing out by its roots. But he had been from the beginning to the end only one person, and to go out now, because just at this moment he stood in need, and scratch up a few people to be his friends would not be easy. He felt a kind of terror that he had never known before. If he kept on acting as he had in the past, anyone at all could cheat him or impose upon him; one lone man could never touch the heavens.

This terror made him begin to have doubts about himself. In the winter time, when his master had a dinner engagement, or perhaps went out to listen to a play, Happy Boy would as of old take the water can from the bottom of the carbide lamp on the rickshaw and hold it inside the front of his gown, because if he left it on the lamp it might freeze. He would just have been running until his whole body was hot with sweat, and to put that ice-cold carbide tin against his bare skin would instantly make him shiver all over. There was no telling how long it would be before the tin would have become a little warmer, like his body. But ordinarily he did not think of this as being anything too unfair or bemeaning. Sometimes, as he hugged the little tin, he thought of the thing as something superlative: those pullers whose rickshaws were tattered and dirty never had such a thing as a carbide lamp in the first place.

But now it was as if he saw clearly; working at a job that paid you only that little bit of money and having to put up with all the bitter things about it, even to pressing the carbide can against your own chest because it mustn't be allowed to freeze —your own chest, as broad as it was, didn't seem to be worth as much consideration as a little tin water can. Originally he had thought of pulling a rickshaw as being the most ideal thing he could imagine doing. From it he could go on to the establishment of a family and the setting up of a business. Now quietly to himself he shook his head. It was no wonder Tiger Girl imposed upon him. He was, to begin with, nothing but a fellow who wasn't the equal of a little tin can.

On the evening of the third day after Tiger Girl had come looking for him, Mr. Ts'ao went with his friends to see the night showing of a moving picture, and Happy Boy waited for him in a little teahouse, taking the ice-cold carbide can with him. The night was very cold and the doors and windows of the teahouse were shut very tight. The place was full of coal smoke, the smell of sweat, the dry smoke of cheap cigarettes. Even so, the panes of the windows were covered with frost flowers.

The tea drinkers were mostly rickshaw pullers who worked by the month. Some of them were sitting with their chairs tilted back and their heads against the wall, taking advantage of the warmth of the room to snooze a while. Some of them had cups of bygar, which, after having made the gesture of offering to share with the whole group, they were slowly sipping. As they took a little in their mouths they would smack their lips, and after they had swallowed it they would blow out their breath as noisily as possible, as if to signify how cold they had been and how warm the wine felt inside them. Some of them had big pancakes that they had rolled up, and they would put a whole half of a cake in their mouths at one bite. Their coarse faces and necks were distended and red with the effort of swallowing so much at one time.

Then there was one of them who had thrust his face forward and was making a full report on his grievances to any and all who would listen. How it was that from the break of dawn until now his feet had only just come to a stop, and how his body had been wet with sweat and got dry again, and wet again and again dry, for so many times that he had lost count. Most of the rest of the patrons had been chatting with one another about nothing at all, but when they heard this one man speak, they suddenly all fell silent for a while, and then each of them, remembering the wrongs that he himself had suffered in the course of the day, they all as suddenly began telling the world in general about them, until the room sounded as if it were full of a flock of birds whose nests had been destroyed.

Even one of the fellows whose mouth was full of pancake managed to move it about until he had a clear space for his tongue, and while on the one hand he was trying to swallow the cake, on the other hand he was saying what he wanted to say. The veins on his head stood out with anger, and his words were punctuated by belches.

"You think his mother's of a puller by the month doesn't have a mean time? I'll smack the mother's of a—uh—uh! From the time I got up at two this morning until now, I haven't had time to draw myself water or to scoop up a bowl of rice. To speak only of going from the Gate Before to the Gate of the Law of Peace—uh—uh—I've pulled his mother's there and back three times! This very day I've frozen even the eye in my bottom until its cracked wide open, and all I can do is break wind."

He took a look around the circle of his audience, nodded his head emphatically, and took another big bite from his pancake.

From this the generality of the talk turned to the weather, and with it as the central topic, each person had a chance to tell of his own hardships.

From the beginning to the end, Happy Boy himself did not say a single word but he paid the closest attention to what the others were saying. Although the matter of their speech, the tones of the dialects in which they spoke, and the things they had to relate were different in each case, they all cursed the unfairness and inequality of their lot.

This kind of talk, touching as it did upon the hurt in his own heart, was absorbed into himself as completely as a few drops of rain falling on parched earth. He had no way, did not know how, to speak out his own story from the beginning to the end to let everyone hear it. The only thing he could do was to assimilate a little of the bitter flavor of life from the things the others said. They were all distressed and in trouble, and he was no exception. Coming to know himself, he was coming at the same time to have a deep feeling of sympathy for others like himself. When one of the others had reached a point of bitter grief in his tale, Happy Boy would knit his brows, and when something laughable was said he would purse his lips. In this manner he felt that he became one of the group; they were all friends together in their bitterness, and even though he said not a word it would make no difference.

In the old days he had thought they were simply all of them possessed of spiteful lips and tongues, and that because they sat around every day from morning until night talking their poverty-stricken talk, they would certainly never get rich. It seemed as if today was the first time he had realized that they were speaking for him as well as themselves, telling of the bitternesses of himself and all other rickshaw men.

Just as they had reached the most interesting point in their

140

discussion, the door suddenly opened, letting in a blast of cold air. Everyone looked up with angry eyes to see who it was so dead to the displeasure he caused in the hearts of others as to push the door open. The more impatient everyone became, the slower the man on the threshold moved, as if he purposely meant to delay his entry. Half urgently, half pleasantly, one of the waiters in the teahouse called out:

"Hurry a little, my uncle. Don't let out all of the little bit of warm air there is in here."

Before he had finished speaking, the man outside had come in. He was a rickshaw puller too. To look at him, he was over fifty and he wore a padded coat that was not short enough to be called short nor long enough to be called long, and was in as many shreds as a reed basket that has come apart. At the lapel and at both elbows the padding showed. His face looked as though it had not been washed for many days, and you could not see the color of his skin except for his ears, which were frost-bitten until they were a bright red, as red as an apple about to drop to the ground. His white hair frizzled out in tangled confusion from under a small cap; on his eyebrows and in his short beard were little drops of frozen moisture. As soon as he got in he felt for a bench and sat down, saying with great effort: "Steep me a pot of tea."

This particular teahouse had always been a gathering place for rickshaw pullers who worked by the month and under ordinary circumstances a puller like this old fellow would never have entered it.

Everybody looked at him, and they all felt that somehow the ideas they had just been expressing were by his coming cut much more deeply into their minds than they could have been by words; no one thought of saying anything more. Ordinarily there would have been sure to be one or two young fellows who had no real understanding of the affairs of the world who would have come forward with their smart talk to ridicule the kind of a teahouse patron that this one was, but tonight not a soul made a sound.

They had not yet brought the tea when the old rickshaw man's head began to sink lower and lower, until his frail body slipped forward from the bench to the floor.

The whole room was on its feet at once. "What's wrong? What's wrong?" Everyone asked it at the same time, pushing forward to try to help.

"Don't move." The manager of the tea shop, a man of experience, restrained the crowd. Going across alone to the old rickshaw man, he loosened his collar and lifted him to a sitting position, resting him against the back of a chair, and putting his hands on the old man's shoulders. "Bring some water with sugar in it—quick!"

He put his ear down to the old fellow's chest and, as if he were talking to himself, said, "His lungs sound all right."

No one of the crowd had moved but neither had they sat down again. They all stood there blinking their eyes in the smoke-filled room and staring at the huddled figure on the floor near the doorway. It was as if, without there having been any agreement between them, they were all saying exactly the same thing to themselves, each to his own heart:

"This shows what we will be! When we have come to the time when our hair is white, there will be a market rate on the life of each of us. Sooner or later there will come the day when the few coppers a fare offers us will be the price for which we will slip and stumble and drop dead between the shafts."

The water with sugar in it had just been put in the old man's mouth. He breathed out two or three times, making a sound in his throat, and lifted his right hand—it was so black it shone, as if it had been lacquered—and wiped his lips with the back of it.

"Drink some of this water," the manager said in his ear.

"Eh?" The old rickshaw puller opened his eyes. When he

realized he was sitting on the floor, he drew up his legs, thinking to get up.

"Drink this water first—there's no hurry," the manager said, relaxing his hold on the man's shoulder.

Everybody rushed over toward him.

"Ai! Ai!" The old fellow looked about him, and gripping the cup with the sugar and water in it in both hands, he tasted it a sip at a time.

Slowly he drank it all, and then glanced up again at the people around him. "Ai, I have troubled you all!" The words were spoken with an extraordinary gentleness and warmth of feeling, and to listen to them you would have felt that they could not possibly have come from the twisted old mouth beneath the dirty scraggly mustache. When he had finished speaking he tried again to get up. Three or four of those about him hurried to support him. With the suggestion of a smile, he said, speaking again in the same warm, friendly, and almost courtly way: "I can manage. It's not serious. I was both cold and hungry, and suddenly I fainted. It's not important."

For all the thickness of the dirt on his face, his smile and his manner made them all feel as if they were looking into the clear clean visage of a man who was warm-hearted, generous and good.

Everyone's heart was moved. The middle-aged fellow who had been drinking the cup of wine had finished it by now. His eyes were bloodshot and there were tears in them. "Come," he called to the waiter. "Bring me two more catties of wine." By the time the wine had arrived the old rickshaw man was seated in a chair nearby. The middle-aged fellow was a little drunk, but with perfect politeness he placed the wine before the old man.

"I'm inviting you to drink. I'm over forty myself, and I'm not going to try to deceive you: pulling a rickshaw by the month is only a makeshift with me, and it can't last anyway. Each year is a year passed: my legs can tell me that. In two or three more years I'll be just like yourself. You'll soon be sixty, won't you?"

143

"I'm less than that. Fifty-five." The old rickshaw man drank a mouthful of the wine. "The weather is cold and I couldn't find a fare. I, uh, ai! I had an empty stomach; I only had a few coppers left and I spent them all buying wine, trying to make myself a little warmer. When I came by here I couldn't bear the cold any longer, and I thought I'd come in here to get warm. The room was so hot, and I hadn't had anything to eat, so I passed out. It's not important, it's nothing at all. I've given you all a lot of trouble and I want to thank you for being so kind."

The old one's white mustache that was like dry grass, the mud on his face, his hands that were like pieces of charcoal, together with the tattered cap and the worn wadded gown, all seemed now to be marks of honor, to possess a pure light of their own. It was as if you were standing before a neglected idol in a ruined temple; however broken-down it might be, the majesty of the Law of Buddha would still shine through it, still command respect.

Everyone watched him and stood in attendance on him, as if they were afraid he would leave. From beginning to end Happy Boy had not uttered a word, but stood there stupidly. When he heard the old man say that his stomach was empty he suddenly rushed out and in a moment was running back again, as

145

quick as he could fly. In his hand he held a big cabbage leaf in which were wrapped ten rolls of meat cooked in a pastry cover. He took them directly to the old man and, placing them before him, said only: "Eat these." After he had spoken he went back to his original seat and sat with his head down, as if overcome by some extraordinary weakness.

"Ai!" The old one seemed at once happy and as if he were going to cry. He nodded his head to the group in acknowledgement. "After all, we are brothers together. When you pull a fare, how great is the strength that you sell him, and yet at the end of the ride it would be a terribly hard thing to get as much as an extra copper out of him."

As he spoke he got up and started out.

"Eat them!" Everyone in the room seemed to be speaking in the same breath.

"I'm going to call Little Horse, my grandson. He's outside watching the rickshaw."

"I'll go. You sit down." It was the middle-aged rickshaw man speaking. "You can't lose your rickshaw here, you can set your heart at rest on that. There's a police sentry box right across the street." He opened the door a little crack and called, "Little Horse, Little Horse, your grandfather is calling you. Bring the rickshaw over here and leave it."

The old one kept rubbing the meat rolls with his hand but he hadn't picked one up. The moment Little Horse walked in the door, he held one out to him. "Little Horse, my beloved boy, I'm giving this to you!"

Little Horse was not more than twelve or thirteen years old, with a very lean face. His clothes were thin and shiny with wear and his nose was red with the cold. His nostrils seemed almost stopped up with mucus, and two dirty white ribbons of it were crusted on his upper lip. Over his ears he wore a pair of tattered ear muffs. Standing beside the old man, he took the proffered meat roll in his right hand, and with his left reached out and

146

took another on his own account, while eating the first one as fast as he could.

"Ai! Slowly!" The old man had one arm around the boy, and with the other hand he picked up a meat roll for himself and without haste put it to his mouth. "I will eat two of them— that will be plenty for me, and the rest are all yours. When we've finished eating them, we will put the rickshaw up and go back home, and not pull it any more this evening. Tomorrow, if it isn't so cold, we start out a little earlier. Isn't that right, Little Horse?"

Little Horse nodded in the direction of the meat rolls—he had never taken his eyes off them—and sniffed back into his nose some of the mucus that was coming out of it. "Granddad, you eat three of them, and what's left over will all be mine. In a little while Granddad can ride in the rickshaw and I'll pull him back home!"

"That won't be necessary." The old man looked very pleased, and smiled at the group. "When we go back we'll both walk. It would be too cold to ride a rickshaw."

The old man finished eating his share, drained the last drop of wine from his cup, and sat waiting for Little Horse to eat the rest of the meat rolls. He brought out a piece of tattered cloth and wiped his mouth with it. Nodding his head to the crowd, he said:

"My son went away to be a soldier, and has never come back. His wife—"

"Don't talk about that!" Little Horse's cheeks were so full of food they looked like two peaches, and he kept on eating after interrupting his grandfather.

"It won't hurt to talk about it," the old man said. "We're none of us really strangers to each other." After that he continued in a lower voice. "My grandson takes everything very seriously, and I needn't tell you how ambitious he is. His mother left, and the two of us, granddad and grandson, earn our rice

147

with that one rickshaw. It's a worn-out cart, but our support is the fact that we own it, we don't have to worry about paying rent on it every day. Sometimes we earn more and sometimes less, and the two of us pass our days in bitter poverty. There's nothing else we can do—nothing else."

Little Horse was about through with the meat rolls. "Grand-dad," he said, "we still have to pull a while—we haven't got any money to buy coal with tomorrow morning. It's all your fault. A little while ago, when that fellow offered you twenty coppers to take him to the Rear Gate, if you'd done what I wanted to do, you'd have taken him. And you were bound you wouldn't do it. We'll see how you manage tomorrow morning when there's no coal."

"There's a way out of that. Granddad will charge five catties of coal balls."

"Do you think they'd let us have some kindling too?"

"That's right. You're a good boy. You go ahead and eat. When you've finished eating, we'll stroll along." As he spoke the old man got up and, glancing at the faces of the people about him, said, "Thank you, brothers, for all your trouble." He took Little Horse's hand in his and started out. The child still had not finished one of the rolls, and he put the whole thing into his mouth at on time.

Some of the group sat still and didn't move, others went out with the old man and his grandson. Happy Boy was the first of those—he wanted to see what the rickshaw looked like.

It was the most broken-down old rickshaw he had ever seen. The paint on the carriage was cracked and half peeled off, and the shafts were so worn you could see the grain of the wood. There was a dilapidated old lamp that rattled in the wind, and the supports holding up the faded cloth top had broken in places and been tied together with twine. Little Horse hunted out a match from one of his ear muffs and, lighting it on the sole of his shoe, held it cupped between his two thin black hands until he had got the lamp alight. The old man spit on his hands, groaned, picked up the rickshaw shafts, and said, "See you all tomorrow, my brothers."

Happy Boy stood dully by the doorway watching the two of them, the old man and the young boy, with their rickshaw. The old man was talking as he pulled the cart along, sometimes in a loud voice and sometimes in a low one. The lights along the roadway were bright and the shadows impenetrably dark. Happy Boy listened and watched, and in his heart he felt a sadness more unbearable than any he had ever known before.

It was as if Little Horse was all his past and his boyhood, and as if in the old man he could see the most that the future could hold for him. It had never been his habit lightly to let go of money, but the one thing that gave him any sense of relief now was the thought that he had bought those ten meat rolls for the old man and his grandson. He stood watching them until they were altogether out of sight before he went back again into the teahouse. The others had already begun talking and joking about other things, but he felt confused, and paid his bill and went out again, pulling his rickshaw back to the moving picture theatre to wait for Mr. Ts'ao.

The night was truly cold. The air was full of fine sand, and, up above, the winds seemed to have marshalled their forces for a rapid march across the world. Of the stars the only ones you could see very clearly were the large ones, and they shivered a little in the heavens. There was no wind along the ground, but the air was frozen everywhere. In the wheel tracks along the road the dirt had frozen and come apart in big cracks. The earth was an ashen white, as shiny as ice and just as hard.

Happy Boy stood a while outside the theatre and was already beginning to feel the cold, but he didn't want to go back to the teahouse. He wanted a chance to be very quiet and think the whole thing over for himself. It seemed as if the old man and his grandson had destroyed his greatest hope. The old man's rickshaw was one that he owned. From the very first day that Happy Boy had pulled a rickshaw he had made up his mind to buy his own. Even now it was still to satisfy this ambition that he worked so hard; he had always felt that once he had his own rickshaw he would have everything. Heng! Just look at that old man!

Was it not also because of this hope that he might some day buy his own rickshaw that he was unwilling to ask for Tiger Girl? Had he not hoped to get his own rickshaw, to save money, and afterwards to take to himself some clean innocent little village girl as his wife? Heng! Look at Little Horse! How could he be sure that his own son would not some day be in the same situation?

Thinking this way, there no longer seemed to be any particular reason why he should resist Tiger Girl's demands. In any case, whatever happened, he could not himself escape the circle that was closing in on him. What difference did it make what kind of wife he married? And, moreover, she might bring him two or three rickshaws. Why not make the most of what little he could get out of her? When you saw through your own self, there was no more need of despising someone else. Tiger Girl was just Tiger Girl, and there was no need to say any more about it.

The movie was over, and he hurried to screw the water can back on the carbide light and to get the lamp itself lit. He took off his gown, and even the little fur jacket underneath it, leaving only a short waist-coat against the cold. He wanted to run as fast as he could, to run until he had forgotten everything, and if he fell and killed himself that wouldn't matter either.

150

11

WHENEVER he thought of the old man and Little
Horse, Happy Boy wanted to take all his hopes and put
them away from him and look to each day for the most pleasure
it could give him, counting only the day itself and never looking to the morrow. Why should he go about the whole day long
gritting his teeth, unable to forgive himself for failing to do
more than he was able? The poor man's destiny, he seemed at
last to understand, was like the kernel of an almond: it was
sharp at both ends. If you could get through your childhood
without starving to death, you had the luck of one in ten thousand, but it was when you were an old man that avoiding starva-
tion got really difficult. It was only during that brief middle
span between childhood and the onset of age, when the years
were light on your shoulders and your strength was full, and you
feared neither the long hunger that sought only for food, nor
the weariness of bodily toil, that you bore yourself with the
pride of a human being. To be in that period of your life when
you should be happy and carefree and gay and in good health
and spirits, and still to be afraid to take advantage of it, was to
be a sovereign fool indeed. This was the village where the
hostel was; you passed the village by and you passed the hostel
too; on the weary road beyond there would be no more of them.
When he thought like this about it all, even the affair of Tiger
Girl didn't seem worth worrying about.

When he caught sight of his porcelain gourd his opinions
would swing back around again. No, he could not simply follow
his own pleasure; he lacked now only a few tens of dollars of

having enough to buy himself a rickshaw. He could not now throw away so completely the results of all his previous labors; at the very least, he could not take the little bit of savings that he had accumulated in the porcelain gourd and blindly yield it up. So difficult as it had been to save! No, he would still have to walk the road of rectitude, that was certain. But Tiger Girl? He still had no plan, still had that hateful twenty-seventh to worry about.

When his harassment had reached the point where the whole thing seemed utterly hopeless, he would take his porcelain gourd in his arms and, holding it tightly to him, talk to it in a plaintive whisper. "They can have it whatever way they want it but, whatever happens, this little bit of money belongs to me! Nobody can take it away from me. As long as he has this money, Happy Boy is not afraid. If they cause me too much anxiety, I can lift my feet and run away. When you have money you can move around."

The streets were becoming more and more bustling and busy; the roadways were covered with displays of candied melons used in the sacrifices to the God of the Kitchen Stove, and wherever you walked you could hear the sound of the hawkers' cry—"Hard sugar candy, hard sugar candy!" Originally Happy Boy had looked forward to the coming of the New Year festival, but now he couldn't get up any enthusiasm for it at all. The more confused and excited the streets became, the tighter became his heart. That day so much to be feared, the twenty-seventh, was before his eyes. His eyes became downcast as if not to see it, and even the scar on his face became darker.

He had to be extra careful pulling his master's rickshaw, with the streets in such confusion and the ground underfoot so slippery. The matter that occupied his heart and the desire to be careful were like two spirits engaged in mortal combat, and he felt as if his own energy were not enough to supply them both. When he thought of one of them, he forgot the other, and time after time, when something brought him up short with a start, his whole body would break out in a prickly itch, like a child coming out with heat rash in the summer time.

On the afternoon of the day of the offerings to the God of the Kitchen Stove there was a softly shifting east wind blowing that brought with it a sky full of black clouds. The weather had suddenly got warmer. When it was close to the time to hang the lanterns, the wind fell even lower and scattered snowflakes began dropping from the heavens. The sellers of sugared melons got all excited and anxious. Warm weather, and add to that these snowflakes! With one motion they all began sprinkling white sand over their candy, for fear it would get soft and stick together. Not many snowflakes fell; soon they changed to small fine particles of snow that came down with a swishing noise and brushed the ground to whiteness.

After seven o'clock they began, in the stores and houses, to make their offerings to the God of the Kitchen Stove, and in the midst of the glowing of incense sticks and the light and shadow of exploding firecrackers, the soft snow fell in unremitting silence and mystery, affording a somber and timeless background to this transient celebration.

The people in the streets all seemed full of a frightened urgency. Those afoot and those in rickshaws or sedan chairs or automobiles were hurrying to get back home in time to make their offerings to the god, but the ground was so wet and slippery they dared not go too rapidly. The small tradesmen selling candies were in great anxiety to get off their hands goods which had been prepared for this festival and would be worthless tomorrow. Without even stopping to catch their breath, they kept calling their wares. But, instead of making you nervous, the sound of their voices was somehow very soothing.

It was 9 o'clock, and Happy Boy was pulling Mr. Ts'ao back from the West Gate to his house. As they passed through the bustling street markets along near the Lone West Honorific

Arch and were headed east along the Street of Everlasting Peace, the people and horses both became gradually fewer. Over the smooth surface of the asphalt road was spread a thin covering of snow that dazzled the eyes a little in the reflected light of the street lamps. Every once in a while an automobile would pass, its bright headlights shooting their beams of light far out into the night through which it moved; in these rays of light the little grains of snow would turn yellowish, like a myriad grains of golden sand.

The stretch of road just before you get to the New China Gate is, to begin with, very broad, and with the covering of snow over it, it served more than ever to give you a feeling of breadth and distance of view and to make your spirits lively and free. And everything seemed more grave and dignified. The Arch of Everlasting Peace, the structure above the New China Gate, the red walls around the Southern Sea, all wore white mourning caps, contrasting with the colors of the red cassia trees and the dull red of the walls, shaded by the night in the light of the street lamps, under whose quiet and tranquil glow the stateliness of the old capital lay revealed.

This time and this place made you feel that Peking was a city in which no one lived, as if it were one wide concourse of lustrous and brilliant palaces, a heaven of soft green jade, with nothing else besides save the old fir trees, receiving in utter silence their burden of the falling snow. Happy Boy had no time to waste looking at this beautiful scenery; when he saw the Jade Road before him he thought only of racing down it to get home in one long stride; that straight, white, dispassionate highway made him feel that the eye of his heart could see straight down it right to the doorway of his home.

But he could not run fast. Although the snow was not thick on the ground, and the separate little flakes were very small, still the snow itself was heavy and weighted, and, because it held your feet and confused your eyes, you could not move

154

through it with fleet strides. The particles that fell on Happy Boy did not melt easily, and before long his shoulders and clothes had a layer of snow on them too. Although this didn't count for much, still the dampness oozed into his inner clothing and irritated him.

Along this run there were not many shops, but from a distance the sound of the firing of firecrackers still continued unbroken and every once in a while the darkness of the sky would be cut by the light of a twice-exploding rocket or by one of those crackers called the "Five Devils Resisting Judgment." When the flying sparks of the rocket had spread across the sky and disappeared, the heavens would seem even darker than before, so dark that it made you afraid. Listening to the sounds of exploding firecrackers and watching the faint fire of the rockets fade against the blackness of the night, Happy Boy wanted to get back home right away. But he did not dare stretch his legs and really run. Aggravating!

A thing that made him feel even more uneasy was that from the western part of the city he had felt that a bicycle was following along back of him. When he reached the Western Street of Everlasting Peace, where the road was quieter, he felt more definitely than ever that there was someone behind him, following him. The wheels of the bicycle crunched the thin snow and, although the sound was not loud, still it was perceptible. Happy Boy, like every other rickshaw puller, hated bicycles more than anything else. An automobile was hateful enough, but it made a loud noise and you could get out of its way while it was still a long way off. A bicycle wriggled its way through the first open crack, swaying first to one side and then to the other, and going east at one moment and west the next. Your eyes got out of focus from dizziness just trying to watch it.

And on no account must you get into trouble with the rider of a bicycle; if there was trouble, it was always the rickshaw puller's fault. According to the calculations in a policeman's

155

heart, a rickshaw man would be easier to deal with than the rider of a bicycle, no matter what the circumstances of the case might be. He would therefore go first about setting out all the wrongs the rickshaw man had committed. Several times tonight Happy Boy had wanted very badly to stop his rickshaw suddenly and throw that little bastard on the bicycle into a tailspin, but he didn't dare. A rickshaw man had everywhere to bear in silence the insults and mistreatment of others. So that every time he stopped to stamp his feet to clear the soles of his shoes, he had to call out, "Stopping."

At the front gate of the Southern Sea, where the street is so broad, the bicycle still clung closely behind him, and Happy Boy began to feel the fire rising inside him. He purposely stopped his rickshaw and started brushing the snow off his shoulders. When he came up short, the bicycle brushed by, close to the rickshaw, and the rider even turned his head to look. Happy Boy purposely dawdled, waiting until the bicycle had gone a long way ahead before picking up the shafts of his rickshaw. As he did so he spit on the ground. "Disgusting!"

Mr. Ts'ao's humanitarianism made him unwilling to use the cloth curtain that spreads across the front of the rickshaw after the passenger is seated in it and serves to protect him from the wind. He would never even let Happy Boy put up the rickshaw top unless it was raining very hard, because both the windbreak and the top, when they were used, made the rickshaw just that much harder to pull, and he wanted to save his rickshaw man the added effort. He had seen no reason why the rickshaw top should be put up on account of this little bit of snow, and besides he coveted the pleasure of watching a snow scene at night.

He, too, had paid heed to the bicycle and when Happy Boy spoke he said in a low voice: "If he keeps on following us, don't stop at our door when you get to the house; just pass right by and go on to Mr. Tso's house, near the Gate of the Imperial Transformation. Don't get flustered!"

156

Happy Boy was already a little flustered. He had only known that he disliked bicycles, but he had never understood before that they were really to be feared. If Mr. Ts'ao didn't even dare go to his own home, the little stinkpot on this particular bicycle must have a long history. Happy Boy hadn't run more than a few tens of paces when they caught up with the fellow again; he had been deliberately waiting for them, and he didn't start until Happy Boy had passed him.

In going by, Happy Boy took a look at him and in a glance understood—the man was a member of the secret police. He had frequently met members of the corps in the teahouses, and although he had never spoken with one of them, he knew the expression of their faces, their manner, and their style of dress. He had seen the style often enough to be well acquainted with it—a dark blue outer gown and a felt hat, the brim of the hat always pulled down very low over the face.

When they reached the mouth of Long South Street, Happy Boy's feet found added strength. There was nothing but the cold light of the street lamps and at his back a detective chasing him! Happy Boy had never had an experience like this before, and sweat broke out all over him. At the Public Gardens he looked around; the man was still following them.

When they reached the entrance way to the door of their own home, he did not stop; it was hard to pass it by, but Mr. Ts'ao made not a sound and the only thing for him to do was to keep on going north. In one breath he ran to the northern mouth of the street, but the bicycle was still with them. He went into the opening of a small lane; it followed them. When he came out the other end of the lane, it still followed them. To reach the Gate of the Imperial Transformation, it was in fact not necessary to have entered the lane. It was not until he reached the northern mouth of it that he realized this, and when he had to admit to himself that he was a little befuddled it made him angrier than ever.

When he had reached a point in back of the Mountain of the Beautiful Vista, the bicycle turned north toward the Black Gate. Happy Boy wiped the sweat off his forehead with the back of his hand. The fall of snow had lessened a little, and in the midst of the fine particles were occasional large flakes. Happy Boy took a great delight in snowflakes that floated and danced between the heavens and the earth with a real abandon, a fine spirit of bravado. They weren't like those petty damp little snow particles that gave you nothing but a feeling of irritation.

He turned his head and asked, "Where shall we go, Master?"

"Still to the Tsos' home. If anyone asks you any questions about me, say you don't know me."

"All right." In the middle of Happy Boy's heart an aperture opened, but he could not very well question his master for the details.

When they reached the Tso house, Mr. Ts'ao told Happy Boy to pull the rickshaw right in through the gate and close it behind them at once. Mr. Ts'ao was still very calm but the color of his face was not very good to look at. When he had finished instructing Happy Boy he went into the house.

Just as Happy Boy had got his rickshaw pushed back into the gate-room and properly placed there, Mr. Ts'ao came out again, this time with Mr. Tso. Happy Boy recognized Mr. Tso, and knew that he was a good friend of the household.

"Happy Boy"—Mr. Ts'ao's lips were moving very rapidly— "you take a car and go back to the house. Tell the mistress that I am here. Tell them to come here, too; to come by car, to call another car. You mustn't have the car in which you go wait for you. Do you understand? Fine! Tell the mistress to bring the things that she'll need, together with those scroll paintings in the library. You hear clearly what I'm saying? In a moment I'll telephone Mrs. Ts'ao, but I'm telling you too for fear she might get excited and forget what I tell her. If she does, you can remind her."

158

"How about my going?" Mr. Tso asked.

"It isn't necessary. It's not certain that that fellow just now was a detective. It's only that I have that other business in my heart, and I can't afford not to be prepared. Do you mind calling a car for me?"

Mr. Tso went to call a car, and Mr. Ts'ao repeated his instructions to Happy Boy. "When the car comes, I'll pay the driver. You tell the mistress to get her things together quickly. None of the rest is important; only by all means bring the baby's things and the scrolls in the library, the scroll paintings! When the mistress has everything ready, tell Kao Ma to telephone for a car and they can come over here. Do you understand all that? After they have gone, you lock the big gate and move into the library to sleep. There's a telephone there. Can you use a telephone?"

"I can't make a call out to anybody but I can take a call that comes in." As a matter of fact, Happy Boy didn't like very much even taking incoming calls but he didn't want to get Mr. Ts'ao excited, so the best thing was to say what he had.

"That's good enough." Mr. Ts'ao went on, still speaking very rapidly: "If by any chance anything happens, if there's any movement or commotion, you mustn't open the gate. With all of us gone, and only you left, they'd never let go of you. If things take a bad turn, you put out the lights, go through the inner courtyard, and climb over the wall into the Wang family compound. You know the Wang family's servants, don't you? Right! Hide a while in the Wang household before you go. You don't need to try to take care of my belongings or of your own things. You just jump over the wall and go, to save their grabbing you. If you lose anything, I'll make it good to you later on. Right now you take this five-dollar bill.

"All right, I'll go now and telephone the mistress, and in a little while when you get there you say it all to her too. You needn't say anything about anyone being grabbed. That fellow on the bicycle a little while ago might be a detective and he might not. And you mustn't get flustered yourself, either."

The car came and Happy Boy climbed into it, his head benumbed. The snow kept falling, neither heavy nor light. You couldn't see very clearly anything on the outside. He sat with his back absolutely stiff and straight, his head almost touching the top of the car. He wanted to think the whole thing over, but his eye was caught by the red arrow on the top of the radiator cap at the front of the car and he couldn't get his mind on anything else. It was so fresh and sprightly and lovable! In front of the driver there was a small wiper on the outside of the glass that swished back and forth all on its own account, sweeping clean the frost and moisture from the semicircle on the windshield over which it moved. It was a cute little thing, too. Just as he was beginning to tire of watching it, the car drew up at the door of the house. Without the slightest enthusiasm in his heart he got out.

Just as he was about to press the bell at the gate, a man appeared from nowhere, as if he had wriggled out of the very wall, and seized Happy Boy's wrist. At first Happy Boy thought of jerking his hand away, but he didn't move; he had already recognized the man: it was the detective who had ridden the bicycle.

"Happy Boy, you don't remember me?" The detective smiled as he let go of his victim's wrist.

Happy Boy swallowed a mouthful of air, and did not know what it was best to say.

"You don't remember when we took you to the Western Hills? I'm that Lieutenant Sun, do you recollect?"

"Ah, Lieutenant Sun!" Happy Boy couldn't recall. At the time, when he was being dragged out into the mountains, he couldn't be bothered with who was a lieutenant and who was a captain.

"You don't remember me, but I remember you. That scar on

your face is a good identification mark. A little while ago, when I was following you around for half a day, at first I didn't dare be sure about it myself, and I looked at you from the right and then from the left, but there's no mistaking that scar."

"Do you have some business with me?" Again Happy Boy wanted to press the doorbell.

"Naturally I have business with you. What's more, it's very important business. What do you say to our going in and talking about it?" Lieutenant Sun—now an operative in the secret police—reached out and pressed the bell.

"I'm busy." Happy Boy's forehead was suddenly dripping with sweat. His heart had all at once been flooded with hate, and at the same time it cried to him, "Can't you get rid of the fellow somehow? How can you be inviting him right into the house?"

"There's no reason to worry. I'm here to do you a favor." A cunning and slippery suggestion of a smile showed on the detective's face. Kao Ma had no sooner got the door open than he thrust his foot through and forced his way into the compound.

"Thank you for your trouble, thank you for your trouble!" He did not give Happy Boy a chance even to exchange a sentence with Kao Ma but pulled him along into the courtyard. Pointing to the room next to the gate, he asked, "Do you live in here?" When they got into the room he looked around him. "This little place is really clean and tidy! Your job's not a bad one."

"Have you business with me? I'm in a hurry." Happy Boy couldn't listen to any more of this piffle.

"Didn't I tell you I've got important business?" Detective Sun was still smiling, but the spirit behind his words was extraor-

161

dinarily sharp and hard. "I'll make it crisp enough for you: I tell you this fellow named Ts'ao is a member of a party that's opposed to the government; as soon as he's caught he'll be shot, and he's got no chance of escaping. We've at least a one-sided acquaintanceship, however you figure it: you were my servant in the army barracks. What's more, we're both people of the street. So I took on myself the very great responsibility of coming here to bring you word of this. If you're one step too late in running away, when we come back it'll be to clean out a burrow from which all escape will be blocked and nobody will slip through. Those of us who are selling our strength to get food to eat, why should we suffer to help our masters win a crooked case at law? Am I right or not?"

"I'd never be able to look them in the face again." Happy Boy was still thinking of the message which Mr. Ts'ao had entrusted to him.

"Who would you be unable to face?" The corners of Detective Sun's lips bore a faint smile, but the corners of his eyes were drawn out thin and hard. "It's a calamity that they brought on themselves. Why should you be unable to face them? They risked doing it; the responsibility for it is theirs. If we had to share their punishment, that would really be an injustice. We don't need to speak of anything else: suppose you're shut up for only three months? Accustomed as you are to living like a wild bird, and doing what you please, you suddenly have to sit for three months in a black room—you think you could stand it?

"Another thing. If they go to prison, they've got money to spend in bribes. They won't suffer. You, my good brother, you won't have a single hard dollar in your hand, and the boys will be sure to tie you over the urine bucket. That's only a small matter. With any luck, the Ts'aos will spend money and use influence and so get off with a few years' imprisonment; but you—you won't have any means of taking care of the officials, and if they don't sink your back ten feet down it'll be a wonder.

"You and me, now, we don't do anybody any harm and we try not to give anybody any cause for offense, and we end up eating a few of the hard black almonds on the execution ground at Heaven's Bridge. Would that not be an everlasting wrong? You understand these things, and nobody who does would take a loss when he can see clearly that it would be a loss. You wouldn't be able to face them. Yo, ho! I'll tell you, my fine young brother, under the whole heavens there has never been a time when anybody felt that they couldn't look us—those of us who live in bitter toil—in the face."

Happy Boy was frightened. When he thought of the sufferings he had endured when the soldiers dragged him off to the mountains, he could imagine how prison life would taste. "Then I have to leave, and not mind what happens to them?"

"You mind what happens to them, and who minds what happens to you?"

Happy Boy had nothing to say in reply. He sat staring into space for a while, and even his conscience bowed its head. "All right, I'll go!"

"You'll just walk off like that?"

Again Happy Boy was thrown back into confusion.

"Happy Boy, my good partner! You are too stupid! Do you think that, seeing as how I'm a detective, I'd be willing to let you go?"

"Then—" Happy Boy was so scared and nervous he didn't know what to do.

"Don't pretend to be a fool!" Detective Sun's eyes nailed Happy Boy to the wall. "You probably have saved up some money. Bring it out and buy your life. I don't earn as much in a month as you do, and I have to eat and wear clothes and support my family, and all I have to depend on is the little money I can scrape together here and there outside of my regular wage. I'm talking to you as a friend who knows my very heart. You think it over. Could I just open my hand and let you go like that? Friendship is friendship: if I weren't a friend of yours would I have come here to urge you to leave? But business is business, and if I don't make a little something out of it, I suppose I should tell my family to drink the northwest wind? People who know their way in the world outside their doorways don't need to waste words—isn't it true?"

"How much will it take?" Happy Boy sat down on his bed.

"Bring out whatever you've got—there's no fixed price."

"I'll wait to be put in prison!"

"Remember that it's you that's saying that. And you won't regret it afterwards?" Detective Sun put his hand significantly under his gown. "Look here, Happy Boy. I could take you right now. If you resisted arrest, I'd shoot you. You add that into your calculations."

Happy Boy sat choking with his indignation for a long time before he spoke. "You've got time to squeeze me, why don't you squeeze Mr. Ts'ao?"

"He's the principal offender. When I arrest him I get a small reward, and if I let him slip I'd be committing a fault. You, you, my stupid younger brother, to let you go would be like letting an air-stench and to shoot you would amount to no more than stepping on a stinkbug. Bring out the money, and get along. Or else don't bring it out, and I'll see you on Heaven's Bridge. Don't dawdle, come clean. A fellow as big as you are! And besides, I can't swallow all of this little bit of money myself. My colleagues all have to get their little patch of it, and there's no telling how many coppers will be left as my share. I'd never sell a life as cheap as this if there were any other way out. How much money have you got?"

Happy Boy stood up, his brain bursting and his fists clenched.

"I warn you," said the detective, "don't raise a hand or there won't be any you. There's a whole gang of men outside. Quick, get the money. I'm thinking of your face. Don't get mixed up as

164

to what's good and what's bad for you." Detective Sun's eyes had a glint in them that was ugly to see.

"When have I ever done anybody any harm?" Happy Boy's voice was a sob, and when he had spoken he sat back down on the edge of the bed.

"You haven't done anything to anybody, but you just happened to hit the exact spot. The only time a human being is really well-off is when he's still in his mother's womb. We're both at the bottom of the scale, and there's no use talking." Detective Sun shook his head from side to side as if he were swept by a feeling of infinite melancholy. "All right, let it go at that. I'm doing you a wrong. But don't keep on dawdling."

Happy Boy thought a while longer, but he could think of no plan. With shaking hands he brought his porcelain gourd out from under his bedclothes.

"Let me look at it." Detective Sun smiled, and no sooner did he have it in his hands than he threw it against the wall, smashing it to bits.

Happy Boy saw the coins scatter over the floor, and his heart split open.

"Is there only this little bit?"

Happy Boy made no sound, but only shivered.

"We'll let it go at that. I'm no one to kill a man in a hurry. A friend's a friend. But you must know, buying a life with this pittance of money, you've got a real bargain."

Happy Boy still made no sound but he was shivering and he started to crawl under his covers.

"Don't touch that!"

165

"As cold as it is . . ." Happy Boy glared at him with fire flaming out of his eyes.

"When I tell you not to touch your bedding, you don't touch it. Squirm away! Get going!"

Happy Boy swallowed a mouthful of anger, bit his lips, pushed open the door, and walked out.

The soft carpet on the ground was already more than an inch thick, and Happy Boy walked through it with his head sunk low. Everywhere there was whiteness and purity, except only for the big black footprints that he left behind him in the snow.

12

HAPPY BOY wanted to find a place to sit down and go over the whole story in his mind, to get the things that had happened all straightened out, so at least he would know what came first and what came next and what came after that. And what if he did weep like a child before his thinking was done? It would be good for him to know what it meant to weep. Affairs had moved too quickly and changed too sharply for him; already his brain was unable to catch up with the events around him. But there was no place provided for him to sit down in. Snow was everywhere. The small teahouses had already put up the boards that shuttered their shop-fronts and had closed their doors. Even if he had found one of them open, he would not have wanted to go into it. He wanted to find a quiet secluded spot because he knew that the tears in which the balls of his eyes were floating might pour out at any moment.

Since he had no place to sit down, the next best thing was to walk slowly on. But where should he go? This silver white world had no place for him to even sit down in, nor was there in its cold infinity any place for him to go. In this limitless flat stretch of whiteness only the hungry little birds with empty stomachs and a lonely rickshaw man for whom there was no escape understood why it was that the wind sighed and moaned.

Where to go? This was the immediate problem, and until it was settled there was no need of thinking of anything else. Should he go to one of the small inns? That wouldn't do. Considering how relatively clean and new the suit of clothing he wore was, he would be sure to lose some of it in the middle of the night. And that was not to mention how much he feared the lice with which such a place would swarm. Should he go to a larger inn? He couldn't afford it. In his hands he had only one five-dollar bill; it was the sum total of all his wealth and assets. Should he go to a bathhouse? They put up their shutters at midnight, and you couldn't stay overnight in them. There was no place he could go.

The clearer that became to him, the more pinched and straitened and harassed he felt. He had run his muddy course within the walls of Peking for so many years, and all he had got out of it was the clothing he wore and a five-dollar bill! Even his bedding was muddled away. From this he thought of tomorrow. What should he do tomorrow? Should he pull a rickshaw? Go again and pull a rickshaw! Heng! The end result of his rickshaw-pulling had been that he could find nowhere to go; all that it had got him was the money he had managed to save, and now that had been stolen from him.

Could he go into a small business? He had only five dollars as capital, and he would have to begin by buying even the flat carrying-pole from each end of which the hawker suspends his baskets bearing the wares he sells. Moreover, could he be sure that such a business would earn him a mouthful of grain to chew on? Starting from level ground and with no backing, a rickshaw puller could earn thirty or forty cents. To be a small business man you had to have capital, and you had, besides, no assurance that you could hope to earn enough to pay for your three meals a day. To wait until you had fed all your capital into such a project and then go back to pulling a rickshaw, wouldn't that be the same thing as taking your pants down when you only meant to fart? Wouldn't that be just losing five dollars to no purpose at all? He couldn't lightly let go of a single ten-cent piece or even one penny of this five dollars; this piece of paper was the last hope he had.

Could he get a job as a servant? It wasn't in his line. When it came to waiting on people, he just couldn't do it. He couldn't wash clothes and he didn't know how to cook. There was nothing workable, nothing that he knew how to do. He was just a big, stupid, black, coarse, useless thing!

Without being aware of it, or knowing by what route he had come, he had reached the Central Sea. From the bridge there was nothing visible but a vast emptiness on either side and, as far away as the eye could see, nothing but falling flakes of snow. It was not until then that he seemed to become aware of the fact that the snow had not abated. He felt the top of his head; the little woolen cap was already soaked with wetness. There wasn't anyone but himself on the bridge, and even the policeman on the beat had ducked away to no one knew where. The few street lights blinked continuously as the fresh flakes fell on the hot bulbs and then melted away, and new flakes fell in their place. Happy Boy looked at the snow on all sides of him, and his heart became vast and vague and empty.

He stood on the bridge a long time. The universe around him was already dead; no sound issued from its death, and nowhere was there even the slightest movement. The gray-white snowflakes had found their time and their opportunity, and in a flustered confusion that was yet light and quick they tumbled continually down, seeking to bury the earth deep in a white grave before anyone knew that it had perished.

Through this quiet solitude Happy Boy heard the frail voice that calls one to the way of virtue. First he must not consider himself; he had still to go back to see how the Ts'ao family was. Only Mrs. Ts'ao and Kao Ma would be left there, and without a man around! Could anyone say that the last five dollars that he possessed had not been given him by Mr. Ts'ao? He did not dare think any further about it, but picked up his feet and started back, walking very fast.

Outside the door there were some footprints, and in the road were two freshly made auto tracks. Could it be possible that Mistress Ts'ao had already gone? Why hadn't that fellow Sun nabbed her?

At first he didn't dare walk across the pavement to push open the courtyard door, for fear he would again be seized. He looked to the right and the left—there was nobody. His heart began leaping up. He would try it and see what happened. Anyway he had no home to go to, and if somebody arrested him they'd just have to arrest him. Lightly he pushed against the door; it swung open. He stepped across the threshold and, keeping close to the wall of the outer courtyard, took a few cautious steps forward. The light in his own room was still burning. His own room! He felt like sobbing out loud. Stooping low, he crept toward the window and stood outside it, listening for any sounds within. There was a coughing noise; he knew from the tone of it that it was Kao Ma. He pulled open the door.

"Who is it? Ai, it's you! You frightened me to death!" Kao Ma pressed her heart, trying to compose herself, and sat down on her bed. "Happy Boy, what happened to you?"

Happy Boy could not get out a reply to her question. He could only feel how many years it seemed since he had last seen her. His heart was stopped up with fever.

"What kind of a thing is this?" Kao Ma's voice seemed ready

to break and become a sob as she went on. "Before you came back, the master had already telephoned to tell us to go to the Tso house. He said, too, that you would be here right away. You did come—wasn't it myself that opened the door to let you in? As soon as I took one look and saw that you were with a stranger, I didn't say a word but went back into the mistress's room as quick as I could to help her get her things packed. From first to last you didn't come in, but left us there in the darkness and with the fires out to crawl about blindly trying to get everything together.

"The little master was already sleeping fragrantly, and we had to lift him up out of his warm bedclothes and wrap him up. Then we had to go into the library and take down the paintings. From first to last you didn't show your face. What were you doing, I ask you? When we'd got things packed in any old way, just thrown together somehow, I came out to look for you. Well, there wasn't the shadow of you anywhere. The mistress was so angry—it was half due to her being so excited—that she trembled. The only thing I could do was to call a car. But we couldn't just act out 'The Plan of the Empty City' like it says in 'The Three Kingdoms'; we couldn't all of us just leave the house empty and open to anybody who wanted to come in. So I stuck out the hard bridge of my nose at the mistress and said to her: 'The mistress may go on, I'll stay here and watch the house. When Happy Boy comes back, I'll come as fast as I can to the Tso house. If he doesn't come back, I'll just accept my fate.' How do you explain it? What happened to you? Speak out!"

Happy Boy had nothing to say.

"Say something! Does that count as settling the matter, just sitting there dumb? What really did happen?"

"You go ahead and leave!" It had been terribly hard for Happy Boy to find this one phrase that he could say.

"Will you watch the house?" Kao Ma's anger had subsided a little.

170

"When you see the master, you tell him that the detective arrested me, but—but, well, he didn't arrest me."

"What kind of talk is that?" Kao Ma was so angry she looked as if she wanted to laugh.

"You listen." Happy Boy was angry now himself. "You tell the master to get away as quickly as he can. The detective said he was going to be sure to arrest him. Even the Tso family house isn't a safe place for him to be. Escape as quickly as possible! You go on. I'll jump over the wall into the Wang family compound and sleep a night there. I'll go hunting for a job. The master will have to forgive me."

"The more you say the more muddled I become." Kao Ma sighed. "All right, I'll go. The little master might have caught cold, and I'll go as quickly as I can to see how he is. When I see the master, I'll say that Happy Boy says he should escape as quickly as he can. Tonight Happy Boy will lock the big front gate and jump over the wall into the Wang compound to sleep for the night; tomorrow he'll go out to look for other work. Is that what you want me to say?"

With ten thousand parts of mortification Happy Boy slowly nodded his head.

After Kao Ma had left, Happy Boy locked the gate and went back into his room. The broken pieces of the porcelain gourd were scattered on the floor. He picked up a piece of it and looked at it, and then dropped it back on the floor. The covers on his bed had not been moved. It was strange. After all, what kind of a business was it? Could it possibly be that Detective Sun was not a real detective at all? It wasn't possible! If Mr. Ts'ao had not seen that there was danger, why should he have abandoned his house and run away? Happy Boy did not understand! He did not understand! He did not understand! Unconsciously he sat down on the edge of his bed, and then suddenly again, as if he had heard something that startled him, he jumped up. He couldn't stay here long. Suppose that fellow Sun should come back. In his heart the whole thing turned round and round: to leave like this was a fault which would make it hard for him to face Mr. Ts'ao again, but with Kao Ma taking the message back to him to urge him to escape quickly, it was after all a thing that he could get over in his heart; it did not make the road impassable for his conscience.

Speaking from the standpoint of conscience, Happy Boy had never deliberately cheated anybody or taken a mean advantage of anyone, but he himself had suffered a grievance. He had lost his own money, and now he had no means of guarding the money and possessions of Mr. Ts'ao. He went on talking to himself in this vein, muttering away, while he was picking up and making ready his bedding.

Lifting the roll of it up onto his shoulder, he put out the light and made his way out through the back courtyard. Then he put his burden down for a moment, gripped the top of the wall and pulled himself up to look over it.

In a low voice he called: "Old Ch'eng! Old Ch'eng!" Old Ch'eng was the rickshaw man in the Wang household.

No one answered, and Happy Boy made up his mind. He would jump over the wall and see what happened. First he put his bedding over, dropping it down noiselessly in the snow. His heart beat fast. Quickly he crawled over the top of the wall and leapt down on the other side. He picked up his bedding and walking very lightly went to find Old Ch'eng. He knew the place where Old Ch'eng stayed. The whole household seemed to be asleep, and there wasn't a sound throughout the courtyard. Suddenly it came to Happy Boy that being a thief wouldn't be a very difficult job after all. He plucked up his courage, and stopped tiptoeing. The snow was firm under his feet and made a little crunching sound as he walked over it. He found Old Ch'eng's room and stood outside of it, coughing a little to awaken him.

Old Ch'eng had evidently just gone to bed. "Who is it?"

"It's me, Happy Boy. Open the door." Happy Boy spoke very naturally, in a warm friendly manner. It was as if, in hearing Old Ch'eng's voice, he heard the voice of a comrade who would comfort him.

Old Ch'eng turned on the light, put a tattered old fur-lined gown over his shoulders and opened the door.

"What's this? Happy Boy! At the third watch, in the middle of the night!"

Happy Boy went in, put his bedding roll on the floor, and took the opportunity to sit down on it, all without saying a word.

Old Ch'eng was thirty years old or more, and the flesh of his body was all covered with pimples, so hard that each one seemed to stand straight out. In ordinary times Happy Boy had no special friendship for him, beyond the fact that when they saw each other they spoke. Sometimes Mrs. Wang would go out shopping with Mrs. Ts'ao, and the two rickshaw boys would go off somewhere and have a cup of tea together and rest a while. Happy Boy did not altogether respect Old Ch'eng. Old Ch'eng could run very fast, but in a very flustered way, as if it took a lot of energy, and moreover he never looked as if he had a really firm grip on the rickshaw shafts. In spite of the fact that as a person Old Ch'eng was a very fine fellow, Happy Boy could never altogether forgive him for this fault, and therefore could never give him his complete respect.

But tonight Happy Boy felt that Old Ch'eng was altogether lovable. Sitting there, Happy Boy could not say anything, but his heart was grateful and filled with warmth. Just a little while ago he had been standing on the bridge over the Central Sea; now he was in a warm room with a familiar person. The scene had shifted with such pressing speed that it had made his mind become suddenly empty and his head hot, as if with fever.

Old Ch'eng had crawled back under his warm covers, and pointing to the tattered fur-lined gown that he had shed again, he said, "Have a smoke, Happy Boy. There are cigarettes in the pocket—'County Villainies.'" From the time that "County Villa" cigarettes had come into existence they had been called "County Villainies" by the rickshaw men, perhaps because of the two similar sounds. They had known more of villainy than of villas.

As a rule Happy Boy did not smoke, but this time he felt as if he could not refuse. Taking a cigarette, he suspended it from between his lips.

"What's happened?" Old Ch'eng asked. "Did you quit your job?"

"No." Happy Boy was still sitting on his bedding roll. "There's been trouble. The whole Ts'ao family have fled, and I don't dare try to watch the house all alone."

"What kind of trouble?" Old Ch'eng sat up in bed.

"I can't tell you clearly. Anyway, it's not just some little thing —it's a plenty big trouble. Even Kao Ma has gone with them."

"All four doors wide open, and nobody caring what happens to the place?"

"I locked the big front gate of the compound."

"Heng!" Old Ch'eng reflected for what seemed half a day, and then asked: "Wouldn't it be a good thing if I said something about it to Mr. Wang?" While he was speaking Old Ch'eng got up and started to wrap his aged fur-lined gown around him again.

"Let's talk about that tomorrow. The whole thing simply can't be clearly explained tonight!" Happy Boy was afraid Mr. Wang would question him closely about it while it was still so confused in his own mind that he'd never be able to get the story straight.

He could not have known then how many months it would be, or how much else would befall him, before the truth of this incident was told him, but one thing was already obvious: the master and mistress and the little master and even Kao Ma had all got away, leaving no one but himself. Everybody had a plan; there was a crack through which they all could crawl—all except Happy Boy. He couldn't escape, because he was only the rickshaw puller. A rickshaw boy swallows a very coarse grain, and what he spits up is blood. He sells the greatest strength and gets the smallest recompense. He stands in the lowest position among men and awaits the blows of all his fellows, of all their laws, and of every bitter circumstance.

When he had finished smoking the cigarette, Happy Boy had still not figured out the principle of the thing, the right and wrong of it. He was like a chicken that the cook holds in his hand: the only thing he knows is that he will be lucky to draw his next breath, and has no other thought. He wanted very much to talk it over with Old Ch'eng, but there was nothing he could say. His words would not be enough to express his thoughts and anxieties. He had experienced every kind of suffering and difficulty, but he could not open his mouth. He was like a dumb person. He had bought a rickshaw, and had lost it; he had saved money, and had lost it; the end of all his labor had been to have someone come along and cheat him out of what he had earned. He had never dared risk exciting anyone's anger, and he even made way for the wild dogs on the street, and the final result was still that he had been so badly cheated that he could hardly draw his breath.

But first he had better not think of what was past and done with: what was he going to do tomorrow? He could not go back to the Ts'ao house—where should he go?

"Will it be all right if I spend the night here?" he asked. He was like a street cur that has found a corner in which to escape the wind, and of which he will have to make the best for the time being. But even in a simple thing like that he had to be careful to see that he did not get in anyone else's way.

"You just stay here. When the heavens are ice and the earth is covered with snow, where would you go? Will you be all right sleeping on the floor? You can crowd in with me in the bed if you'd like to."

Unwilling to discommode his host, Happy Boy answered that the floor would be fine.

Old Ch'eng went off to sleep. Happy Boy tossed back and forth, turned over and over, and from the beginning to the end never slept at all. In a little while the cold air sweeping across the floor froze his bedding into an ice-cold sheet of iron. He doubled his feet up under him, and his legs felt as if he was about to have cramps in their calves. The frigid winds that came in through the crack in the door were like a flock of cold needles stuck into the top of his head. With a fierce desperation he closed his eyes and ducked his head down under the covers, but still he couldn't sleep. He heard the heavy, even breathing of Old Ch'eng, and his heart filled with irritation and envy. Just then it would have made him extremely happy to get up and strike his friend, to wake him up too, and he was vexed at not being able to do that. The later it got, the colder it became; he was so frozen that his throat itched, but he was afraid that if he coughed he would wake up Old Ch'eng.

Unable to sleep, he thought in all earnest of getting up stealthily and going back to the Ts'ao house to take a look around. In any case, he had quit his job; there was no one in the compound; why shouldn't he go take a few things? His own few dollars of money that it had been so hard for him to save up had been stolen from him. It was on account of the Ts'ao family affairs that they had been stolen from him. Why could he not himself go over there now and steal a few things? Because of his working for the Ts'ao family he had lost his money; now to recover his loss from the Ts'ao family, was not that precisely proper? What could be more appropriate? Thinking in this way, his spirits rose and forthwith he forgot the cold. He would go right away. The money it had been so hard for him to come by was lost, and now he could get it back again so easily. Go now!

He had already sat up, and then suddenly he laid himself as speedily back down again. It seemed as if Old Ch'eng had seen him. His heart started beating very rapidly. No, he could not be a thief. A little while back, in order to shake himself clear of the danger, he had failed to carry out Mr. Ts'ao's instructions. On account of that he would be unable to face his master; how could he go, on top of that, and steal his master's things? He could not do it! If he died of his poverty, he would not steal!

How could he know that someone else would not go and rob the place? If that fellow Sun had taken away some of the things, who would know the difference? Again Happy Boy sat up. In some distant place a dog barked several times. He lay back once more. He still could not go. If other people were going to steal, they'd just have to steal: that would not be a thing for which his own conscience would have to bear the shame. It was bad enough to be as poverty-stricken as he was now; he couldn't put another black spot on his heart.

Another thing to be said was that Kao Ma knew he had come to the Wang house; if something were lost during the night, whether he did it or not, he would still have done it. Not only was he unwilling to go steal anything himself; he was afraid that someone else might do it. It was very true that if during this particular night something was stolen, he might jump into the Yellow River and still not wash himself clean of the suspicion. He wasn't cold now—he was hot. He was so hot that the palms of his hands were perspiring. What should he do? Should he jump back over the wall into the Ts'ao compound to keep watch? He didn't dare. He had bought back his own life for a price in money; he could not again knowingly blunder into a trap like that. If he didn't go, and by some unlucky chance something was lost, what then?

He could think of no clear course of action. For a third time he sat up, with his legs drawn up under him like a bow and his head so low that it almost touched the grass matting on the floor. His mind was heavy with a great weight, and his eyes wanted to close, but now he didn't dare sleep. The night was so terribly long: only for Happy Boy was there no time to close the eyes.

He sat he did not know how long, and changed his plans he did not know how many times. Suddenly there was a light in his heart, and he leaned over and pushed at Old Ch'eng. "Old Ch'eng! Old Ch'eng! Wake up!"

"What's the matter?" Old Ch'eng was very loath to open his eyes. "If you want to urinate, there's a night pot at the bottom of the bed."

"Wake up! Turn on the light!"

"Is there a thief or what?" In muddled bewilderment Old Ch'eng sat up.

"Are you fully awake, so that you understand what's said to you?"

"Uh!"

178

"Old Ch'eng, you take a good look. This is my bedding. These are my clothes. This five-dollar bill Mr. Ts'ao gave me. That's all there is, isn't it?"

"That's all. Why?" Old Ch'eng yawned.

"Are you wide-awake? That's all there is of my things. I haven't taken a blade of grass or a stick of wood that belongs to the Ts'ao family?"

"No, of course not. We brethren who eat long the food of a household, how would it do for us to have sticky hands? If it's work that we can do, we do it. If we can't do it, we don't. How could we steal our employer's things? Is that why you woke me up?"

"Did you get a good look?"

Old Ch'eng smiled. "Yes. There's no mistake. I say, aren't you cold?"

"I'm all right."

13

BECAUSE the snow caught the light and sent it glistening back to the sky again, the day seemed to come a little earlier than before. It would soon be the year's end, and many people had bought chickens to fatten them up; the sound of the cocks' crowing was many times what it would have been at other seasons. Everywhere there was the caw of chickens and over everything the promise of plenty and prosperity that the auspicious snow had brought.

But Happy Boy had not slept all night. In the very first hours of morning, before daybreak, he had managed to close his

179

eyelids and doze a while. It was sleep without sleeping, like float-ing in water where the waves suddenly carried you high up and as suddenly slid you down again, so that your heart could not be at peace. The longer he slept this way the colder he got, and outside the house there came from all four directions the sounds of the chickens. It was the actual truth that he could stand it no longer. He did not want to disturb Old Ch'eng, so he buckled his legs up under him and stopped his mouth with a corner of the bedding quilt to muffle his coughing. He still did not dare get up, and endured the waiting until his heart was parched with vexation. It was no easy thing for him to wait until daylight, to wait until the sounds of turning wheels and the calls of the cart-pushers came to the streets.

He sat up but he was just as cold that way as he had been lying down. He got all the way up, looped the cloth loops on one side of the front of his gown over the little round balls of cloth that were the buttons on the other side, and opened a crack in the door to look out. The snow was not very deep: it had probably stopped falling sometime in the middle of the night. The weather seemed already to have cleared, but in the oozing gray of the morning mist he could not see very distinctly, and even the snow seemed to be covered with a pallid shadow of gray. In his first glance he saw the big footprints that he him-self had left the night before; although snow that had fallen afterward had buried and blurred them a little, they could still be seen, one depression after another.

In the first place because it gave him something to do, and in the second place because he wanted to eliminate these traces of himself, he felt around inside the room until he found a broom and without a word went out to sweep away the snow. It was heavy and not easy to sweep; the broom he had found in his short minute of searching was not a large one, and he had to bend way over, using all his strength to get the snow off. When he had swept off the top layer, there was still a layer of very fine snow that seemed already to have stuck itself fast to the ground. His posture was so tiring that he had twice to straighten himself up and rest a while before he had finally cleared the entire courtyard and got the snow all piled up around the trunks of the two young willow trees. There was by now a light sweat on his body; he was warmer and felt a little more relaxed. Stamping his feet to get the snow off them, he exhaled a long breath, very long and very white.

Going back into the room, he put the broom down again in its original place, and was trying to put his bedding in order and get it rolled up when Old Ch'eng woke up, yawned, and, before he had properly closed his mouth again, asked, "Is it late?" The tones of his language were confused: he did not speak any one dialect clearly, but a mixture of all of them. He rubbed the moisture away from the corners of his eyes and as a part of the same gesture reached over to the pocket of his old fur-lined robe and felt out a cigarette. Only after he had had two or three puffs was he wide-awake.

"Happy Boy, you mustn't go yet! Wait until I boil a little water and we have a pot of steaming hot tea. Last night must have been enough for you to bear!"

"Can't I go get the water?" Happy Boy said with a gracious air. But he had hardly spoken when the feeling of fright that the night before had brought him came back to him again, and suddenly the middle of his heart was so stopped up as to become one single hard little ball.

"No, I'll go. You are still my guest." As he spoke, Old Ch'eng very quickly threw on his clothes, leaving the whole of his buttons unbuttoned, only throwing his tattered gown about his shoulders, so that it hung like a bundle suspended from a stick, and with a cigarette clinging to his lips he ran out of the door.

"Heh! You've already got the courtyard swept clean. You're a good one, in all truth. You'll have to accept my invitation."

Happy Boy felt a little lighter at heart.

He had not waited long when Old Ch'eng came back toting two big bowls of sweet broth of congee, along with he did not know how many horse's-hoof cakes and crisp "little devil" biscuits fried in oil.

"I haven't steeped the tea yet. First let's drink a little of this broth. Come on, eat. If there's not enough, we'll go buy some more. If we haven't any money, we'll buy it on credit. Those of us who earn our living in bitter labor must not try to cheat our mouths of the food we need. Come on!"

It was full daylight now, and the room was clear and cold in the transparent brightness. The men held their bowls to their lips with both hands and the noise they made in drinking was loud and sweet to hear. Neither of them said anything and, almost as if it had been in the same long inhalation, they ate up all the cakes and biscuits.

"How about it?" Old Ch'eng finally asked as he picked a sesame seed from between his teeth.

"I must be going." Happy Boy looked at his bedding roll on the floor.

"Tell me about it. After all I still don't understand what happened or how it happened!" Old Ch'eng held out a cigarette, and Happy Boy accepted it, nodding his head.

Thinking it over, Happy Boy felt a little ashamed not to tell the whole story to Old Ch'eng. So he went over the affair of the night before, one thing following the other and all connected together just as it had happened. And although it cost him a tremendous effort, it could not be said that the result was incomplete in any detail.

Old Ch'eng sat for what seemed half a day with his lips pursed, as if he were tasting the flavor of the chronicle.

"According to the way I view it, you should still go hunt up Mr. Ts'ao. You can't just give up your job like this, and you can't just lose your money like that. Didn't you say a moment ago that Mr. Ts'ao had given you instructions, had told you that if you saw that things were going badly you should run away? Well, then, as soon as you stepped out of the car you were blocked off by a detective. Whose fault was that? It wasn't that you weren't loyal and faithful, it was because the whole affair was too crooked, and you had no other course but first to consider your own life. From the way I look at it, there's nothing in that that would make it hard for you to face the Ts'aos. You go and hunt for Mr. Ts'ao, and tell him the true facts from one to ten and from beginning to end. I don't think he can possibly hold it against you, and there's even a chance that he might make good your loss! You go ahead—leave your bedding roll here, and make an early start to look for him. The days are short and by the time the sun is up it will be eight o'clock. Hurry along and don't lose any time."

Happy Boy's heart came alive again. He still had a little feeling that it would be hard to face Mr. Ts'ao, but Old Ch'eng had spoken very close to true reason. When a detective with a gun under his gown had pushed him back into a hole and stopped him up, how could he at that moment still have regard for the affairs of the Ts'ao family?

"Go on," Old Ch'eng urged him. "I think last night you were so tied up in your mind you couldn't think. Nobody can guarantee that when they meet up with an affair of great urgency they won't be befuddled in the head. I can assure you that the road I've suggested to you is not the wrong one. I'm a little older than you are, and I can't help but have had more experience. You go ahead—isn't the sun already coming out?"

The light of the morning sun had borrowed the brightness of the snow and already had illumined the whole city. The blue heavens, the white snow, the light in the sky and the light on the snow, with the gold of the roofs shimmering between, was so thrilling that one could hardly open one's eyes to look at it. Happy Boy was about to be on his way when someone knocked at the gate.

Old Ch'eng went out to see who it was, and from the gateway he called back, "Happy Boy, it's someone looking for you."

It was Wang Two from the Tso household. His nose was so cold that clear water was dripping from it, and he stood outside the gate-room stamping his feet to get the snow off of them. When Old Ch'eng saw Happy Boy coming out toward the gate too, he offered them his place. "Let's all of us go inside and sit down." The three of them went into the room together.

"Well, then—" Wang Two rubbed his hands. "I've come to watch the house. How do I get in? The big gate is locked. Well, then—the cold that comes after the snow is truly cold. Well, then—Mr. Ts'ao and Mrs. Ts'ao both left early this morning; they went to Tientsin or maybe to Shanghai, I couldn't say very clearly which. Mr. Tso charged me with coming to look after the house. Well, then—it's certainly cold."

Suddenly Happy Boy felt like sobbing. Just as he was about to follow the advice and urging of Old Ch'eng and go look for Mr. Ts'ao, Mr. Ts'ao himself goes away. He stood stupidly for a long time, and then asked:

"Mr. Ts'ao didn't say anything about me?"

"Well, then—no, he didn't. Before daylight they all got up. There simply wasn't a chance to say anything. The train, well, then—left at seven-forty. Well, then—how will I get across the courtyard?" Wang Two was in great hurry to get over into the Ts'ao compound.

"Jump over the wall!" Happy Boy looked at Old Ch'eng, as if to turn Wang Two over into his care, and began rolling up his bedding.

"Where are you going?" Old Ch'eng asked.

"To the Human Harmony Rickshaw Shed—there's no other place I can go." This one sentence was laden with all the grievances and bitterness in Happy Boy's heart, and all the mortification, and all the feeling of helplessness. He had no other way—

the best he could do was to surrender. Every other road was sealed against him, and he could only make his way through the beautiful white world of snow to the wretched black pagoda that was the Tiger Girl. He had put store by honor, ambition, loyalty, integrity; all these things were utterly useless to him; his was the destiny of a dog.

Old Ch'eng walked over to him. "You go your way. And it isn't to be saying it in front of Wang Two that I tell you that I know you haven't taken a single blade of grass or one splinter of wood that belongs to the Ts'ao family. May you find good fortune on the road, and whenever you get back to this street you must come in and while away some time with me. It might be that I will hear of a good job, and I could recommend you for it. When you've gone, I'll take Wang Two over to the other side. Is there coal there?"

"The coal and kindling wood are all in the little room off the back courtyard." Happy Boy swung his bedding over his shoulder.

Already the snow on the streets was no longer so white. On the avenues the wheels of passing cars had packed it down so tight it showed something of the color of ice. In the unpaved byways the hoof prints of horses had trampled it into dark splotches only interspersed with a white that was pitiable to see. Happy Boy thought of nothing, attending only to the toting of his bedding and his own forward steps. Without once stopping or slackening his pace he walked straight to the Human Harmony Rickshaw Shed. He did not dare stop at the gate: if he paused just once, he knew he would not have the courage to go in. So he walked directly in, his face so hot it was burning.

He had already prepared a speech that he would say to Tiger Girl:

"I have come. Do what you see fit. Anything you do will be all right. I am helpless."

When he did see her, he turned this statement around many times in his heart, but from first to last he remained unable to speak it out. He had no such facility with his lips.

Tiger Girl had just got up, her hair was all grizzled and sticking out at angles, her eyelids were swollen, and over her black face was a layer of little white chicken-pimples, like a frozen capon from which all the feathers have been plucked.

"Yo! You've come back." Her voice was warm and intimate, and the laughter in her eyes made them bright.

"Rent me a rickshaw." Happy Boy kept his head down and his eyes fixed on the snow that was still unmelted on his shoes.

"Go tell the old man about it." She spoke in a low voice, and as she finished the sentence she pursed her lips and moved them to indicate the direction of the east room.

Fourth Master Liu was in his room and in the act of drinking tea. In front of him was a great white chafing stove, the flames from which reached up over six inches from the coals. When he saw Happy Boy come in, he said, half in vexation and half in jest: "You're a slick one! Let me count—how many days has it been since you were here last? How's your work? Have you bought a rickshaw yet?"

Happy Boy shook his head, the words jabbing so deep in his heart that it was like a pain that he could feel. "Fourth Master, you still have to give me a rickshaw to pull."

"Heng! you've puffed away your job like you'd blow out the light of a candle, haven't you? Again! All right, you go pick out a rickshaw for yourself."

Fourth Master Liu emptied a teacup. "Come. First drink a cup of tea."

Happy Boy picked up the cup in both hands and, standing before the stove, drained it in one big gulp. The tea was extraordinarily hot, the fire extraordinarily warm, and suddenly he felt a little sleepy. He put the cup down and was just about to go out when Fourth Master called to stop him.

"Wait before you go. What are you in a hurry about? I want to tell you: you've come just at the right time. The twenty-seventh is my birthday, and I want to put up a matshed and invite guests. The thing for you to do is to help out for two or three days—there's no need of your going out right away again to pull a rickshaw. None of them"—Fourth Master waved his hand in the direction of the courtyard—"can be depended on. I don't want to call any of those profligate and dissipated wretches in to help and have them stumbling around raising a blind rumpus. If you'll help me it'll be all right. When something should be done, you go ahead and do it, and don't wait for me to tell you. First go out and sweep up the snow, and at noon I'll invite you to share a bowl of food that'll have fire under it."

"Yes, Fourth Master." Happy Boy had thought it out: since he had come back to this place, he would put everything in the hands of the father and daughter of the Liu family. However they wanted to push him around would be all right; he would take his orders and accept his fate.

"Didn't I tell you?" Tiger Girl chose this time to come in.

"Happy Boy is still the one. Everyone else lacks just a little something of his."

Old Liu smiled. Happy Boy's head hung even farther down.

"Come, Happy Boy!" Tiger Girl was calling him to go out with her. "I'm giving you money to go buy a broom, one made of bamboos so that it'll be good for sweeping the snow. You must hurry and get it swept up. The man who puts up the matshed is coming today."

As they walked across to her room she was counting out the money for him, and at the same time whispering to him, "Look a little brighter and more alert. Try to please the old man. There's hope for our business."

Happy Boy said nothing, nor did he get angry. It was as if his heart were dead. He thought of nothing, only that one more day dragged through would be one more day gone by. If there was food he would eat, drink he would drink, work to do he would do it. As long as his hand and feet were not idle he need only turn about a few times and the daylight was gone. The best thing he could do would be to study the ways of the blindfolded mule that patiently pulls the upper grindstone. Were you to ask it one thing there would be three that it did not know; all it could do was to plod darkly through its circuit, turning the grindstone round and round.

At the same time he could feel that no matter what he did or didn't do he could not find delight in it or real elation. In spite of his unwillingness to think, to speak, or to be angry, his heart was blocked up with something as completely as if it had been a bottle with the stopper stuck way down into its long neck. During the time when he was working he could forget temporarily, but if he had only the shortest period of leisure he would feel that piece of something again—as soft as cotton but always large; it had no distinct taste or flavor, and yet he felt terribly choked by it, as he would have been by a great sponge down below his throat.

188

With his heart stopped up by this thing, he forced himself to work up enough energy to go about the tasks given him, in order that he might get so tired in doing them that he wouldn't be able to move any farther, and then he could fall into a heavy fevered sleep. The night he turned over to the governance of his dreams, the daytime to that of his feet and hands. It was as if he were a dead man who could do the work of a living one. He swept away the snow, he bought things, he ordered the kerosene lamp, he polished rickshaws, he moved tables and chairs, he ate the dinner that Fourth Master Liu prepared as a reward for his workmen, he went to bed at night and got up in the morning; he did all these things without clearly knowing that he was doing any of them. There were no words in his mouth and no thoughts in his heart; all he could feel was that dark, hidden, sponge-like thing that had sopped up the whole of his spirit.

The snow on the ground had been swept clear, and that on the roofs had gradually melted away. The matshed builder had shouted the words that told everyone he was climbing up to the housetop, and from there he raised the bamboo framework over which the matshed was to be built. It had all been described and agreed upon: it was to be a shed large enough to cover the whole courtyard, and completely enclosed so that it could be heated. There were to be coverings and balusters and trimmings on three sides, and glass windows on all three sides as well. Inside the matshed there were to be glass partitions, and scrolls hung along the walls; wherever the wood showed it was to be wrapped in red cloth. The center door and the doors on either side of it were all alike to be festooned in cloths of brilliant coloring; the shed to house the kitchen was to be put up in the rear courtyard. Because it was the Fourth Master's sixty-ninth birthday, one year short of his seventieth, and he wanted to carry out an uproarious celebration of it, the first important step was to put up a handsome matshed, a really respectable one.

189

On account of the shortness of the winter days, the matshed builder was only able to put up the structure of the shed itself and the balusters with the cloths with the lucky characters on them; the paintings and the hangings he would have to come back the next day to put in place. Fourth Master Liu got in a great rage about this builder of harmonious matsheds, a rage that made his face a flying scarlet. It was because of this that he sent Happy Boy scurrying out to hurry up the man who was to send them the kerosene lamp, and to tell the cook on no account to neglect his duties. As a matter of fact, neither of them was at all likely to forget, but the old man was not easy in his mind.

When Happy Boy had just come running back from this errand, Fourth Master sent him out again to borrow sets of the ivory counters with which machiang is played; he was to borrow three or four sets—when the day came nothing was going to do but that the old man should gamble until he was content. Once the counters were borrowed, Happy Boy was told to go out again to borrow a phonograph—when you celebrate a birthday you certainly have to have a little noise. Happy Boy's legs never stopped even for a little while; he kept running from one place to another until eleven o'clock at night. He had grown accustomed to pulling a rickshaw—to go racing about without the shafts in his hands made him even more weary. The last time he came back to the shed even he, even Happy Boy, could hardly lift his feet.

"You're a good one," the old man said. "You'll do! If I had a son like you, even if I had to live two or three years less, it would still be good. You go rest—tomorrow there'll still be things to do."

Tiger Girl, standing to one side, winked at Happy Boy.

Early the next morning the matshed builder arrived to supply the deficiencies in his labors. He hung the brightly painted cloths—there were pictures of war scenes from "The Three

Kingdoms": the three battles in which Liu Pei fought Lü Pu; the fighting on the hillside where Chao Yun saved the defeated Liu Pei's son; the debacle in which Liu Pei's encampments were destroyed by fire, and from which the hero himself escaped only by the grace of a miracle; and other storied happenings—the big painted faces and the small ones were all astride their horses, flourishing spears and swords. Old Man Liu stretched his neck to look them all over carefully and felt well satisfied.

Close on the heels of the matshed builder came the furniture store men. They set up eight tables inside the matshed; the table aprons, the chair cushions, and the stool covers were all of silk with great red flowers embroidered on them. An altar to the God of Longevity was set up in the ceremonial room; the censers and the candelabra were of cloisonné enamelware in a beautiful blue, and before the table were four red rugs. The sight of them reminded Old Man Liu that they hadn't any apples to set around, and he sent Happy Boy off in a hurry to order some. Behind the old fellow's back Tiger Girl slipped two dollars into Happy Boy's hand, telling him to get peaches and cakes of longevity and to have baked on each of the peaches one of the Eight Immortals; these were to be as if they had been a present from Happy Boy himself.

When he had bought the apples, they went to work to set them out, and after what was not a very long while the peaches and cakes of longevity that he had ordered arrived too, and they put them in back of the apples. The peaches were so large that the lips of the cleft near the top looked like a mouth, and the figure of the Immortal as if he were issuing from it; it was marvelously genteel and large-spirited.

"Happy Boy bought them as presents for you. See how the eyes of his heart overlook nothing!" Tiger Girl was stuffing the ears of her father with good words for Happy Boy. Fourth Master looked at him and smiled.

The hall for the celebration of the aged one's birthday still lacked the one immense character "Longevity" which should hang in the center of the back wall behind the long table on which the censers stood. According to custom, one need not prepare this character oneself: one's friends presented it. Up to now no one had sent one; Fourth Master was of a hasty and impetuous disposition, and once more he flew into a rage.

"Whenever there's a red affair—a wedding or a birthday—or a white one, a funeral, I always run over to be down in front, but when I have a celebration, his mother's!—they walk off and leave me on an empty stage."

"Tomorrow's only the twenty-sixth, and the tables won't be ready until then. Why are you in such a hurry?" Tiger Girl called out across the shed to console him.

"I want to get everything prepared and set out at once. It grieves my heart to look at it when it's put together piecemeal like this, all in little fragments and odds and ends. I say, Happy Boy, the carbide light has to be installed today. If they haven't sent it here by four o'clock this afternoon, I'll cut their flesh into little strips and hack them to death."

"Happy Boy, you go once more to hurry them up." Tiger Girl purposely leaned heavily on his aid and always she was calling him and asking him to do something when her father was in earshot. Happy Boy didn't utter a sound; when he understood what was being asked of him he went off to do it.

"It isn't because I'm saying it, Old Pa." Tiger Girl pursed her lips a little as she spoke: "If you had had a son, if he wasn't like me, he'd be like Happy Boy. It's a pity that my spirit stole into the wrong womb, but there's no help for that now. As a matter of fact, it wouldn't be too bad to have a fellow like Happy Boy as an adopted son. Look at him—he doesn't even let a fart the whole day long, but he gets all the work done just the same."

Fourth Master Liu made no answer, but sat thinking. Then suddenly he asked: "The phonograph? Is it here? Let's have a song!"

A broken-down old phonograph, borrowed from no one knew where, was brought out and wound up. The needle was old and the record worn-out: every sound the machine let out was like the howl of a cat when someone steps on its tail, and the shrill shriek twisted in your heart like an awl. But Fourth Master didn't mind that—just so it made a noise it was all right.

By that afternoon everything was in readiness, and only awaited the coming of the cook on the following day to prepare the tables. Fourth Master had gone all over the place on a tour of inspection: everywhere the flowers were red and the willows green, and he nodded his head in approval.

That evening he went down to the Coal Store In Accord With Heaven to invite the manager to keep the accounts of the celebration for him. His name was Feng, he came from Shansi Province, and he kept very careful accounts. Mr. Feng came right over to see about it, and sent Happy Boy out to buy two large red account books and a scroll of paper glazed in a felicitous scarlet. He unrolled the scroll, inscribed a series of "Longevity" characters on it, and then cut it up into sections, each with a character, and went around pasting them up in appropriate places. Fourth Master Liu felt that Mr. Feng truly had a clear concise mind, and immediately wanted to invite two more people over so that they could have a round of machiang. Mr. Feng, knowing how sharp a player Fourth Master was, didn't dare accept.

His failure to get up a game left Fourth Master a little angry, and he called together several of the rickshaw men. "How about playing a game of Pawn the Jewel? Have you the guts to do it or not?"

They would all have liked to play, but none of them had the courage to play with the Fourth Master. Who didn't know that in the old days he had owned a gambling house?

"You flock of stuffed toys! How did you ever come to be alive." Fourth Master was working himself into another rage.

"When I was as young as you are, I wasn't afraid to play even if I didn't have a copper in my pocket. I'd talk about losing when I'd already lost, and not before. Come on!"

"Can we play for coppers?" one of the rickshaw men asked tentatively.

"Keep your coppers! Fourth Liu doesn't play at coaxing children." The old man swallowed his cup of tea in one mouthful, and rubbed his bald head. "Let's count that settled. If you invited me to play, I wouldn't play. I say, you fellows tell all the others: tomorrow the tables are going to be set out, and in the afternoon my relatives and friends will be coming. All the rickshaws must be in the shed at four o'clock, and you can't be pushing back and forth crowding and confusing everybody with your rickshaws after that time. Tomorrow's rickshaw rental you needn't pay; you can all pull your rickshaws for nothing for one day, and you must all recite over in your hearts the lucky phrases that will bring me good fortune. Don't be unkind and don't act without conscience.

"Day after tomorrow is the birthday itself, and nobody is permitted to take out his rickshaw. At eight-thirty in the morning I will spread out for you six main courses with as many large bowls and two seven-inch bowls, four small plates and one chafing dish; I will be able to look you all in the face. You must wear your long gowns, and the man who comes in dressed in a miserable short jacket is the man who will get kicked out. When you've finished eating, do me the favor of squirming away, so that I can receive my relatives and friends fittingly. They will be served three large meat courses, six platters of cold meats, six bowls of vegetables roasted in a frying pan, four more large dishes, and a chafing dish. I'm telling you plainly ahead of time: you mustn't stand around and look on greedy-eyed. Friends and relatives are friends and relatives; I'm not asking anything of you. Those of you who have any sympathy in your hearts for your fellow man can give me ten large coppers each as a birth-

194

day present, and I won't consider the amount too small; if you don't bring me a single copper, but only knock your head on the ground three times before me, I will still accept that. Only you must be well-behaved and orderly, do you understand? In the evening anybody who still wants to eat my food can come back after six o'clock, and whatever is left over, whether it's much or little, all belongs to you. But it won't do to come back early. Do you hear? Have you all understood?"

"Tomorrow some of the fellows are pulling the night shift, Fourth Master," a middle-aged rickshaw puller said. "How can they put their rickshaws up at four o'clock?"

"Those who are pulling the night shift can come back for their rickshaws after eleven o'clock. In any case they can't be crowding and pushing around while there are people in the matshed. You are rickshaw pullers: Fourth Liu is no fellow craftsman of yours, do you understand?"

There was nothing that anyone in the group could say, and they felt as if they were on a high stage with no steps leading down from it by which they might leave. There was no way for them to make a graceful exit, and they all stood there as stiff and numb as if they had been so many mummies. Fourth Master's words had enclosed in the heart of each a feeling of anger and resentment and inequality. Although having one day's rickshaw rent remitted was an advantage, still who among them would be willing to eat a free meal? Did not each of them have to give out at least forty coppers as a present to the old man? And, moreover, Fourth Master had spoken so discourteously to them that it was as if, when he celebrated his birthday, they should all scamper away like rats and hide.

And then again, on the main day, the twenty-seventh, not to let any of them take their rickshaws out, just at the time when the New Year was near and there was plenty of business! Fourth Master Liu could well sacrifice one day of income from rentals, but the crowd could not endure keeping company all day with a bursted bubble. They stood there daring to be angry but not daring to show it in speech, and the words they were saying over and over in their hearts were not lucky phrases to bring good fortune to Fourth Master Liu.

Tiger Girl tugged at Happy Boy's sleeve, and he walked out with her.

It was as if the anger of the group had found the opening through which it could spend itself. They glared at Happy Boy's retreating form. For these last two days they had all felt that Happy Boy had become the running dog of the Liu family. He was toadying to them for all his life was worth, laboring uncomplainingly and bearing every grievance, just for the honor of being their little scullery boy.

Happy Boy himself knew nothing of this; he was helping the Liu family prepare for its big affair because the work helped him drive away the vexation in his own heart. In the evening he said nothing to the others because there was in the nature of things nothing that he could say. They knew nothing of his grievances and therefore imagined that it was because he was so busy currying favor with Fourth Master that he had no time to make conversation with them.

The care that Tiger Girl took of Happy Boy had a particularly sour taste in the hearts of the others. When they thought of the things before their eyes, how Fourth Master Liu would not even let them go in and out of his matshed of felicity at will, and yet Happy Boy would certainly be able to eat the best food all day long—weren't they all rickshaw men together? Why, then, have a third class, and a sixth class and a ninth class? Look at that—the Tiger Girl was calling Happy Boy out! The eyes of every man in the group followed him; their legs, too, felt like moving and they shuffled out, abusive words behind their lips. As they came through the door, Tiger Girl was just in the act of talking to Happy Boy under the kerosene light, and they all looked at each other and nodded their heads.

14

CHE Liu family affair was carried out with much color and bustle and commotion and ado. Fourth Master Liu was very well satisfied to have so many people coming and knocking their heads on the ground before him and offering him their birthday congratulations. Especially sufficient to make him proud of himself was the fact that many of his old friends hurried themselves over to proffer their felicitations. From the presence of these old friends he could see that not only was the affair a huge success, but that it showed how completely he had reformed and changed for the better. In the clothing that his friends wore they had already dropped behind in the ranks, while Fourth Master's fur gown and silken fur-lined jacket were both newly made. From a business standpoint many of these old friends of his had in former years been better off than himself, but now—in the changes of fortune through which they had all passed in the last twenty or thirty years—the further the muddy river had rolled the dirtier it had become, and the longer they lived the worse off they became. Some of them found it very difficult now to eat a full meal. Looking at them and then looking at his own matshed of felicity, his chapel of longevity, the cloth scroll so bravely painted with the Battle of the Long Incline, and the feast of the three great bowls, he felt how true it was that he had grown taller than them all by a head; he had "reformed." Even when it came to gambling, he had prepared machiang sets for his guests; that was much more refined and polished than playing the lottery game called "Pawning the Precious Thing."

For all that, in the midst of this appearance of gayety and life, he still felt a sense of cold loneliness, of a sadness that made it difficult for him to carry on. He had grown accustomed to a single life, and he had originally thought of the guests at his birthday party as being limited to the managers and staffs of the shops in the locality or with which he had dealings, together with some of the "bare sticks," the unmarried rogues and bachelors, with whom he had been associated in earlier years when he lived in the outside world and went freely about the town. He had not thought that there might be a few women guests. Although Tiger Girl could receive them for him and take care of them, still their presence made him feel suddenly the solitude of his house. He had no woman to keep him company, but only his daughter, who moreover had grown up to look more like a man than a woman. Supposing Tiger Girl had been a boy, naturally he would early have established his own home and would by now have children. Then, even though he himself were an old widower, he would still not be so lonely and wretched. Yes, he lacked nothing himself. All he lacked was a son. The greater his own age became, the slimmer and slimmer grew his chances of having a son. Receiving felicitations on the length of one's life was by right a very happy occasion, but it seemed at the same time as if one ought to be weeping. No matter how completely he had "reformed," or how much better off he was, if he had no one to carry on his business after him, had he not taken all his pains to no purpose?

Throughout the forenoon he had been extraordinarily pleased to have all these people prostrating themselves before him and wishing him a prolonged life; he had puffed himself up to seem very big and put on a grand manner indeed, as if he were a hero so great that he had wrested from the mystic sea turtle the position of world-supporter, and was now due all the reverence that once was paid to that fabulous godhead.

By the afternoon a little of this air with which he had been inflated had leaked out. Seeing the children that the women guests had tugged along with them, he was both admiring and envious. At the same time there was the problem of how to act toward the children themselves: he did not dare assume an air of too great intimacy toward them, and yet not to do so left him feeling constrained and unnatural. It irritated him so that he felt like flying into a rage, but again he was unwilling to do that forthwith because he knew that he was himself a man of the world and therefore could not put out into the very faces of his friends and relatives a stench like that. He hoped that the day would be over quickly, very quickly: he could bear this punishment no longer.

There was also a further circumstance which lent imperfection to his felicity: Happy Boy almost got into a fight.

The food had been set out for the rickshaw pullers at a little after eight o'clock. They were all a little grudging about it; although they had had a day's rickshaw rental remitted the day before, still none of them had come empty-handed this morning to eat a free meal—whether it was a ten-cent piece or forty coppers, much or little, each had brought his share of gift-money. In other times they were just laborers, sons of bitterness and toil, and Fourth Liu was the master of the rickshaw yard; today, according to the way they looked at it, they were guests and shouldn't receive this kind of treatment. What was more, when they finished eating they had to leave, and weren't going to be permitted to take their rickshaws out, right at the year's end, the one time that business was really good!

Happy Boy knew for a certainty that the "finish eating and be on your way" rule did not apply to him, but he wanted to have his meal with the crowd. First, the earlier he finished eating the sooner he could be about his work and, second, it seemed more friendly. When he sat down with the crowd, they turned all their displeasure with Fourth Master Liu upon him. He had hardly got into his seat when someone said, "Ai! You are an honored guest. How can you be sitting at the same table with us?"

Happy Boy smiled his good-hearted silly smile without having caught the idea or tasted the flavor of the remark. In the last few days he had not opened his mouth to say a single idle word, and for that reason his mind did not seem to be functioning now.

The group did not dare to make their feelings manifest to Fourth Master Liu: the best thing they could do was to eat a few mouthfuls more of his food than otherwise they would have done. There were no extras of the meat and vegetables, but there was no way of limiting the wine—was it not the wine of felicity, and how then could you be niggardly of it? By a kind of tacit agreement they all took to the wine to work off the violence of their anger at Fourth Master.

Some of them drank in a kind of depressed solitude; others boisterously played the fingers game with one another. Old man Liu could not prevent their doing that. Seeing the crowd drinking, Happy Boy felt that it was not convenient for him to be too much out of things, so he drank a couple of cups with them. As they drank and drank, everybody began to get red-eyed, and their lips got past the point where they could govern them.

One of them even said, "Happy Boy Camel, that job you've got is a beautiful one! It gives you enough food to eat each day, waiting on the old master and his daughter. And when tomorrow comes you won't have to pull a rickshaw—you can perform two different kinds of jobs at the same time."

Happy Boy got a little bit of the idea but he still didn't take it to heart. From the time he had come back to the Human Harmony Rickshaw Shed he had determined to put aside altogether any idea of acting the "hero" or the "real son of Han"; he sought only to submit to the will of heaven in all things. Whoever wanted to say whatever they wanted to say could say it. He would repress his anger.

200

Then someone else said, "That fellow Happy Boy walks a road of his own. We depend on the strength of our legs to earn our money: that fellow Happy Boy is an inside worker." Everybody started to laugh loudly. Happy Boy could feel that they were all snapping at him, but he had borne so great a grievance, why should he pay any attention to a few idle words? So again he made no sound.

When they saw they were getting something for nothing, the people at a nearby table joined in, one of them calling over, "Happy Boy, when tomorrow comes and you're the master of the yard, you mustn't forget your fellow rickshaw men."

Still Happy Boy said nothing, and one of the men at his own table spoke up, "Say something, Camel."

Happy Boy's face flushed red, and in a low voice he asked, "How could I become master of the yard?"

"Heng, why can't you? Under the very eyes of the beholder the magic happens, and the rickshaw man is a rickshaw man no longer."

Happy Boy could not quite thread the maze and get the thought untangled; he did not know exactly what the idea behind this talk about magic was, but he guessed intuitively that they were speaking about the relationship between himself and Tiger Girl. Slowly the color of his face turned from red to white, and all of the wrongs and grievances he had suffered in the past came into his mind at the same time; they were all there, blocking up his heart. It came to him that he could no longer maintain the silence of those latter days, no longer go on enduring; the thing was like water at flood inside himself, stopped up and overflowing, that would rush out in a turbulent flood through the first opening it could find.

Just in this interval of crisis, another of the rickshaw men pointed his finger in Happy Boy's face and said: "Happy Boy, I'm talking about you—you're the real dumb man eating meat dumplings; while the talkers are wrangling you get the meat.

Your heart keeps a clear count. Isn't that so? Admit it, Happy Boy, admit it!"

In a sudden mad rage Happy Boy stood up, his face a malevolent white. Of the man who had last spoken he demanded: "Come outside and say that, do you dare?"

The crowd became wooden in speechlessness. In their hearts they had really thought only of snapping at him, to throw out a little idle harassment just to pass the time, but they had certainly not intended to prepare for a fight.

Suddenly they had become perfectly silent, like a forest full of twittering little birds when unexpectedly an eagle appears. Happy Boy stood there alone, much taller than any of the others. He felt his isolation, but his anger was at the window of his heart, and it was as if he were possessed of a deep conviction that even should they all move against him at once, still they would be no match.

He drove home another sentence as if he were driving a nail: "Does anybody here have the courage to step outside of the door with me?"

All at the same time they recognized the taste of their situation, got the point of it, and almost together they cried out: "Enough of this, Happy Boy. We were only teasing you."

Fourth Master Liu saw them. "Sit down, Happy Boy!" Turning to the group, he said: "Don't pick out a person to ridicule just because he's quiet and inoffensive. If you cause any trouble I'll kick everyone of you out. Hurry up and eat!"

Happy Boy left the table. The crowd picked up their rice bowls again, watching Old Man Liu out of the corners of their eyes. In no very long time they were all whispering and chattering to each other again, like birds in the forest when the danger is past twittering lightly to each other.

Happy Boy squatted for half a day outside the door, waiting for them. Supposing any one among them dared repeat any of that idle talk, his mother's! He had nothing himself and nothing to lose: he'd give them something that would show them he didn't care what happened.

But they came out together in little groups of two or three, and did not come to seek him out at all. And although the fight hadn't occurred, he felt that he had given vent to some of his feelings. But when he thought about it a little more, he could see that this act he had put on today had given offense to a great many people. In ordinary times, it had been in the nature of things that he had no close friends, which was how it came about that when he had been deeply wronged there had been no one to whom he could go to confide his troubles; how could he afford to go about offending even more people?

He began to repent a little. The little bit of food that he had just eaten had got stuck crosswise in his stomach, and it was beginning to ache. He got up. Why should he worry? Didn't the fellows who got in two fights every three days over their accounts get a lot of fun out of life? Because you acted according to the proprieties and were well-disposed and well-behaved, did that necessarily mean that you got some advantage out of it? Or any good out of it?

Thinking about it from this point of view, his heart traced out another road for him to follow. The Happy Boy who walked on this new road would be altogether different from the Happy Boy who in the past he had hoped he might sometime become. This new individual would be one who would make friends with anyone he met, would take every mean advantage that was afforded him, would drink the other fellow's tea, smoke the other fellow's cigarettes, borrow money and not return it, see an automobile coming down the street and not turn aside to avoid it, piss wherever he happened to be when he felt like pissing, spend the whole day trying sly little tricks to evade or get the better of one policeman or another, and counting it a matter of no importance to be held in the precinct station for two or three days on end.

Yes, it was true. A rickshaw man like that went on living, and was happy too. At the very least he was as happy as Happy Boy. All right, since being well-behaved, law-abiding, and ambitious were all useless, there could be nothing wrong, no mistake, in changing oneself into this kind of a thoroughly undependable and worthless character. Not only was it all right, Happy Boy thought, but there was something of the bearing and spirit of the hero, of the real man, about such a person. There was nothing in heaven he feared, and nothing on earth, and never would he hang his head and suffer for not taking his own part. Right! He ought to be like that! The lowest rowdy is cut of the good man's cloth.

Now he began to repent a little for just the contrary reason: he was sorry that the fight hadn't come off. Fortunately he needn't be in any hurry about it. From today on he'd never lower his head again to anybody.

There was no sand in Fourth Master Liu's eyes. He had taken the things he had heard and the things he had seen and put them all together in the same place; in his heart he already understood eight or nine parts of the whole. In these last few days, his daughter had been extraordinarily obedient. Heng! Because Happy Boy had come back! Her eyes were always following him. The old man hid this affair in his heart, and he felt more cold and desolate and miserable than ever. Thinking about the thing, and looking at it—to begin with, he didn't have a son and you could not just in a blaze of fire bring together a family. And now if his daughter went off with some man, the trouble and thought and scheming of his whole life would be only a vain expenditure.

Happy Boy was in truth all right, but if you considered him as occupying the position of both son and son-in-law, he was a long way from being fit to be either one: a stinking rickshaw man! He, the Fourth Master, had gone through the toil and anxieties of life for his whole generation, he had fought mob battles, he had borne the cruel torture of kneeling before the government yamen on chains of iron—was he to come in the end to this, to seeing a fellow with the head of a village farmer on his shoulders move out with his daughter and all his property? Nothing came as cheap as that! Nothing came as cheap as that! If there were bargains like that to be had, there was no use thinking you could come here to Fourth Liu to get it! Fourth Liu who from his youth had blown a hole in the ground every time he farted!

At three and four o'clock in the afternoon there were still a few people coming to pay their ceremonial call on Fourth Master on the occasion of his birthday, but the old man had lost his taste for it, and the whole thing was insipid and meaningless to him. The more people complimented him on his vigorous and hearty look and assured him that good fortune was certainly his, the sicker he got of it and the more of a sham it seemed to him.

After the lanterns had been hung, the guests began to disperse, leaving one after the other. Only some ten, those who lived closest or whose friendship had been the longest, had not yet gone. They got up a machiang game among them. Seeing the empty matshed over the courtyard, the tables with their aprons pulled away, all illuminated with the ghostly green light of the acetylene lamp, made the old man feel endlessly remote, as if he had been made to understand that after his death things would not be very different from this: the matshed of felicity need only change its name and become a matshed of mourning; the colors of the now disarrayed hangings would be white instead of red. There would be no son or grandson to wear the mourning robes and kneel before his coffin; there would only be a few people, to whom it was a matter of no concern, who would sit there playing machiang by way of keeping the night watch by the lighted coffin. In all truth he thought seriously of running these guests who had not had the good sense to leave out of the place; he owed it to himself to take advantage of the living breath still left in his lungs to show a front to the world that would really be awe-inspiring. But when it came right down to it, he felt a certain hesitancy, a degree of inappropriateness, in venting his murderous temper on his friends.

His wrath then turned a corner; the more he looked at his daughter the less she pleased his eyes. Happy Boy was sitting inside the matshed, a fool with the form of a man and the face of a dog; the light that issued from the endless hissing of the acetylene lamp made the scar on his face green in color, like a piece of jade stone. How was it that the more he looked at this pair the more the sight irritated him?

Customarily Tiger Girl paid no regard to her clothing or her manners—she was like a wild song without either rhythm or tune. Today she was elaborately garbed from head to toe, and the airs she was putting on in the reception and entertainment of the guests!—if her purpose was to secure everyone's approval and praise, it was still at least partly to show off her wifely skill before Happy Boy. In the earlier part of the day she had found this tremendously interesting and diverting, but as the afternoon passed and she grew a little weary she began to feel that on the contrary it was a disgusting show and to long to find somebody at whom for a change she could curse and shout. By evening she did not have as much as even a half of a dot of patience left, and if the black eyebrows that she had painted diagonally across over each eye to her temples stayed straight and stiff in the mask-like make-up on her face, it was only through a grim effort of will.

It was after seven o'clock and Fourth Master Liu was a little sleepy. But he would not give in to old age and was still unwilling to off to bed. The crowd invited him to join their game and play a few rounds with them. He was unwilling to say that he didn't have the energy to do it, and told them instead that he didn't find any release in machiang; "Pawning the Jewel" or

"Nine Cards" were more to his taste, for all they were low class gambling games. The crowd didn't want to change midway, and the best he could do was to sit at one side watching them. To get up a little energy he drank a few more cups of wine, and with every sound that came out of his mouth he was saying that here he'd given a party and didn't even get enough to eat himself; moreover he bore a grudge against the cook for squeezing too much money; the food had not really been plentiful at all.

With this question of the insufficiency of the food as a starting point, he took every item with which in the course of the day he had felt well content and reversed himself on the whole lot of them. The matshed, the furnishings, the cooking, were none of them worth what he had paid for them. They were snatching at his big head, all swindles!

By this time Mr. Feng, who had charge of the accounts, had got them all recorded and added up. The receipts were: twenty-five scrolls inscribed with verses of longevity; three chapel-sets of longevity cakes baked in the shape of the peaches of immortality; a similar quantity of the noodles of long life; an earthenware jug full of the wine of the undying; two sets of candles of endless light; and a little less than twenty dollars in ceremonial money. The list of the contributors was not a short one, but the greater number had given forty coppers or ten cents in large money.

Hearing this report, Fourth Master Liu's fire blazed even higher. If he had known ahead of time that this was the way it would be, he should properly have prepared fried noodles with a few chopped vegetables! Eat a feast of three great courses, and give out only a ten-cent piece in friendship money? In simple truth this was taking the old man for a big-headed simpleton asking to be defrauded. From this time forward he would never hold another affair; he could not afford to lose the money that he had thrown down this black hole! There was no use talking about it: everybody, including both his relatives and his friends, all of them, had thought of nothing but eating a free meal off him. A man of sixty-nine, clever all his life, had turned around and played the fool for this one time, and let a flock of turtle-egg bastards whose real fathers had been monkeys eat him alive!

The more the old man thought about it the more enraged he became. Even the fact that during the daytime he had felt pleased about some of the things was now only further evidence to him of his stupidity. With these thoughts filling his heart, his lips were giving continuous voice to them, embellished by many an ancient epithet that long ago had dropped out of currency in the streets.

Not all of his friends had left and in her solicitude for the face of all concerned, Tiger Girl thought to check her father in his loud bluster and deliberate rudeness. But seeing that the guests were all engrossed in their machiang counters, and were apparently taking no note at all of whatever the old man might be muttering about, she felt it a little inconvenient to open her mouth in the matter, lest she make it only the more obvious. Let him go ahead with his grumbling: if everybody pretended to be deaf, it would pass off harmlessly.

How was she to know that the old man would keep on talking and talking until he had got the subject worked around to herself? She determined that she was not going to swallow this particular line of talk: he wanted to celebrate his birthday, and she had rushed about in all the confusion for many days, and in the end she was to get no good out of it. She wouldn't accept that complaisantly. Whether he was sixty-nine or seventy-nine, he had to have some regard for straight reasoning. Quickly she turned it back on himself: "It was you yourself who wanted to spend your money in a celebration. What harm is that to me?"

Meeting with this resistance, the old man's energy leapt suddenly upward. "What harm is it to you? You're to blame for the whole thing! Do you think my eyes see nothing of what goes on around them?"

"What have you seen? I've worked myself weary all day, and at the finish of it you take out your temper on me. Wait a little, wait a little. Say it, what did you see?" Tiger Girl's weariness was all gone too, and her lips were exceptionally quick and handy.

"You needn't watch over my celebrations with your hot eyes. See? I saw the whole thing long ago. Heng!"

Tiger Girl's head shook from side to side in anger. "What are my eyes hot about? What have you actually seen?"

"What haven't I seen! Isn't that—" Fourth Liu pointed into the matshed; Happy Boy was there, his back bent over in the act of sweeping the floor.

"Him?" Tiger Girl shuddered; she had not thought the old man's eyes could be as sharp as that. "Heng! What about him?"

"Don't press so closely that the thing becomes clear. Talk stupidly about it, as if you didn't understand." The old man got to his feet. "If you want him, you won't have me. If you want me, you can't have him. I'm telling you crisply and directly. I'm your father, and it's proper that I should make this my business."

Tiger Girl had not anticipated that the affair would break so quickly; her own plan had only been carried to the halfway point, and the old man had already punctured the cunning behind her campaign. What should she do? Her face grew red, a dark purple red; add to that the half-death-like hue of her powder, and the gray-green whiteness of the light of the carbide lamp, and she looked like an overcooked piece of pig's liver, her coloring was so splotched and repulsive. She was tired, this thing had sharply excited her, the fire in her spleen had leaped in flame, she could think of no plan, and her heart was terribly confused. She could not just crawl back into her hole like a whipped animal; for all the confusion in her heart, she must still find a course of action to follow, and find it quickly. The worst and most unsound plan would be better than not having any plan at all. Never had she submitted, never had she accepted the part of the weaker person in the face of any man. All right, she would come out with a clear frank heart and make a clean-cut issue of it, and let success or failure, a good result or a bad one, all depend on this one hammer blow.

"All right," she said, "that's good enough. We'll talk the whole thing out clearly today. Let's figure that you've got the account straight, that your statement of it is right, what are you going to do about it? I'd just like to hear! But remember that you found this sickness for yourself. Don't claim that I've got it in my heart to deliberately upset you!"

The machiang players acted as if they heard the father and daughter quarreling, but could not bring themselves to divide their attention between their ivory counters and the affairs of the household of their host, and so, to resist the noise which would have distracted them, they were all slapping their counters down on the table and shuffling them back and forth with the greatest éclat; their lips were loud with the phrases of the play, and a player who filled his hand would shout "Strike" with almost too great a vehemence.

Happy Boy had overheard the affair and already understood it. He kept his head low as before and went on sweeping, but in the waters of his heart his feet had touched bottom. To say what he felt in another way: "Their mothers'!"

"You're simply trying to anger me!" The old man's eyes had already grown round with glaring. "You want to drive me into such a rage that I'll die of it, so you can use my money to buy yourself a man? There's no use in your planning on that. I still have a few years longer to live!"

"There's no use in your dragging out a lot of idle gossip to put on display. What are we talking about? I asked you, what are you going to do?" Tiger Girl's heart was beating so loudly she could hear the pooh-tung, pooh-tung of its rhythm above the sound of her voice, but her lips still moved facilely and with speed. "What am I going to do? Haven't I already said—if you want him you can't have me, and if you want me you can't have him. I can't give everything I've got to a stinking rickshaw man just because he's looking for a mean advantage."

Happy Boy threw his broom aside, straightened his waist and stood erect. Looking squarely at Fourth Liu, he asked:

"Who are you talking about?"

Fourth Master Liu broke into mad laughter. "Ha, ha! You, you're a slick one! You're thinking of rebellion, are you? I'm talking about you. Who am I talking about! Squirm away from here, in a hurry! Squirm! Because I thought you were all right, and gave you countenance, you dare to dream of digging foundations on the face of the planet Jupiter. What I am and what I do, you didn't stop to inquire. Squirm! Never again let me see you. You come his mother's over here to take a cheap advantage, ah?"

The sound of the old man's voice had grown overly loud, and had attracted some of the rickshaw men who came out to see the excitement. The machiang players were under the impression that the Fourth Master had got into another of his quarrels with some rickshaw puller, and went on with their play, still unwilling to raise their heads from it long enough to look and see what was going on.

Happy Boy was not facile in the use of his lips; the things he thought of saying were very numerous, but not a single sentence of all of them ever came to his tongue. So he stood there in dumb silence, stretching his neck and swallowing spittle.

"Squirm away from here! Squirm, quick! So you were going to play a cheap trick on me? I was dealing in trickery before there was such a person as you! Heng!" In his shouting at Happy Boy the old man seemed a little as if he were shouting purely to be shouting. The hatred he had in his heart for Happy Boy was nowhere near so sharp and bitter as that he felt for his daughter. It was as if even in his anger he recognized that in all truth Happy Boy was well-disposed and decently behaved.

"All right, I'll leave!" There was nothing more that Happy Boy could say. All he could do was to get away from here as quickly as possible. However things might come out, he knew he could not match either of those two in quarreling.

The rickshaw men had originally come in to see the excitement, but when they saw that Fourth Master Liu was cursing out Happy Boy, they all remembered the act that morning and felt delighted. But when it came to hearing that the old man was driving Happy Boy out, they all went over to his side. He had labored at so wearisome a task, and now that the river was crossed the old man was tearing down the bridge; he had no more use for Happy Boy, and was turning his face against him and would not recognize him. They all felt for Happy Boy the unfairness of this treatment. Several of them hurried over to him.

"What's the trouble, Happy Boy?"

Happy Boy could only shake his head.

"Wait a little before you go!" It was as if the lightning had struck in Tiger Girl's heart. She saw with full clarity: her plan was useless now. Haste is not the equal of speed. She must quickly grab hold of Happy Boy: if she had scared away the chicken she must not at the same time break the egg. "The two of us are alike a couple of crickets tied to one string: neither can run away from the other. You wait, wait until I have explained things clearly."

She turned her head about and plunged the knife of her words straight at the old man. "I'll tell you crisply: I'm with child—Happy Boy's! Wherever he goes, I'm going with him. Will you give me to him or are you going to drive us both out together? We'll listen to a single sentence in answer."

Tiger Girl had not imagined with what speed affairs would move, or how early she would be obliged to fall back on this, her last stratagem. Fourth Master Liu was even less prepared for this turn of the play, or for the fact that it could ever have been brought to such a pass as this. But it had already come to it. He could not submit, especially before so many people.

"You really have the face to say a thing like that openly? This old face of mine blushes for you, burns with fever for you!" He slapped himself hard across the mouth. "P'ei! You are shameless!"

The machiang players brought their quick fingers to rest, feeling that there was a little something going on that lacked somewhat of the right flavor. But they were in complete confusion, not knowing what business this was or how it had come about. They could not join the conversation, or make any reasonably sensible remark; some of them stood up, and others sat stupidly staring at the ivory counters lying on the table before them.

Having said everything that she could say, Tiger Girl felt

213

happy. "I'm shameless? Don't force me to tell about you and your affairs. There isn't any kind of excrement you haven't pushed out of your bowels. This is the first time for me, and it, too, is all your fault. When a boy grows to manhood, you should find him a wife, and when a girl matures she should be given in marriage. You're sixty-nine years old—you've wasted your life and learned nothing! It isn't because there are people here that I'm saying this." Tiger Girl paused to point to the group about them. "The best thing is to get everything clear. Let's act with clear eyes and understanding hearts. We'll take this matshed of felicity—you have only to perform one more ceremony in it, and everything will be all right."

"Me?" Fourth Master Liu's face turned from red to white, and bringing out all the spirit of the earlier days when he was a "bare stick" and a tough on the streets of the old capital, he said, "I would burn this matshed down before I would let you use it."

"Good!" Tiger Girl's lips were trembling, and the tone of her voice was unpleasant to hear. "If I roll up my bedding and leave, how much money will you give me?"

"The money is mine, and I'll give it only to the people I want to give it to." When the old man had heard his daughter say she was going to leave, his heart had been pained, but he had steeled himself to have out this quarrel.

"Your money? I've helped you all these years, and no part of it's mine? You think about it in your own heart. It'll be a wonder if you don't spend all your money supporting prostitutes. We'll let the good in our hearts be our guide!" Her eyes sought out Happy Boy. "Say something!"

Happy Boy only stood there, very erect, without a thing to say.

214

15

REGARDING the use of violence, Happy Boy could not hit an old man nor could he raise his fist against a woman. There was no direction, then, in which to employ his strength. And to act the part of the slick scoundrel, so as to turn the situation to his own advantage and play these two off against each other for what he could get out of them, was a thing he could only think about and could not actually carry through. Concerning Tiger Girl, he was fully ready to shake his feet and run away. On account, however, of the scene that was being acted out before his eyes, in which it was made to appear that she was sacrificing herself for him, there was nothing he could do before all these people but put on something of a heroic and protective air. There was nothing that he could say; all he would do was to stand there waiting for the unending flow of water finally to reveal the stones. But that, as least, he must do; anything less would make him appear to be lacking in the qualities of the true son of Han.

And all that there was left for the father and daughter of the Liu household to do was to glare fixedly at each other, since there was already nothing more that could be discussed and Happy Boy had closed his mouth tightly and would let no word escape from it.

As for the rickshaw men, it looked as if it would be very difficult for them to stick their lips into the matter, whichever side it was that they might favor. The machiang players could not remain silent: they had to speak, the absolute

215

quietness had already been so unbearably prolonged. The only difficulty was that they could only float with trivial lightness over the outside skin of the thing, saying a few sentences composed of surplus words, urging the two sides in conventionally acceptable phrases to desist, and not to hook too much of anger's hot fire on themselves, to talk the thing over in a leisurely way, that there was no barrier in the affair that could not be got over—this sort of thing they could say, but they couldn't solve anything and didn't want to solve anything. Seeing that neither side was willing to give way, there was nothing to do but slip away as soon as the opportunity afforded.

Without waiting for everyone to get away, Tiger Girl grabbed hold of Mr. Feng of the Coal Store In Accord With Heaven. "Mr. Feng, isn't there some room in your store? First let Happy Boy live there for a couple of days. If there's to be a ceremony for the two of us, it will be quickly carried out; he won't take up your space for any length of time. You go along with Mr. Feng, Happy Boy, and I'll see you tomorrow to talk over our affairs. I tell you, if I'm going out of the door of my father's house, I'll go in a flowered sedan chair as becomes a bride or I'll never step over the threshold. Mr. Feng, I'm handing him over to you, and tomorrow I'll hold you for his safe return to me."

Mr. Feng could do nothing but gulp. He did not want to undertake any such responsibility. Happy Boy was in a frantic haste to get away from there under any terms, and he spoke one sentence: "I wouldn't be able to escape—I won't run away."

Tiger Girl glared once more at the old man and went back into her own room, locking it from the inside. Then she cleared her throat and broke into loud sobs.

Mr. Feng and the others urged upon the Fourth Master the propriety of his going back into his room as well, but the old man managed to bring back into play some of the energy and spirit that belonged to him in his character as a man of the world, and he invited his guests not to leave, insisting instead on their having a few more cups of wine.

"All of you gentlemen may make yourselves easy in your hearts: from now on she is she, I am I, and we will never quarrel again. She may walk her own way, and it will only be as if I had never had any such little slave girl around me. For the whole period of my generation I have been out in the world, and here in one evening she has caused me to lose every vestige of face I ever had. If we could turn back twenty years, I would tie them living between wild horses and rend them apart. In this present time, I'll let her leave. But if she counts on getting a single copper from me, it will be ten thousand times difficult. A single copper—I won't give it! I won't give it! We'll see how she lives. Let her taste of it and she'll know whether in the end her father was good, or it's some ignorant scoundrel, some wild man, who is good. Don't leave, have another cup of wine!"

The crowd found a few pointless sentences to say, and all made haste to get away, to avoid being involved in scandal.

Happy Boy went to the Coal Store In Accord With Heaven.

In all truth the affair was carried out very quickly. In the Cove of the Mao Family Tiger Girl rented two small rooms with a northern exposure that were on one of those large courtyards which a number of leaseholders share in common, the living quarters around it being cut up, tenement-like, into a number of little cubbyholes. Immediately she called in a paper hanger and had the four walls covered with bright clean whiteness right down to the floor. Then she entreated Mr. Feng to write a few felicitous characters, and when he had done so, she had them pasted up on the walls of the room. When the rooms were ready, she went out to bargain for a sedan chair, one with all the silver stars in the heavens, sixteen musical instruments to accompany it, but no gold lanterns and no conductor. When the terms had been talked out and agreed upon, she got out her red satin, embroidered, sedan-chair dress; she had prepared it before

217

the New Year celebrations so that she would not have to break the taboo that forbids one to move one's needle until the fifth day of the New Year has passed. The sixth was appointed the Day of Felicity since that was a lucky day in the calendar of astrology, and also it would not be necessary on it to follow the superstitious usages about the birth-dates of those who cross the threshold of the newly married.

All of these things she arranged herself, and instructed Happy Boy to go out and buy a new set of clothes from his head to his feet. "There's only one time like this in one lifetime."

In his hands Happy Boy had only five dollars.

Once more Tiger Girl glared. "What? The thirty-odd dollars that I turned over to you?"

There was nothing Happy Boy could do but tell the truth, so he took the whole story of the Ts'ao family affair and told it all to her. She blinked her eyes at him as if she half believed and half suspected him. "All right, I haven't any time to quarrel with you. Each of us must act according to his own conscience. I'll give you fifteen dollars. And if when the day comes you aren't fitted out like a new fellow, you better be prepared to defend yourself."

On the sixth day of the New Year Tiger Girl climbed into her sedan chair. She had not exchanged a sentence with her father; she had neither elder nor younger brothers to escort her; she had no relatives or friends there to tender felicitations; she had only the gongs and the drums to make their loud clamor along streets that had so recently seen the celebrations of the New Year. Moving in a stable and even progression, firm and secure, the sedan chair was borne through the Gate of Western Peace and under the Four Western Arches; and in the hearts of people in the streets, wearing their new clothes for the New Year, and especially among the helpers in the shops, it aroused a certain feeling of admiration and stimulated emotions of longing or remembrance.

Happy Boy wore the new clothes he had bought near the Bridge of Heaven, and above his red face, scrubbed clean, there sat one of those little velvet caps that cost thirty cents apiece. It was as if he had forgotten himself and was watching everything with a dumb unreflectiveness, unaware that he had any part in it. Listening to all of it, he did not even recognize himself. From a coal store he had moved into a new room that was freshly papered and as white as snow. He did not know how that had come about: everything that had happened previously was exactly like a coal store—there was one heap after another and all of them black. Now suddenly he had been transported into a new room, so white that it dazzled his eyes, with the walls stuck over here and there with writings as red as blood.

He felt somehow as if he were being manipulated, played with, made sport of. It was a vague, misty, limitless feeling of resentment and depression, all glaring in white.

The rooms were furnished with the table, chairs, and bed that had been Tiger Girl's in her father's house; the stove and the kitchen table were in truth new, and in the corner was hung a duster made of chicken feathers of many colors. He recognized the old table and the chairs, but toward the stove, the kitchen table, and the chicken-feather duster he felt estranged and at variance. Mixing the old furniture up with the new and putting it all in the same place within the same four walls made him recollect the things that had passed, the old things, and confronted him with the uncertainty and anxieties of the future, with all the fears that new things bring. In everything he was allowing some other to do with him as that other pleased; he, too, was some kind of piece of furniture or ornament, some strange, queer thing that seemed at the same time to be completely new and to be identical with something out of the past; he did not know himself, was not sure of his own name and identity. He could not think to cry, nor think to laugh; moving about in this warm little room, acutely conscious of his big hands and feet, he

felt like a great rabbit caught in a frail little bamboo cage, looking with avid eyes at the world outside and then glancing around at the cramped wooden space within; legs that could run with the speed of flight were useless now—he could not get out.

Tiger Girl wore her red jacket, and on her face she had rubbed white powder and red rouge. Her eyes flowed after him, lapping like water around every move he made. He did not dare look straight into those eyes of hers: she, too, was some strange thing that was both old and new, both familiar and unfamiliar; she was at once a girl and a woman; she had the seeming of being a woman and yet the seeming of being a man; she was like a human being and at the same time was like some evil, savage, malignant beast. This beast in the red jacket had already pounced upon him, captured him, and now she was preparing to dispose of him bit by bit, very carefully and with relish. Anybody could do what they wanted with him, but this beast was dangerous and sharp and cruel beyond any of the others. She kept guard over him every moment, never letting him get an inch away, glaring at him, laughing at him, and then pulling him to her, holding him very tightly in her arms, her legs locked around him, her lips on his to silence him while by another soft function she sucked out his strength until all his strength was gone.

He had no way to escape her. He took his little round velvet cap in his hands, staring stupidly at the red button on top of it until his eyes became blurred, and when he turned his face up again the white wall was covered with red buttons swirling about, shimmering up and down, until from their center there evolved a red button larger than any of the others, that splotched the whole wall with red, and the face of it was a human face, smiling a stinking, leering, ugly smile: the face was the face of Tiger Girl.

It was not until the evening of their marriage, their first wedding night, that Happy Boy understood: Tiger Girl was not pregnant at all! Like a magician in a juggling act, she explained the whole thing to him with the greatest ease: "If I hadn't deceived you that way, how would you ever have come to deaden your heart and walk the hard earth of reality and lower your head in submission? I put a pillow inside the waistband of my trousers. Ha, ha! Ha, ha!" She laughed until the tears came to her eyes. "You stupid thing! Let's not talk any more about it. At any rate, I have no reason to be ashamed to face you—I owe you nothing. You're the kind of a person you are, and I'm the kind of person I am. You ought to thank the heavens and thank the earth—I came right out and fought with my father to follow you."

On the morning of the second day, Happy Boy got up very early and went out. Most of the stores had already opened up for business again after the holidays, but some of the private residences still had their front gates closed. The New Year mottoes written on strips of red paper and pasted on the doors were as full and red and voluptuous as before, but the strings of yellow paper ingots had some of them been torn by the wind. The street was quiet and cold and unstirred by any warmth of feeling, but for all of that there were still quite a number of rickshaws passing up and down it. The rickshaw pullers seemed to have more energy than on other days; they nearly all of them wore new shoes, and on the back of their rickshaws they had pasted squares of red paper for good luck. Happy Boy admired and envied these rickshaw men: he felt that they really had the manner and bearing, had caught the spirit of passing the New Year as properly it should be, while he had for many days been caught up inside of a dark suffocating gourd. They all seemed to be on their way, each contented with his lot and minding his own business, while he had no occupation and was idling along the highway as aimlessly as one of the long wooden signs hung over the sidewalk as a store-mark waves back and forth in the breeze.

He was not at peace in this complete idleness, but if he calculated to give some thought to tomorrow's affairs, the only thing he could do would be to go and discuss them with Tiger Girl—his wife! His wife, the kind of a wife he had, was keeping him and he was eating the food that she fed him. It was for an empty nothing that he had grown so tall, and for nothing but emptiness that he had such great strength: neither was of any use. His primary reason for being was to provide his old woman with the service she incessantly required—she, that red-jacketed and tiger-toothed creature who was neither man nor beast, who sucked his blood and siphoned off into her own body the very milk of his virility. Already he was no longer a man, but a single

222

piece of bone, a single extension of flesh. He had no self that was his self, but was the prey that she had got her teeth into, that was hanging from her jaws, like a little mouse dangling from the mouth of a cat.

He did not want to go discuss anything with her. The thing for him to do was to go away, to think out his own plans carefully, and to part from her without so much as taking his leave of her. There was nothing in such a course that would make it difficult for him to face her before his own conscience; she was an evil spirit in the shape of a woman who had been capable of using a pillow to play him a cheap trick of sleight-of-hand.

In the dark den of his heart his spirit lay sick, gnawing out the walls of its house. He wanted to tear that new suit of clothes of his into strips and fragments, and, more than that, he wanted to put himself into a pool of pure water and cleanse himself; inside as well as out; he felt that his whole body was covered with some stinking, sticky impurity, some unclean thing that gave him a feeling of nausea, that vexed him from his very heart. He did not want ever to see her face again.

Where should he go? He had no objective. Ordinarily, pulling a rickshaw, his legs went in the direction set for them by the lips of his fare. Today, although his legs might take him where they chose—they were free—his heart was surprised and confused. Following along the Four Western Arches, he turned due south and came out through the Gate of Martial Display: the road was so straight that his heart was less able than ever to turn the corner that it had to turn. Coming out of the city gate, he kept on walking south until he saw a bathhouse. He decided to go in.

He undressed himself and stood in his complete nakedness looking down at his body, feeling the deepest sensation of shame and mortification. When he got down into the bathing pool the hot water boiled him so that he became wooden with numbness all over. He closed his eyes and lay back, his body relaxing in a

223

drugged drowsiness and giving forth all the collected filth within it as it would give forth sweat. He was almost afraid to soap himself; his heart was empty of everything and his forehead was wet with big pearls of sweat. Only when his breathing was becoming labored did he manage slowly and lazily to crawl up out of the tub, his whole body as red as that of a new born baby. It was as if he did not dare step out all naked like that; with a towel around his middle he still felt unsightly and ugly, and with the dripping perspiration dropping *bee-da by-da* to the rattan mat on which he stood, he still felt that he was not clean: it was as if the stain of impurity, the spot of filth in his own heart could never in any eternity be washed away. In the eyes of the Fourth Master, in the eyes of everyone who knew him, he would always be a man who stole women.

Before his perspiration had gone completely down, he dressed himself in the greatest haste and rushed out of the bathhouse. He was afraid that people would see him naked, would guess the shame of the way he was living. On the street again, with the cold wind blowing on him, he felt light and easy and free; the tension seemed gone. The streets were busier and much more gay than they had been earlier. The resounding clarity of the bright heavens lent everyone's face a little of its gayness and light, but Happy Boy's heart still felt as if some hand were clutching it, and he didn't know where it was best to go.

He turned south and then east and then south again, crossing over by the Bridge of Heaven. At nine o'clock on a morning just after the New Year, the apprentices in the shops would already have finished their early rice and come here. Every color of street stall, every kind of acrobat's tent, had all been set up and arranged very early. When Happy Boy arrived, the place was already surrounded by circle after circle of people, and in the center were men beating on gongs and drums. He had no heart to watch any amusement; he was already incapable of smiling.

Ordinarily the mimics that were here, the men with their trained Tibetan bears, the magicians, the counters of coming treasures, the singers of the rice-planting songs, the tellers of the stories out of the ancient books, the war dancers, could all of them give him a little of true happiness, making him open his mouth wide and laugh. The fact that he could not do without Peking, that he could not bear to leave the city, was at least half due to the Bridge of Heaven. Whenever it came into his mind, or he had a chance to go there, it would bring to his memory countless laughable and lovable things. Now he had no spirit to press forward among the crowd, and the sound of the laughter at the Bridge of Heaven already lacked for the share that he had always contributed. He turned away from the mobs, seeking to walk towards some spot where he could be quiet and alone, but again he felt loath to leave. No, he could not leave this lively, colorful, bustling place that was so much to be loved. He could not leave the Bridge of Heaven, he could not leave Peking.

Go away? There was no road along which he could walk. He would still have to go back to her—to her!—and discuss what to do. He could not leave, and he could not go on in idleness. He would have to retreat one step in his thinking, exactly as everyone does in that hour when there is no other recourse. He had suffered every kind of wrong, and why should he go now screaming for the truth at this one added grievance? He could not straighten out all the crooked things in the past, and so the best thing he could do was to keep on walking down the road that he was already on.

He stood still, listening to the confused sounds of people's voices, of the beating of drums and songs, and watching the endless currents of those who came and those who went away, and the carriages and the horses, and suddenly he thought of the two little rooms. It was as if the sound that had been in his ears was gone, as if the people and things that had been before his eyes had disappeared. There was nothing but the two white warm little rooms with the red characters pasted on the walls, clean and straight and in good order before his eyes. Although he had only lived there one night, the place was still extraordinarily familiar and intimate. Even that woman who wore the red jacket seemed now to be something that could not be forsaken at pleasure. Standing there on the Bridge of Heaven, he had nothing and was nothing; in those two little rooms he had everything. He would go back: only by going back would he find the means of meeting his situation. Everything that belonged to tomorrow was in that little room. Shame, fear of involvement, the feeling that things were hard to live through, were all useless; if he calculated to live, he would have to go back to the place where he could find a plan.

He walked back in one breath; when he entered the room, it was just eleven o'clock. Tiger Girl had finished cooking the forenoon meal: steamed dumplings, boiled cabbage with meat balls, cold pig's skin, a dish of pickled turnips. Everything was on the table except the cabbage, which was still on the fire and giving out the most beautiful of fragrant odors. She had already taken off her red jacket, and wore again the cotton trousers and cotton jacket of ordinary times, although she still wore in her hair the little cluster of red velvet flowers, a tiny ingot of gold paper in their midst. And she still wore, too, a little of that air of self-satisfaction, of pleasure with one's self for having got what one wanted.

Happy Boy glanced at her. She did not look like a new wife. Every act and movement was that of a woman who has been married for many years. She was quick, ready, expert, and old in experience. In spite of the fact that she did not seem like a new wife, at bottom she made him feel a little something new, something that he had never felt before: her cooking for him, her cleaning the room, the faint fragrance of the place, its warmth, all were things that he had not experienced before. It did not matter what sort of person she was; he felt that she had

226

made him a home, and a home always has points about it that a person can love.

"Where'd you go?" She served the cabbage as she questioned him.

"I went to have a bath," he answered, taking off his long gown.

"Ah! After this, when you go out, say something to me about it. Don't just heedlessly fling up your hands as if you were angry and walk off."

He said nothing.

"Are you able to say as much as 'heng' or not? To show at least that you've heard what I said? If you can't, I'll teach you how."

He made the sound, "Heng!" There was nothing else he could do. He knew he had married the bitch that whelps the night demons that fly like meteors, messengers of hell, but this mother of the night demons could cook and she could keep the room clean; she could curse him and she could help him too. But whatever she did for him, the taste of it would always be wrong. He started eating the dumplings. It was a fact that the food was more appetizing, and came hotter from the fire, than he was used to eating. For all of that, he ate without relish; as he chewed the food his heart could not find the joy that was ordinarily his in his wolfish appetite. This was not one of those meals where he could eat until he perspired.

When he had finished eating, he stretched out on the brick bed, linking his hands behind his head for a pillow and looking up at the ceiling.

"Hi! Help me clean the dishes! I'm not somebody's slave girl!" she called from the outer room.

Reluctantly he got up, looked at her, and went through the door of the paper partition to help her. Usually he was extraordinarily diligent and hard-working, but now he worked with his lips closed tight to keep the anger from coming out. At the rickshaw shed, he had frequently helped her out, but now the more he saw of her the more she disgusted him. Never in all his life had he hated anyone as sharply and as deeply as he hated her. He could not explain why it was. Turning around and around in these tiny rooms, he felt as if his destiny was just one long grievance, as if it were a sin against him that he should ever have lived.

When they had finished putting the dishes away, she swept the four walls with a glance, and sighed. Then she began to smile.

"How about it?"

"What?" Happy Boy was squatting down by the stove warming his hands. His hands were not cold at all, but because there was no proper place to put them, the best he could do was to warm them. In truth these two little rooms did seem like a home, but he never knew where best to put his hands and feet when he was in them.

"Won't you take me out? Can't we go some place to amuse ourselves? To the White Cloud Monastery? No, it's a little late for that—couldn't we just go out and saunter on the streets?" She wanted to taste to the very fullest all the joys of the new bride. Although her wedding had not been fit to behold, on the other hand it was good to be so completely without all the ordinary conventional restraints, and the best thing about it was that she could be more with her husband, and could spend these few days with him in abandoned play. In her father's house, she had not lacked for food or clothing or money to spend. The one thing she had lacked had been a man whom her heart could know. Now she wanted to make good for all the years of drought; she wanted to swagger about the streets, in the temples and the market places, with Happy Boy to play with her.

Happy Boy was unwilling to go. In the first place he felt that to go all over the world sight-seeing with your old woman in tow was a thing to be ashamed of, and in the second place he held that an old woman acquired in the way he had acquired his old woman could only properly be hidden away in the home; this affair was not one to be proud of, and the less you waved it before the eyes of other people the better it would be. There was one more thing: once they went out, how could they avoid meeting people they knew? There wasn't a rickshaw boy in the western half of the city who had not heard the story of Happy Boy and Tiger Girl; he could not go out on the streets just to give occasion to people to titter behind his back.

"Let's discuss it, shall we?" He was still squatting by the stove.

"What is there to discuss?" She strode across and stood by the side of the stove.

He took his hands down and put them over his kneecaps. Dumbly he watched the flames of the fire. He was stuck like a wooden pole in this distraught vacancy of his for a long time, and finally he spoke a single sentence: "I can't be idle like this."

"Your destiny is to work and be weary." She laughed shortly. "When you go for a whole day without pulling a rickshaw, you begin to itch all over. Isn't that true? Look at the old man—he spent all his life in idleness, and when he was old he opened a rickshaw shed. He never pulled a rickshaw, and never sold his strength. He depended for his rice on the ways that opened in his heart. If you insist on pulling a rickshaw all your life, what reward do you expect to get for that? Let's first enjoy ourselves for a few days, and then talk about it again. It's not just in these two or three days that business will be good. Why are you in such a hurry? You're just taking advantage of the fact that I don't mean to quarrel with you these two days, and you're purposely trying to make me angry."

"We'll first discuss it." Happy Boy was determined not to give in. Since he could not simply shake his feet and be gone, he had to think of some way of getting to work. And the first thing that he had to do was to take up a firm position—he could not keep going back and forth like a child in a rope swing.

"All right, tell me what you want to say." She moved a stool over and sat down by the side of the stove.

"How much money have you got?" he asked.

"Isn't it true? I knew you were going to ask me just that. You didn't marry a wife, you married that bit of money, didn't you?"

It was as if Happy Boy had been caught in a sudden strong gust of wind and knocked breathless. He swallowed several mouthfuls of air. Old Man Liu and the rickshaw men at the Human Harmony Rickshaw Shed, all thought it was because he was covetous of her money that he had been brought to form his illicit connection with Tiger Girl. Now she herself had put that same suspicion into words. Without cause or reason he had lost his own rickshaw and then later his own money, and now he was to be crushed beneath a few dirty dollars of his old woman's. It was as if the very food he ate had to go down his backbone instead of his gullet, it was that hard to swallow. He hated himself for not being able to clench his two hands around her throat and choke her and choke her and choke her until her eyes turned back into her head and only the whites of them showed. He would choke it all to death, the whole thing. He felt his own throat. They weren't people, either of them. They should both die. He wasn't a human being himself—he should die too; neither of them, none of them, need hope to live.

Happy Boy stood up, thinking to go out to walk a while. His coming back to the place a little while ago had been a mistake.

Seeing that Happy Boy's color and expression were not right, she became again a little more easy and accommodating. "All right, I'll tell you. I had a little less than five hundred dollars to start with. Counting the sedan chair, the rent—three payments —papering the room, having clothes made, buying utensils and things, and adding in what I gave you, throwing it all in to- gether, it comes to less than a hundred dollars, and I've still got a little less than four hundred dollars left. I tell you, you've no reason to be anxious or get excited. When we have a chance to be happy, let's be happy. You—the whole year through you pull a rickshaw and are stinking with sweat. You ought to just play for two or three days, and be smart and fresh and attractive. For my part, I've filled the post of an old maid for all these years—I ought to have a few days of pleasure too. Wait until we've spent almost all our money, and then we can go back again and seek the old man's help. I—if I hadn't fought with him that night, I would never have had to leave. Now that my anger's gone, papa after all is still papa. From his side, he's only got me for a daughter—there are no other children, and you're a person that he's very fond of. We have only to be a little meek and submissive, and apologize for our fault, and in all probability there's nothing in the matter that can't be got over. How made to order it all is! He's got money, we're in the direct descent, and in perfect seemliness and propriety we inherit it from him. There's nothing in the slightest wrong or unreasonable about it. And how much better that is than your going out and being a transport animal for anybody who hires you.

"After two or three days, you go once—he probably won't be willing to see you. If he won't see you the first time, go a second time. That will give him all the face, and then there'll be nothing for him to do but repent and change his ideas. When that has happened, I'll go and right or wrong I'll give him a few sentences that it will please him to hear. I wouldn't say for certain but that we won't be able to move back. And once we move back, I guarantee that if we hold our chests out, there won't be anyone who will dare look askance at us. If we just go on indefinitely putting up with this, we'll always be like a pair of branded people, or criminals—don't you agree with me?"

Happy Boy had never thought this over. From the day that Tiger Girl had come to the Ts'ao family house to look for him, he had taken it for granted that after he took her to wife he would use her money to buy himself a rickshaw, and go out himself and pull it. Although using your old woman's money

231

was not a very self-respecting thing to do, still, since the relationship between himself and her was one of those that you could not explain even if you had the mouth with which to tell about it, there just wasn't any help for it. He had not thought that Tiger Girl had a stratagem like this one in her mind. If you put aside the mask, and gave up all idea of face, naturally there was in all truth a real scheme. But Happy Boy was not that sort of a person. Thinking of all that had happened, of the things that had happened before and the things that had happened afterward, he seemed to begin to understand a little. His own money —he would let somebody else steal it from him without any cause, and without giving him any return, and he had no one to whom to take his grievance. So that you're in a position where if someone else gives you money, you have no choice but to accept it, and after you have accepted it, you are absolutely unfitted from that time forward to regard yourself as a man. Your chest is for nothing, your strength is for nothing—you must be another person's slave, you must afford your wife her favorite plaything, you must serve as the male slave of an aged father-in-law. It seemed that at the roots of a thing a man was nothing; he was at best like a bird. If it goes itself to find its food, it may well fall into the trapper's net; if it eats the grain that another provides, it must remain obedient and well-behaved within its cage, singing its shrill song when that is required of it, and facing the possibility of being sold by its master whenever he chooses to do so.

He was unwilling to go hunting for Fourth Master Liu. With Tiger Girl his relationship was one of flesh within flesh; with the Fourth Master he had no connection whatever. He had already suffered by reason of this woman, and he would not on her account go begging of her father.

"I don't want to go on being idle." Of all that he had thought he spoke only this one sentence, in order to avoid wasting words and quarreling futilely.

"Destined to toil and be weary." She said it as if it were a club with which one could pound one's opponent at will. "If you don't want to be idle, go into some kind of business—sell something."

"I can't do it. I wouldn't make money. I can pull a rickshaw—I love to pull a rickshaw!" The blood vessels stood out on top of Happy Boy's shaven head.

"I tell you, I just won't permit you to pull a rickshaw! I just won't have you coming onto my brick bed with me when your whole body is red from running and stinking with sweat. You've got your plans and I've got mine. You see which of us can irritate the most. You took a wife, but I spent the money. You didn't find a little copper of it anywhere else. Think about that for a while. Of the two of us, who should obey who?"

Once again Happy Boy had nothing to say.

16

$\mathcal{I}$T was already the time of the festival of the fifteenth day of the first lunar month, and Happy Boy was still loafing around. He could stand it no longer.

Tiger Girl was in high spirits. She had set about cooking the food of the festival, the little round rice balls that have year after year for hundreds and hundreds of years been appropriate to it, and the wrapped meat dumplings that Happy Boy loved. In the daytime she would have it that they sight-see among the many Buddhist temples, and at night they must go out and stroll about the streets to see the lighted lanterns that had been hung out before shops and homes. She did not permit Happy Boy to put forward a single proposal of his own on any subject, but she took care that he should never lack for tasty food to put in his mouth. She was always reforming her methods, continually changing her approach, contriving to buy and prepare fresh new dishes for him to eat.

In the common compound, sharing this one courtyard, were seven or eight families, the majority of them having only one room apiece. In that one room would be seven or eight people, old and young, all living together. Some of the men were rickshaw pullers, some of them street-hawkers, policemen, and others were household servants. Each had his work to do, and none had any leisure. Even the children would each of them shoulder a basket and go in the morning to collect a bowl of congee from the free rice kitchen, and in the afternoon to pick among the ash piles for pieces of unburned coal. It was only the very smallest children who resorted to the courtyard, their bare little behinds frozen a rosy red, to play and shriek and quarrel with each other.

The ashes from the stoves, the dust and dirt, the unclean water, were all thrown into the middle of the courtyard, and no one took any responsibility for cleaning it up. The water that had collected in the center was frozen solid, and the larger children, when they returned in the later afternoon from their coal-collecting expeditions, would use it as an ice rink, sliding back and forth on it, pushing each other over it, beating it with sticks, and all of them yelling at once.

The most miserable were the very old people and the women. The old people had neither food nor clothing, and lay all day on brick beds as cold as ice, waiting in empty idleness for the young to earn a pittance in coppers and bring it back at night, so that they could drink a bowl of thin rice gruel. Perhaps by the sale of their strength the young would have been able to earn that pittance, but it was just as likely that they would come

234

back with empty hands. When that happened they would come back angry and search for any opening to quarrel. Then the old people with their empty stomachs would have to take their tears for water and swallow them down.

The womenfolk had to take care of the old, mind the very young, and at the same time string along the younger men of the household who earned the money. They had to carry on their labors as usual even though they were pregnant, with only the same old flour cakes in the shape of birds' nests and congee made from white sweet potatoes. Not only would they carry on with their work just the same, they would try in some way or other to keep things going; they had to make shift to keep the others and themselves alive. If by good fortune the old and the young alike would all have had enough and have gone to bed, the women would have to cherish the scant light of a little kerosene lamp by which to wash and bake and sew and mend for the whole family. The room would be so small, the walls so dilapidated, that the cold wind would bore in through one side and blow straight out through the other, carrying off with it every breath of warm air there might have been.

About their bodies there would be wrapped a strip of torn cloth for clothing, and in their stomachs might be left a cup of thin gruel, and in their bellies might be a child six or seven months on the way. They had to do their work, and they had to do their best to see that old and young all had enough to eat. They would be sick in every part of their body, they would be losing their hair before they were thirty, but they could not rest for one minute or one second, and from sickness they walked on to death, and to buy their coffins it would be necessary to collect subscriptions from the charitable.

The growing daughters, sixteen or seventeen years old, would not even have a decent pair of trousers to wear, and could only wrap themselves in what tattered rags of garments their mothers could give them, and stay inside the room—a natural prison for them—helping their mothers do the work and mend the men's clothing. If they wanted so much as to go to the privy, they would have to look out first to see that there was no one in the courtyard before they scuttled across it like sneak thieves. Once winter came, they would not see the sun or clear weather. Those among them who were growing up to be ugly would in the future inherit everything that was their mothers', all the sickness and pain. Those who were nice to look at, who had an appearance, even they themselves knew that early or late their parents would sell them away—to "enjoy happiness."

It was just in this kind of a "common courtyard" that Tiger Girl felt very well pleased with herself. She alone had food to eat and clothes to wear, and did not need to be anxious. And, moreover, she could stroll about or go sight-seeing, all at her leisure. She stuck her face up high and proud both going out and coming in, and since she felt that her situation was due to her personal excellence, and was afraid that the others would

defile or provoke her, she gave no sign that she knew those poverty-stricken people so much as existed.

Almost all of the hawkers and hucksters who came to the place to carry on their trade were sellers of the cheapest grade of things, like scrapings of meat from the bone, frozen cabbage, thin bean gruel, horse and donkey meat. It was in places like these that they found their customers. From the time that the Tiger Girl moved in, the hawkers of sheepshead meat, of smoked fish, of hard biscuits made of wheat flour, of bean curd cooked in brine and then fried, would stop at the gate in passing to cry out their wares. She would come forth with her face stuck up and a bowl in her hands, shortly proceeding back to her room again, her bowl full of this miscellany of food. The children, sucking their bony fingers that were black and thin like little twisted strands of iron wire, would watch her in awe, as if she were some princess from a different world. But she had come here to receive, not to give, and she could not, would not, see the bitter sufferings of the others.

Happy Boy in the first place could not but regard this behavior with contempt. He was born in poverty, and he knew what deep poverty meant. He was not happy to eat all these miscellaneous odds and ends of stuff, all these tidbits—he regretted the money. In the second place—a thing which was even more unbearable: he had gradually worked through to the suggestion of an idea, as the stone polisher rubs through to the stone, that she was not permitting him to pull a rickshaw, and was seeing to it that he was well nourished every day on good meats and vegetables and good rice, just as you would fatten a cow to squeeze more milk out of her. He had become completely her plaything. He had seen it before: in the streets a lean old bitch in heat would choose the fattest and strongest of the young male dogs. Tiger Girl would know what she wanted and would know how to get it. When this thought was uppermost in his mind he not only abominated the kind of life he was living, but he was even concerned for his own proper person. He knew how carefully a man who sells his strength should protect his physical well-being: it was everything to him. Supposing that he should go on living like this, eating and sleeping with no other purpose than to build up virility for a bitch to suck out of him, would he not become one day nothing more than a dried-out framework of bones? Still the same height and the same size, but with only emptiness where his guts should be?

The thought made him shiver. He calculated that even if it meant risking his life he was still going out right away and pull a rickshaw, going out to run all day and come back at night and put his head down and sleep unconscious of everything else. He would not eat anymore of her tidbits, nor would he serve any more in her night-long games. He decided definitely on such a course of action, and he could not again give way; if she wanted to put out the money to buy a rickshaw, well and good; if she didn't want to, he would go rent one. Without making a sound about it, he thought the thing out in his own mind, and went and rented a rickshaw.

On the seventeenth of the first moon he started rickshaw-pulling again, renting his cart by the day. After he had pulled a couple of fares on relatively long jobs, he began to notice several slight weaknesses that he had never felt before. The calves of his legs became knotted and hard, as if he were about to have cramps in them, and in the groins and the joints of the thighs, the place where the thigh bones join the rest of the body, he was aware of a vague aching sensation. He knew well enough the source of his own illness, but in order to console himself he pretended that it was due to not having worked for over twenty days; that his legs were out of practice. When he had taken a few more trips and got used once more to running, there probably wouldn't be anything more to it.

Again he took a fare. This time it was in a group, four rickshaws together. Picking up the shafts of their rickshaws, the

238

company all gave way to a tall fellow in their midst, over forty years old, and asked him to lead. The tall one smiled: he knew that actually any one of the other three was a stronger staff than he was. But he was not afraid to use his strength, and although he knew clearly enough to begin with that he could not outrace these three young fellows, he was still not willing to trade on his age. When they had run for something over a third of a mile, one of the men behind called out to him in praise, "How's this? Are you trying to prove to us how good you are? You're certainly not far from one of the best."

In all truth he was not a slow runner; even Happy Boy had to bring out seven or eight parts of his strength just to keep up with him. But the way he ran was hard to look at. As tall as he was, he didn't seem to be able to bend at the waist. It was as if his back and waist were one solid flat piece of board plank, so that his whole body had to lean forward. This posture made his hands—gripping the shafts—seem to be too far back; he didn't look as if he was running, but as if he were weaving his way forward. With such a dead board as a backbone, his hips and buttocks could do nothing but flop back and forth and up and down, while his feet slipped along the ground, his whole body twisting forward with what seemed an always augmenting urgency. The twisting process was in effect a rapid one, but you knew from watching it that it cost a great deal of wasted strength. When it came to swinging around a circle or turning a corner, his whole body turned, like a man with a stiff neck who can't turn his head without turning his whole body in the same direction. The group sweat in their sympathy for him; he seemed always to think only of somehow getting forward, and the job seemed so grim a one for him that he had no energy left to pay any attention to what happened to the rickshaw he was pulling, or to the person who happened to be his passenger.

When he reached the destination, big drops of sweat that had formed on his head and face ran down from the tip of his nose, from the lobes of his ears, and from his lips, dripping down *pea da py da* as if they were racing to get to the ground. He put down the rickshaw shafts, straightened up quickly, and opened his mouth, peeling his lips back over his teeth. When he took the money that his fare proffered him his hand shook so that it did not look as if it had the strength to lay firm hold of anything.

Because the four rickshaw pullers had hauled a group-job together, they counted as friends, and they all stayed together when the job was done to wait for new fares. Happy Boy, like the others, wiped himself clean of perspiration while he joked and laughed with them. Only the tall one kept sweating for half the day, spending a long time coughing, a dry retching cough, and spitting out quantities of white spittle, before he gradually came around and could begin talking to them.

"I'm finished. My heart, the small of my back, my legs—there's no more strength to be got out of them. No matter how much I strain my thighs, I just can't make them lift my legs up in a free running stride—I only fret myself for nothing."

"Just now, those few paces we ran together, you were not lacking in much—do you regard that as slow travelling?" A short young fellow, twenty years old or so, had taken the conversation into his own hands. "I'm not trying to deceive you; honestly, the three of us are all stout enough sticks, and which one of us hasn't sweat as much as you have?"

The tall one was pleased a bit by that, but he sighed as if in mortification.

The short fellow said: "If we're speaking of the way you run, it doesn't lack by much of throwing you forward on your face, am I right?"

Another youngster said: "I'm not joking with you: I think it's a question of your age."

The tall one smiled a little and shook his head. "And yet it's not altogether a matter of age, my brothers. I'm going to tell you one sentence of the truth: people who follow our profession should never get married. It's the truth!" Seeing that the whole group had respectfully tendered him their ears, he dropped his voice a little. "Once you get married, in the deep of the dark night and the brightest daylight as well, you have to spend yourself, and the time comes when you're played out. Look at my torso—it's as if it were no longer a live, flexible thing. There's no more give left in it. I'd best not press myself too hard in my running: once I grit my teeth and really try to move, I begin to cough and my heart becomes a jungle of bitter confusion. There's no use talking about it—his mother's! When you do our work you've got to be a bare stick for your whole generation. Even the house sparrows travel in pairs, but it's not allowable that we should marry.

"Then there's another thing to be said. After you get married, you have a child every year. I've got five of them now. All with their mouths stretched open waiting to be fed. The rental for my rickshaw is high, grain and food are dear, my business is bad—what can I do? It would be better to have been a bare stick all my life, and whenever my strength flopped up at me, I'd go to one of the white houses where you pay to have it taken care of. And if later you break out with syphilitic sores, you just have to accept your fate. A single man can die, and when he's dead he's dead—that's all there is to that. But with a toy like this, if you ever get married, with all those mouths, you could die and you still wouldn't be able to close your eyes. Isn't that true?" he turned to ask of Happy Boy.

Happy Boy nodded his head, but said nothing.

Just then a fare came up, and although the short young fellow was the first to accost the prospective passenger and they settled upon a charge, he stepped aside, making way for the tall one to take the job. "Old Elder Brother, you take him. You've got five children at home."

The tall one smiled. "All right. I'll make one more trip, but I wouldn't take advantage of an offer like that ordinarily. But we'll let that be—when I go back to the house in a little while I'll be able to take one more piece of hard bread to the youngsters. See you soon again, my brothers."

Watching the tall one until he had gone off into the distance, the short fellow spoke as if to himself: "It's mother's! You drag along through a whole generation, and you can't even rub up a woman. And the others—their mothers'!—in one household one man hugs four or five women to himself."

"Don't talk about what the others do." The third among their number was speaking now. "You can see that in this business of ours you really do have to be careful. The tall one was not wrong in what he said. Let's just take what you were talking about. What is it that you get married to do? Can you take your wife and set her off somewhere as an ornament, a toy that's pretty to look at? You cannot. All right, then, there's where your trouble comes in. All day long you have nothing to eat but hard biscuits baked in the shape of birds' nests, and the strength you get out of them is attacked from two sides; no matter how husky a pole a youngster may be, he'll still have to crawl down."

When he had heard this much, Happy Boy picked up the shafts of his rickshaw and said in an offhand way over his shoulder: "I'm going to the southward a ways to wait for a fare—there's no business here."

"See you again," the two young fellows replied.

Happy Boy did not seem to have heard. As he walked along he picked his feet up. It was a certain fact that his loins still ached a little. Originally he had thought to put his rickshaw up and not pull any more fares for the day, but to tell the straight truth he just didn't have the courage to go back home. It was no proper wife who awaited him there, but an old bitch possessed of the spirit of the she-wolf who steals at night into the darkened chambers of lonely men and sucks them empty of semen, drinking so deep of their manhood that the well runs dry, and they wander through the rest of their time staring

242

vacantly at the world about them and mumbling to themselves.

The days had very gradually grown longer, and when he had swung back and forth across the town several more times, it was still just five o'clock. He ate a pound of meat cakes and drank a bowl of millet congee cooked with red beans. Walking slowly homeward, he kept time with his own steps with a loud and musical belching. He knew for sure that there was a clap of thunder waiting upon his return, but he was very calm. He had made up his mind: he would not quarrel with her, would not be angry with her, but would just lay his head down and go off to sleep. Tomorrow he would go out as he had today to pull his rickshaw. She could do what she liked.

As soon as he got in the door, he saw Tiger Girl sitting in the outer room. She looked at him, her face so deep in storm it seemed as if torrents would pour out of it in that instant. Happy Boy sought to follow a slippery way, putting face aside, to speak to her. Unfortunately he was not accustomed to doing that sort of thing, and he went on into the inner room without uttering a sound, his head down. She, too, was silent and the little room was as quiet as an ancient grotto deep in the mountains. The coughing of their neighbors in the compound, their talking, the crying of children, all could be heard with an absolute clarity that at the same time seemed to belong to sounds that came from some remote distance, exactly as if from a mountain peak one had heard voices that came from far away.

Neither of them was willing to be the first to speak, and first one and then the other lay down on the brick bed, their lips still tightly closed, like a pair of great turtles. After they had awakened from their first sleep, Tiger Girl spoke, the tones of her voice carrying a note of jest as well as one of anger:

"What did you go off to do? Away the whole day!"

"I pulled a rickshaw." He spoke as if he were half awake and half asleep; his throat seemed to have something stuck in it.

"Oh! If you're not out making yourself smelly with sweat,

your heart itches, you cheap piece of bone! You didn't come back to eat the food I cooked for you. Are you more comfortable wandering stupidly all over the face of the earth? Don't deliberately try to turn me against you. My father began his career as a bachelor—a tough, unsheathed cudgel in all truth—and I'm his daughter. There isn't anything I'm not capable of doing. If you dare go out again tomorrow like this, I'll just hang myself to give you something to look at. And if I can say it, I can do it."

"I can't go on being idle."

"You can't go look up the old man?"

"I'm not going to."

"It's the truth, you're ugly-tempered and overbearing."

Happy Boy had fire hooked onto his heart, and he could not forbear longer to say the words that were in his mind.

"I'm going to pull a rickshaw, and I'm going to buy my own rickshaw. If anybody tries to stop me, I'll just leave and never come back again."

"Uh-uh-h." The sound revolved in her nostrils, rising and falling and long drawn out. In it was expressed her pride and her conceit and her contempt for Happy Boy, but at the same time she had turned a corner in her heart. She knew that, for all his good disposition and his simple honesty, Happy Boy was a firm and determined person. And such a person never spoke in jest. It had been no easy thing to catch him; he was an ideal man to have: well-behaved and well-disposed, frugal, vigorous and strong of physique. Considering her age and looks, it wouldn't be so simple to lay her hands on another such a jewel as he was.

You are only really able if you can be hard at one moment and soft at another. For the next move she would have to be as yielding as virgin cotton or soft felt.

"I know how ambitious you are, but you must understand how much I really feel for you. If you're not willing to go looking for the old man, we'll do it this way: I'll go hunt him up.

After all, I'm his daughter, and it doesn't matter much if I lose a little face."

"Even if the old man will take us back, I still have to have a rickshaw to pull." Happy Boy wanted to make his point absolutely clear.

For a long time Tiger Girl said nothing. She had not thought Happy Boy could be so clever. In spite of the simplicity of the words he was using, he was yet telling her very clearly that he was through with her tricks. He was no stupid donkey after all. On this account particularly, she felt an even greater interest in him. She would certainly have to use her wits to rein in this great fellow who could kick like a mule when he was really exercised. Or maybe he was not a person, but just an immense thing; in any case, she must not press him too hard—it wouldn't be so easy to find another thing as big as that. She would have to be measured in the strength of her pressure on him, her use of him: she could grip him tightly but not for too long, and then she must relax her grip and caress him lovingly, so that he would never quite get out of reach of her hand.

"All right, if you like to pull a rickshaw, there's nothing I can do to stop you. You must swear an oath that you won't take a job in some household to work by the month—that you'll come back every evening. Just think of that; you can see for yourself that if I have to go a whole day without you my heart gets frantic. Promise me that you'll come back home early every night."

Happy Boy thought of what the tall one had told them that day, and he opened his eyes wide and stared into the darkness, seeing there a whole battalion of rickshaw men, an army of those who lived by the sale of their strength: their backs were all round and bent over, and they could only shuffle their feet along the ground. At some future day he, too, would be that way. But right now it was not convenient to exasperate Tiger Girl; if he could only pull a rickshaw, that alone would count as one victory for him.

"I'll keep on picking up fares on the street, and won't take a private job," he promised her.

In spite of what she had said, Tiger Girl was not very enthusiastic about going to hunt up Fourth Master Liu. Even when the two of them, father and daughter, had been living in the same house, they were continually quarrelling, but the present situation was more complicated. This was a fog that you couldn't disperse in a single day's time by speaking thrice now and twice more a little while from now; aside from the seriousness of their split, she could no longer be counted as a member of the Liu family. Whatever the particular circumstances might be, the relationship between a daughter who has left home to go to her husband's home and her parents whom she has left is bound to become more or less distant. She did not dare go directly back like some brash litigant walking straight into the public hall of the magistrate's yamen, without having things arranged in advance.

Suppose, on that one chance in ten thousand, the old man should in truth turn his face away from her and refuse to acknowledge that she was his daughter. All she could do then would be to create a disturbance, shouting and brawling around, but if he kept a death-grip on his property, and would let none of it out of his hands, there wasn't the slightest thing she could do about it. Even supposing there was someone present to come forward and try to make peace between them and bring them to agreement, the most such a person would be able to accomplish, if no other course were open, would be to urge her to go quietly to her own home. The Liu house was no longer her home.

Happy Boy went on as usual pulling a rickshaw, and she was alone in the empty rooms, walking back and forth. Three times over many times she started to put on her best clothes and go out to look up her father, but for all the intent in her heart, her hands were reluctant to move. She was in a dilemma. For her own comfort and happiness, the only course open was to go

246

back; from the standpoint of her own self-respect and the looks of the thing, the best thing was not to go back. Supposing the old man's anger had spent itself, all that she would have to do would be to drag Happy Boy back to the Human Harmony Rickshaw Shed, and naturally it would be possible to find work for him to do, so that he wouldn't have to pull a rickshaw. Moreover, they could very firmly and securely lay hold on the old man's business.

But here a sharp flash spread a cold illumination through her heart: suppose the old man remained unyielding to the very end? She would lose face. She would not only lose face, she would have to bend her head and recognize that from then on she could be no more than the old woman of a rickshaw man— she, heng! There would be not the slightest difference between herself and the other women in the courtyard. Suddenly her heart grew as black as the blackest enamel. She almost regretted that she had married Happy Boy. No matter how ambitious he might be, if her own father did not nod his head, Happy Boy could be nothing more than a rickshaw puller for all the days of his generation.

When she had reached this point in her thinking, it even occurred to her that it would be better for her to cut her connection with Happy Boy as you would cut a cord with a knife, and go back alone to her father's house. She could not on his account afford to lose everything that was her own. But as she continued along the unravelling thread of her thought, it came to her that the happiness that she had known with Happy Boy was something that no word or phrase could embody. She sat on the edge of the brick bed staring vacantly into space, wandering absently through the vague afternoon of her sensations, pursuing in her thought the essence of the joy that had been hers after her marriage. It was a joy that was not really here, nor there, but resided in an idea, a flavor, that she could not name or describe. It was as if her whole body had been a bouquet of flower buds, and all of them had burst into the warm fragrance of their flowering under the heat of the sun.

No, she could not give up Happy Boy. She would let him have his way about pulling a rickshaw. If he wanted to beg for his food on the streets, she would still stay with him forever. Look—look at the women with whom she shared this courtyard. If they could bear it, she could bear it. And even if she and Happy Boy broke up, she would not want to go back to the Liu household.

From the day he left the Human Harmony Shed, Happy Boy had been unwilling even to go down the Avenue of the Gate of Western Peace. In these last few days that he had been pulling a rickshaw again, he had always gone out the gate and toward the East City to spare himself the embarrassment of a meeting with any one of the many rickshaws from the Human Harmony Shed that would be sure to be circulating around the West City.

But on this day, after he had put up his rickshaw, he purposely walked past the gate of the shed, for no reason except to take a look at it. What Tiger Girl had said was still in his heart, and he thought that before he returned to the shed he should first experiment a little to see if he would dare to walk down the road that Tiger Girl wanted to take. With his hat pulled down well over his face, he sauntered along on the other side of the street from the shed and some distance from it, the one fear in his heart being that someone he knew would recognize him. From far off he could see the light over the gateway through which the rickshaws were taken into and out of the shed; he could not have said why the sight of that lamp turned his heart into a turbulent stream that was hard for him to cross. There rose before his mind all the circumstances of his first coming to this place; he remembered how Tiger Girl had tempted him into a fatal course, and there was before him, too, the scene that took place on the night of the old man's birthday.

All of these things he could see before his eyes, like a series of paintings hung there, extraordinarily clear and distinct in every detail. Among these paintings there were others, of another time, smaller and simpler but just as distinct: they were of the Western Hills, camels, the Ts'ao household, the government detective; separate and clear and sharply lined, they formed one long connected gallery, fearful to behold and awful to think about. They were so real for him that his heart turned round in its confusion, and a vagueness and uncertainty and insecurity blocked away everything that was real; the actuality lost its identity in the dream, and he had no way of knowing whether the tissue of memory could breathe and live or how it was that he had gone back among them or where they were or where he himself—alone in the dusk when they had all gone —could be.

Without there having been any beginning to his thought, he was thinking again about himself and wondering why after all it was that he should suffer so much affliction and wrong. The time that he had been standing across from the front of the shed seemed very long, and yet again it did not seem that there had been any interval of time at all, or any passage of it. He could not figure out clearly how old he was, but he could only feel that, compared to the Happy Boy who had first come to the Human Harmony Rickshaw Shed, he was much older, much, much older. In that period his had been a full heart, and all of hope; now he had only a stomach crammed with anxieties. He did not understand why, but he knew that these pictures were not cheating him.

In front of his eyes was the Human Harmony Rickshaw Shed, and he was standing across the street from it, staring stupidly at that bare electric bulb, still terribly bright. He watched and watched, until suddenly his heart moved. The four characters in gold on the metal plaque beneath the light had changed their appearance. He did not recognize characters—he

249

had never learned to read—but he could remember the look of the first character of the four: it was like two sticks leaning toward each until their tips touched at the top, and with their sides bowed in a little—λ. It was not a cross, and it lacked one side of being a triangle. That very simple and very strange character would be, according to the order of words in the name of the shed, the one that stood for "human" or, more commonly, just "man." The first one of the four characters that was there now was an even stranger one, and altogether different. The name of the shed had been changed. He could not think of any reason for it or of any principle that would explain it. He looked again at the east and west rooms—never in all his life would he forget those two rooms—and in neither of them was there a light.

It was only when he had been standing there so long that even he had grown impatient with himself that he turned and walked off homeward, his head low. While he walked he kept pondering what he had seen: it couldn't mean to say that the Human Harmony Rickshaw Shed had failed and gone out of business? He would have to question people about it, slowly and in his own time; until he had done that it would not be convenient to speak of the matter to his old woman.

When he got back home Tiger Girl was opening melon seeds between her teeth and eating them to have something to do to relieve the boredom of waiting.

"Again you come back as late as this." There was not even a little spot of anything but hostility and hard bitterness in her face. "I'm telling you, if you keep on like this, I'm not going to put up with it. When you go out it's for the whole day, and I don't dare go outside of this hole—the whole courtyard full of thieving beggars—I'm afraid of losing something. All day until evening there's no place I can go even to say a single sentence. It won't work. I'm not made of wood. You think of some plan—it won't work like this."

Happy Boy made never a sound.

"Say something, you! What are you doing, deliberately try-ing to drive me into a burning rage? Have you got lips or not? Have you or haven't you?" The more she talked the faster the words came, and the more sharp and crisp they were, like the sound of a small-calibre artillery piece, firing one shell after another.

Happy Boy still had nothing to say.

"We'll do this—" she broke off the sentence in her frenzy, but even in her frenzy there was something that suggested that she really was without recourse, that she knew she had to have him; she was neither crying nor smiling, and her face was burn-ing with a fire that could not break into flame. "We'll buy two rickshaws and rent them out. You can stay home and we'll live off what we make in rental. Will you do that?"

"Two rickshaws would only bring in thirty-some cents a day —that's not enough to feed us. Rent one, and I'll pull the other, and together it'll do." Happy Boy spoke very slowly but very naturally. When he heard talk of buying a rickshaw he forgot everything else.

"Won't that be just the same thing as now? You still wouldn't be at home."

"Or we could do this"— Happy Boy could think of many schemes as long as the object of them was a rickshaw—"we could rent out one rickshaw and get a full day's rental from it. I could pull the other one myself for half a day and rent it out the other half. If I pulled it in the daytime, I could go out early in the morning, and come back at three in the afternoon. If I worked in the afternoon, I could go out at three and come back late at night. That would be fine."

She nodded her head. "Wait until I think it over, and if there isn't a still better scheme we'll do just that."

Happy Boy's heart was elated. If this plan could be brought to realization, it would amount to his pulling his own rickshaw

251

once again. Although it would have been bought with his old woman's money, still he could slowly save more money of his own, and in a while buy another rickshaw himself. It was not until this time that he felt that Tiger Girl was worth something. Unexpectedly he turned to her and smiled—a natural, simple, unaffected smile that came from inside his heart. It was as if all the poverty and hardships were crossed off with one stroke of the pen, and the old world had become a new world, as easily as one would change from old clothes into new.

17

SLOWLY Happy Boy managed to piece together, by asking one person and then another until he had the story clear, what had happened to the Human Harmony Rickshaw Shed. Fourth Master Liu had sold a part of the rickshaws, and the rest he had turned over to a well-known rickshaw owner in the West City. Happy Boy could guess that, the old man's age being upon him, he could not keep the business turning round without his daughter to help him, and he had therefore clearly and crisply given it up, and taken the money away to enjoy himself. Where had he gone? But this Happy Boy had been unable to find out.

He could not say whether he should properly be glad for this news or not. From the standpoint of his own inclinations and his obstinate purposes, Happy Boy felt that since Fourth Master Liu had definitely made up his mind to abandon his daughter, Tiger Girl's plans and schemes could be counted as having fallen completely into emptiness, and he himself could go ahead in simple honesty pulling his rickshaw without any other thought than earning the rice that he ate, and without relying on anyone else. Speaking from the standpoint of the little bit of money and property that Fourth Master Liu had, it was in all truth a somewhat regrettable thing. Who could have known that Old Man Liu would throw his money away like that? Not a single copper of it had so much as stained the hands of the Tiger Girl or himself.

But affairs had already come to this pass, and he did not give ten parts of his mind to meditating on them, and there would be even less basis for saying that his heart had been moved in the slightest. The way he felt about it was this: whatever happened, his strength was his own, and as long as he was willing to sell his strength to earn money, there would never be any question of not having rice to eat. Very simply and without any emotion whatever, he told Tiger Girl.

Her heart, though, was deeply and terribly moved. Almost in the instant that she heard it she saw her own future with utter clarity: she was finished! Everything was finished. The best she could do now was to be the wife of a rickshaw man for the whole of her lifetime. She would never escape from this common courtyard. She had anticipated the possibility of her father's taking another wife, but it had never occurred to her that he might just shake his hands free of the whole thing and go away. Supposing it had come about that he had taken a young woman to wife, Tiger Girl could have gone to her and disputed the property, and there would have been no certainty but what she might have been able to join forces with her stepmother, a situation from which she could have gained some advantage at least. She had plenty of schemes, as long as the old man kept the rickshaw shed.

The one thing she had never dreamed might happen had happened: that the old man could be that hard and unyielding and malicious as to turn his property into cash, and steal off somewhere and hide himself with it! Originally when she had fought with him she had regarded it as a type of maneuver, and had been sure that when the time had come to do so she could with the appropriate language turn the thing so that it would come out all right. She knew that the Human Harmony Rickshaw Shed could not run without her; who could have believed that the old man would open his hands and let the rickshaw shed drop?

There was even now a whispered rumor of the coming of springtime; the buds on the twigs of the tree branches already seemed full and red. But in this courtyard the spring did not first come to the branches of the trees: there wasn't a single tree or flower anywhere around. In this place the spring announced itself in the pock-like holes the melting ice had left in the center of the yard and in the rank, sickening stench which floated up with the spring breezes from the filth that the cold had covered. And the same breezes would pick up all the old chicken feathers and garlic skins and shreds of torn paper and blow them into the corner of the wall, making a tiny whirlwind of them there. The people who lived in the courtyard had their troubles for every season of the year. Only now would the old folk dare to come out to bask in the sun, and only now it was that the young girls wiped some of the soot smudge off their noses and faces, showing something of the natural yellow and rose of their skins. Then, too, it was that the women drove their children out into the yard to play, there being less reason now for them to be ashamed of the inadequacy of the youngsters' clothing. The children could find a piece of paper and try to make a kite of it, and could run about the courtyard as they pleased, without being afraid that their black little hands would be so badly frozen by the cold that they would split open in places. But the public kitchen that served the free congee put out the fire under its big cauldron; the distributors of relief stopped giving away rice; those who practiced doing good deeds stopped giving money to the needy; it was as if they took all those who were poor and in distress and turned them over to the care of the sunlight and breezes of the spring.

It was just at this time that the early wheat was as green as new grass, and the stores of the old grain were beginning to run out, so that wheat and rice became as usual more dear. The days too were longer, and the old people could not very well go to bed as early as was their wont in the wintertime; it was no longer as easy to use their dreams of food in plenty to cheat the hungry rumblings of their stomachs. The entrance of spring into the life of man had only one effect for this courtyard: it deepened the distress.

Lice that had grown old and wily—the worst kind, and the hardest to catch—would sometimes hop out from inside the wadded cotton of the garments of one of the old men, or of one of the children, and sit in the sun, to gain some experience of its warmth.

Tiger Girl looked out into the courtyard at the freshly melted ice, at the unbearably tattered clothing, smelled the mixed hot odor, heard the sighs of the old men and the cries of the children, and her heart grew half cold. In the wintertime the people all stuck to their rooms to avoid the cold; the filth and garbage was all frozen under the ice; now the people had come out, and the filth had reassumed its original form. Even the wall —built of the fragments of broken bricks held together by mortar—was shedding dirt and dust, as if it were preparing to collapse on the first day that a heavy rain fell. The whole court-yard was bright with flowers and the soft green of their leaves: the flowers were these broken blossoms of poverty, and the green was the sick green-purple of rotting filth. It was many times more ugly and horrible than in the deep of winter. Heng! That it should be precisely at this time that she should be faced with the realization that she would have to live here forever;

that that little bit of money of hers would some day be all spent, and Happy Boy was nothing but a rickshaw man.

She told Happy Boy to watch the house while she went to the Southern Park to find her father's sister, to ask after any news of the old man. Her aunt said that Fourth Master had in fact come on one occasion to her house—as best she could remember, it was on about the twelfth day of the first month. For one thing, he wanted to thank her, and for another to tell her that he calculated to go to Tientsin or maybe to Shanghai to have himself a good time. He said he'd passed his whole life without once having got outside the gate of Peking; after all, that could not be counted as anything very brave. He would take advantage of the fact that he still had a breath of life left in him to go to all these various places and increase his knowledge. He had also said he didn't himself have the face to spend any more time in the city because his daughter had lost all his standing as a man for him. This little bit was all his sister had to report; her judgment on the matter was even more simple and to the point: it might be that the old man had in truth left the city, or it might be that he only said he was going to, and had gone into hiding in some little house down one of its countless lanes. Who could tell?

When Tiger Girl got back home she threw herself down on the bed, and in the depth of her sadness began to cry. For a long time she lay there weeping, and her eyes grew red and swollen with tears.

The crying done, she wiped her face and said to Happy Boy, "All right, you've won! You can have everything your way. This time I bet on the wrong number. When you marry a rooster, you've got to be content to be a chicken like the rest. I'll give you a hundred dollars, you buy a rickshaw to pull."

Behind this speech there was a sly thought of her own: originally it had been planned that they would buy two rickshaws, one for Happy Boy to pull and the other to rent out. Now she changed her plan, and would buy only one, for Happy Boy to pull. The rest of the money she would still keep in her own hand. As long as she had the money, she would have the power. She was unwilling to dig it all out: suppose by some remote chance that after she had used the money to buy· rickshaws, Happy Boy's heart should change, and he should desert her? She could not but make some preparation for such a contingency. And, moreover, old man Liu's going off this way had made her feel how little reliance one can put on anything. No one can be certain of what tomorrow may bring; the best course of all was to take pleasure where you found pleasure. For that you had to have a few pennies in your hand, so that if you felt like eating a mouthful of something you could eat that mouthful. She had always been fond of tidbits, and now she was thinking only of those few joys that were still before her eyes and that she could still hope to grasp.

There would come a day when the money was all spent forever. Marrying a rickshaw man—although there was no help for that now—was already perpetrating a wrong against herself; she could not add to that humiliation of going every day to him with the back of her hand turned down asking for money, and be without a copper in her own pocket.

This decision made her feel a little more lighthearted again: although she understood very clearly that it meant that the future was impossible, still she would not immediately have to bow her head. It was as if, walking into the sunset with the distance already shadowed and obscured by the coming of night, one sought to take advantage of the remaining light to walk on a little farther without any thought of what one would do when darkness came.

Happy Boy did not dispute with her. It would be good enough to buy just one rickshaw, so long as it was his own. Good or bad, he could make sixty or seventy cents a day, and that would be enough to supply them both with a mouthful of nourishment to chew on. Not only did he not argue—he even felt a certain lift in his spirits, a kind of joy. Had he not undergone all those hardships in the past for nothing else than to buy a rickshaw? Now he could buy one again—well, then, what had he to complain of? Naturally, when you depend on one rickshaw to feed two people, you can't save money; there would be danger ahead when this rickshaw began to wear out and you had made no preparation to replace it. But considering how difficult it was to get the money to buy a rickshaw in the first place, he should certainly be satisfied now that he was in a position to get one. Why should he spoil what pleasure there was in it for him by thinking of anything so remote?

One of those who shared their courtyard, he who was called Second Vigorous Son, was just at this time trying to sell his rickshaw. In the summer of the preceding year he had sold his daughter, Little Lucky One—she was nineteen years old—to an army officer for two hundred dollars. After Little Lucky One had gone, her father had for a time put on a great air of wealth. He redeemed all the things he had pawned at the hock shops, and even had a few pieces of new clothing made, so that the whole family looked strangely neat and well-dressed.

The wife of Second Vigorous was the shortest and ugliest woman in the compound. Her forehead protruded, her jowls were heavy, she didn't have much hair, her teeth stuck out over her lower lip, and her face was covered with freckles, so that all in all you almost felt nauseated simply from looking at her. Her eyelids were red and swollen; the while she wept for her daughter, she wore her new blue cotton gown. Second Vigorous Son's temper had always been violent, and after he had sold his daughter he would often drink several cups of wine; with the wine in him, the balls of his eyes would become oiled with his tears, and he would be particularly given to finding fault with those around him.

For the wife, although she wore her new dress, and got one

really full meal to eat, still the pleasure did not balance the suffering: the number of times she had to suffer herself to be beaten up was now double what it had been.

Second Vigorous Son was over forty, and he calculated that he would no longer pull a rickshaw. Wherefore he bought a pair of wicker baskets and rigged them up at each end of a shoulder carrying-pole, to go about hawking general merchandise. He had a complete line of goods: melons, fruits, peanuts, and cigarettes. After carrying on this business for two months he struck a rough balance and discovered that he was not only losing, but losing a great deal. Accustomed to pulling a rickshaw, he could not meet the demands of business; the rickshaw man's job was a matter of bumping into a customer on every street you went down; if you got the job, all right; if you didn't, there was an end to it. To carry on a small business, you must sweat over every little detail, over every half copper, and be quick to see your chance to cheat your customer. Second Vigorous wasn't capable of it.

Rickshaw pullers know how to buy things on credit, and they are therefore unable to get by with a whole face in refusing to let people whom they know well owe them their accounts; once owing, it is no easy thing to collect the money.

Proceeding on this basis, it was impossible for Second Vigorous to draw any good customers to himself, and those who had business transactions with him were almost exclusively people who coveted the opportunity to buy on credit things for which they never had any intention of paying. He had no way to avoid losing money, and when he lost money he would be sad, and when he was sad he would drink even more wine than usual. Drunk, he was constantly quarreling with policemen on the street, and at home he would take out his anger on his old woman and his children. He would offend the police, and beat his wife, all on account of wine.

When he got sober again, he would be extraordinarily repentant and swallowed up in an aching regret. And when he gave the matter further thought, and realized that this little bit of money had come from the sale of his own daughter, and he was losing it like this without getting any return for it, and was even drinking wine and hitting people, he would feel that he was hardly worthy to be called a human being. At times like these he was capable of going off and falling into a vexed slumber for the whole day, turning his bitterness and his distress over to his dreams.

He made up his mind to abandon his business and go back to pulling a rickshaw; he could not simply fritter that money away. He bought a rickshaw. During his drunken periods he would never talk reason and had no use for the proprieties, but when he was sober he had the greatest love for respectability and an impressive front. Because he had this predilection for face, he was forever putting on the airs a poor man affects when he wants to impress people. Everything had to be according to the book. The rickshaw he bought was a brand-new one, and the clothes he wore were neat and clean. On account of the fact that he felt himself to be a high-class rickshaw man, he felt obliged to drink the better-grade tea, and that it would be beneath him to haul any but smart-looking and well-dressed fares.

He was capable of standing at the mouth of some lane for long periods of time, letting the bright sunlight shine on his new rickshaw and on his white vest and trousers, gossiping with the crowd, but never deigning to try to do any business. Every few minutes he would bring out his new duster made of strips of blue cloth at the end of a stick that served as a handle and make a great display of brushing off his rickshaw; again he would stamp his feet on the ground, bringing his new double-lined, white-soled shoes down on the roadside; yet again he would stand with one foot crossed over the other one, one arm akimbo and the other resting on the mudguard of his rickshaw, his eyes looking down his nose and a faint smile on his lips, waiting for someone to praise the rickshaw, whereafter they could find a topic of discussion, and once they had gotten started talking there would be no end to it. In this way he could soak away two or three days on end without any result. When it did come to the point that he got a good fare, his feet would be no proper match for his rickshaw and his clothes: he would be unable to run. This again made him extraordinarily sad; once this sadness came upon him, he thought of his daughter, and the only thing that there was to do was to go drink wine. In this way all of his money had soon been squandered, and all he had left was his rickshaw.

Sometime near the Day of the Winter's Beginning he got drunk again. As soon as he came in the door his two sons—one was thirteen and the other eleven—thought to get out of his way. This enraged him and he gave each of them a good hard booting. His wife said something, and he bore down on her, trampling on the lower part of her stomach. She lay down on the ground and for a long time emitted no sound. The two boys were frantic, and one took the coal scoop and the other the pole used in pounding grain, and entered a battle to the death against their father. The three were rolled into one struggling mass, and the seven hands and eight feet that flew about in all directions managed to trample the mother several more times. The neighbors came over and with the greatest difficulty were able finally to get Second Vigorous laid out on the brick bed, while the two children embraced their mother and wept.

Mrs. Second Vigorous came to, but from that time on until the end she was never again to set her feet on the ground. On the third of the twelfth lunar month her breathing stopped, and she lay dead on the brick bed, dressed in the long blue gown that had been bought for her after her daughter had been sold.

Her own family would not stand for their daughter's being brought to such an end, and nothing would do but that they must have a lawsuit over it. Friends on both sides came forward and entreated them in the name of the living and in the name of the dead before the wife's family was finally willing to give way, although Second Vigorous Son was on his part obliged to promise that he would see that the dead was properly escorted to her grave, and he had moreover to pay her family fifteen dollars.

He pawned his rickshaw for sixty dollars. After the New Year he wanted to get it off his hands entirely, since he had no hope of ever being able to redeem it himself. In his drunken periods he would in all truth think of selling one of his sons, but there was never a chance of anyone's wanting to buy one of them. Also on one occasion he hunted up Little Lucky One's husband, but the fellow refused from the very beginning to acknowledge that he had any such father-in-law at all, so there's no need relating again how that turned out.

Happy Boy knew the history of this rickshaw, and he did not very much like the idea of taking it. There were plenty of rickshaws to pull—why should they buy this particular one, this rickshaw of ill omen that had been bought at the price of a daughter, and was being sold because of the murder of a wife?

Tiger Girl did not look at it that way. She thought that with the use of a little more than eighty dollars, you would be able to buy it—a bargain! The rickshaw had only been in service for a little less than half a year, and even the color of the tires hadn't changed much. Moreover, it was a known fact that it had been made by the famous Virtue Achieved Factory in the West City. If you bought one that was seven parts new, wouldn't that cost you fifty or sixty dollars? She could not forego so cheap a price. She knew, too, that so soon after the New Year money was tight everywhere; Second Vigorous Son would not be able to get a high price, and he was in urgent need of the use of the money right away. She went herself to look at the rickshaw, herself bargained with Second Vigorous over the price, and handed over the money.

Happy Boy could do nothing but wait to have the rickshaw brought to him for a trial pull. He said nothing, nor was it convenient for him to say anything, since the money was not his own. When the cart had been fully purchased, he looked it over with minute care. In all truth it was strong and solid. But he had always a certain slight feeling of irritating constraint about it. The thing that he was least enthusiastic about was the fact that the body of it was in black lacquer, while the brass fittings were all finished in white enamel. When Second Vigorous was having the cart made, because white and black are in such sharp contrast with each other, and tend each to accentuate the other, he felt that it would make a handsome appearance; Happy Boy, on the contrary, felt that it was ill-omened, like a person dressed in mourning. He was very much tempted to change the cover, perhaps to a chrome yellow or a moon white; that might be enough to lessen a little the austerity of the rickshaw's decor. But he never discussed the matter with Tiger Girl, the better to avoid just another spate of her barbed and malicious mouthings.

When he drew this rickshaw out to pull it, the crowd all took especial notice of it. Some people would call it only "the Little Widow." Happy Boy's heart was not at ease on that score, although he managed in ways of his own to keep his mind off it. But the rickshaw itself was always with him, from early morning until late at night, and he was always nervous and apprehensive, as he never knew at what moment it might jump the track. Sometimes he would suddenly think of Second Vigorous Son, and the misfortunes with which the fellow had met; it would be then as if it were not a rickshaw at all that he was pulling, but a coffin. It seemed to him that he was constantly seeing the shadowy spirits of the dead riding for nothing in this rickshaw of his.

In spite of the tick-tick sound of unreasoning restlessness that his heart made, he had no trouble at all with the rickshaw

263

from the first day forward. The weather grew warmer as the weeks passed; he took off his cotton padded garments, and it was almost as if you could do without any lined clothes at all, and wear only a jacket and trousers of a single thickness of cloth; Peking does not have much springtime. The days grew so long that people seemed as if they were growing impatient with the whole thing; they were all sleepy and tired. Happy Boy went out at dawn, and went round and round through the streets until four o'clock in the afternoon, when he felt that he had already sold enough of his strength; the sun, though, would still be very high in the heavens. He didn't want to run any more, and yet he was unwilling to put up his rickshaw. Caught in this perplexity, he would yawn long and lazily.

If this length of the days made Happy Boy feel weary and spiritless, Tiger Girl back at home was even more dejected and solitary. In the wintertime she could warm herself by the stove, listening to the sound of the wind outside, and even though she would be depressed she could always console herself with the thought that it was better not to go out into such weather. Now the stove was moved out under the eaves, and there was just nothing at all left for her to do in the room. The courtyard, too, was so filthy and stinking; there was not even a single blade of living grass to be found in it. If she went out on the street, she would have to be uneasy about the neighbors; even if it was just to go buy something, she still had to go straight there and come straight back, without daring to loiter on the way. She was very much like a bee that has been shut up inside a room; it is in vain that it watches the sunlight outside, because it cannot fly out into it. With the other women in the courtyard she felt that she had so little in common that she could not get up a conversation with them. The thing they talked most about was the latest gossip of the neighborhood, while she had been so long accustomed to being completely free, like a wild hill song with neither tune nor rhyme, that she didn't like to talk about, or hear about, all this pettiness. Their grievances arose from the miserable lives that they led; every little unimportant thing was enough to bring tears to their eyes. Her grievances arose from her discontent with the life she was leading; she had no tears to weep, and when she wanted to let out some of her stored-up resentment, she would think to find someone to whom she could give a good cursing. She and the other women could have no mutual understanding of each other, so it was best that each minded her own affairs and neither spoke to the other.

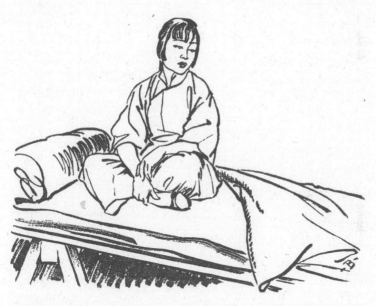

It was not until the fourth month was half over that she found a companion. Little Lucky One, the daughter of Second Vigorous, came back. Her "man" was a military officer; wherever he went it was his custom to establish a very simplified "family." He would spend one or two hundred dollars to buy himself a young virgin, and besides that he would purchase a large-size bed of boards and two chairs, which was enough to make it possible for him to pass a few days in pleasure.

When the troops were transferred to some other place, he would open his hands to let the whole affair drop from them and turn his back and walk away, leaving the woman and the board bed stretched out where they were. He took no loss at all on the transaction, spending one or two hundred dollars for a year or a year and a half's time. Counting only the washing and mending of clothes, cooking, and all the other little things that have to be done around the house, if he had hired a servant to take care of them, would he not have had to spend eight or ten dollars a month, not counting the money it would cost to feed him? By this method of taking a wife, he not only got a servant, but someone to sleep with as well. Moreover, she was absolutely guaranteed to be clean and without disease. If he was enthusiastic about her, he would have a brightly flowered calico dress made for her that would cost something over a dollar. If she gave him no particular pleasure, he would buy her no clothes at all and keep her kneeling on her haunches in the room bare-holed and helpless.

So when the time came for him to be moved on, he would not in the least regret the bed-board and the pair of chairs, because the last two months' room rent he would be owing would be left for the girl to find some means to pay, and pawning the board and anything else that might have been accumulated would hardly cover the full amount.

Little Lucky One had simply sold the bed-board, paid the rent, and come back home wearing her calico dress and a pair of silver-plated earrings.

After Second Vigorous had sold the rickshaw, aside from the repayment to the pawn shop of the principal and interest they had loaned him on it, he had about twenty dollars left. Sometimes he would get to feeling that it was a terribly pathetic thing for a middle-aged man to have his wife die; since no one else had any sympathy for him, he would go off and have a cup of wine with himself for the sake of consolation and commiseration. At such times it was as if he had a feeling of enmity for money and was determined to squander it no matter how great the effort or risk involved. On occasion it would come over him that it was more than ever necessary that he put forth every bit of energy in his rickshaw pulling, in order to properly drag his two boys up to manhood, so that the future might hold a little hope for all of them. When these thoughts of his sons would occur to him he would chirp seven times like a bird and neigh eight times like a horse, rush out to buy a whole stock of food and stagger back with it to give it to the two of them to eat.

Watching them gulp it down with tiger-like appetites, his eyes would hold back their tears, and he would make conversation with himself, saying: "Children without a mother! Children of bitter destiny! Papa lives in poverty and works hard, all for you children. Without any deception I can tell you, whether I get enough to eat or not counts for nothing; first my children must have their fill. Go ahead and eat. The only thing I ask is that when you grow up and become men, you just don't forget me."

In moods like these he also spent no small amount of money, and gradually the whole twenty dollars was used up.

Being without money, when it came again time for him to drink, he would go into a rage and for two or three days on end pay no attention to whether the youngsters had anything to eat or not. There was nothing that they could do. The only course they knew of was to think of some schemes of their own for scraping together a few coppers to buy something to eat. They could act as guides and runners in weddings or funerals; they could follow along after the trash cart and pick up a few scraps of broken copper or a few torn newspapers. Sometimes in that way they could get enough to buy a roll baked with a meat filling, but sometimes they could only afford a catty of wheat husks and yams, which they would gulp down whole, skins, roots and all. And at yet other times the two of them would have only one copper between them; the best thing they could do then was to buy a handful of broad beans and peanuts; you couldn't ward off the pangs of hunger that way, but at least you could chew on them a little longer.

When Little Lucky One returned, and they saw someone who was one of them, there was nothing that they could say: one took hold of her right arm and the other of her left, and they both just looked up at her, smiling, their faces streaming with tears. Mother was dead! Big Sister was Mother now!

Second Vigorous gave no sign either of pleasure or displeasure at his daughter's return. Her coming back only added one more person to be fed. But, seeing how happy the two youngsters were, he was forced to admit that there ought to be a woman in the home, to cook for the family and to wash its clothes. It was thus not convenient for him to make any objection, and he thought it best simply to keep on going and calculate where you were when you got there.

Little Lucky One had grown into a girl who was not hard to look at. Although originally she had been very thin and slight, since she had gone to live with the army officer she had filled out a great deal, and had even grown a little taller. Her face was soft and round, her eyes and eyebrows very even, and although there was no one thing about her that was particularly striking or above average, she was solidly pretty in all truth. Her upper lip was very short, and no matter whether she was angry or about to smile, this upper lip drew back a little, showing a row of teeth very even and very white. The thing that the army officer had been especially fond of about her had been those teeth. When she showed them, her face took on a simple bewildered look, like that of a person who does not know what to do next, and at the same time it gave her the air of a petted and innocent child.

This guileless expression gave her—in common with all girls who come from poverty and are yet pretty—something of the natural beauty of the flowers and grasses of the forests, and made it certain that, like them, they need only have a little fragrance or coloring of their own for them to be duly plucked and taken to the market to be sold.

From the beginning Tiger Girl had taken no notice of the other people in the courtyard, but she regarded Little Lucky One as worthy of being her friend. In the first place, she had some looks; in the second place, she wore a long gown of flowered calico; in the third place, Tiger Girl was convinced that since she had been married to an army officer, she would certainly have seen something of the world; and therefore she was willing to be seen in her company. It is not easy for women to make friends, but if they are going to associate with each other the relationship is very quickly established. It was not many days before they had become intimate friends.

Tiger Girl loved to eat tidbits, and every time she got hold of a few melon seeds or anything of that sort she would be sure to call over for Little Lucky One to come across and share them with her. As they ate they would talk and laugh. In the midst of this chatter, Little Lucky One would show her white teeth, and in her simple-minded bewildered manner tell Tiger Girl many things that she had never heard of before. Living with her army officer had not been any business of "enjoying happiness," but when he was in high spirits he would sometimes take her to a hotel to dinner, or to the theatre, so that she had plenty of things to tell about, and as she related them Tiger Girl would listen to her with admiration.

There were also many things that it was very hard to speak of: she thought of them as kinds of ill-treatment to which she had been subjected, humiliations too lecherous to be discussed, even with one's closest friend, but to Tiger Girl all of these things were thrilling experiences. Tiger Girl begged and entreated her to tell her all about them, and for all the embarrassed constraint Little Lucky One felt in discussing them, she still could not quite bring herself to refuse her friend.

Little Lucky One had seen one of those books entitled "The Palace of Springtime" which are shown to virgins on their wedding night before their husband takes them, and in which in a long series of beautiful paintings are shown all the ways in which virile strength may approach the soft cushion that so tingles to receive it and absorb its heat. Because Tiger Girl had first given herself a long time ago and without formality to a man who was practically a stranger, she had never looked inside "The Palace of Springtime" and she must needs hear in detail from her more fortunate friend about every position and posture, and about what he does when she does this, and what she does when he does that. With everything of this sort it was the same: when Tiger Girl had heard about it once, she wanted to have it told to her all over a second time.

In her eyes Little Lucky One was an altogether lovable, altogether admirable, and altogether enviable person. When she had finished listening to one of these recitals, and turned to consider herself—her looks, her age, and her husband—she felt that in everything in life she had been deeply wronged. She had never known the springtime of passion, the future held no hope for her, and as for the present—Happy Boy was so dead and heavy, like a brick! The more discontented she became with her husband, the more she loved Little Lucky One; although she was so poor, and so pitiable, still, in Tiger Girl's eyes, she was a person who had seen better days, who had lived and seen life; if Little Lucky One were to die that same day, she would still have no cause for complaint. In Tiger Girl's way of looking at it, Little Lucky One was a sufficient example of the joys that every woman should know.

But Tiger Girl had not seen the depth of her friend's poverty, nor understood the bitterness of her distress. Little Lucky

270

One had brought nothing back with her, and yet, no matter how worthless her father was, she had to take care of her two younger brothers. Where was she to go to get the money to feed them?

Second Vigorous in his drunkenness proposed a way: "If in your heart you have any true feeling for your brothers, there's a way that you can make money to take care of them. Everything's up to me; I have to spend the whole day playing pack horse for the public, and I've got to have enough to eat before I can do that—do you think I can run when my stomach's empty? Would you think it was funny if I tripped and fell and killed myself, or what? And you're just spending your time in idleness —you've got something ready-made that would bring a good price any time you were willing to sell it—what are you waiting for? Why don't you get out and start selling it?"

Looking at her sodden alley-cat of a father, and at herself, and at her two little brothers who were so starved they were like sick rats, Little Lucky One could do nothing but cry. But her tears would not move her father, they would not feed her brothers; she would have to bring out something much more helpful than that. So that her brothers might have food, she must sell her own flesh—she must open up the portal of her womanhood to any who had the price; she must nominate the number of coppers for which she would lay down her body and spread wide her legs.

She took the youngest of the boys in her arms, hugging him tightly to her. He did not feel her tears wetting his hair: there was only one thing he could think of: "Sister, I'm hungry!" Sister! Sister was a piece of meat herself, to be given to her brother to eat!

Not only did Tiger Girl refuse her any comfort—just the contrary, she wanted to help. She volunteered to put up a little capital so that Little Lucky One could dress herself up and have rouge to put on her lips. She could pay her back, Tiger Girl said, from her earnings. The older woman also wanted to lend her young friend the space necessary for her contemplated venture. Little Lucky One's own room was too dirty, but Tiger Girl's had at least something of an appearance, and with the two rooms together, there'd be more space to move around in. Since Happy Boy would certainly never come back during the daytime, Tiger Girl was pleased to help out a friend. Moreover, since the partition was of paper, and you could make a place to peep through just by wetting your finger and putting it against it, she could hardly contain her composure in the thought of all the things she would see and all she would learn: all the things that she herself had missed, that she wanted to do but couldn't do.

But there was one condition that Tiger Girl put forward: each time Little Lucky One used the room, she must pay her twenty cents. A friend is a friend, but business is business: on account of Little Lucky One's project, she had to put the room in the very best order, and since it was necessary to do that work, certain expenditures were entailed—was anyone going to claim that it doesn't take money to buy brooms and dustpans? Twenty cents could by no means be considered high—it was because the two of them were such good friends that Tiger Girl was considering her face to the extent of renting the room to her at so cheap a price.

Little Lucky One showed her white teeth, but the tears she shed fell in her own heart.

That night when Happy Boy came back, Tiger Girl told him nothing of what had happened but he paid, too, in the sleep that he lost. With a full, deep, passionate joy Tiger Girl went after him: she had broken her father, she had just that day helped ruin the friend that she hated and envied, and now she would take it out of Happy Boy.

18

WHEN the year had reached the sixth month, the courtyard was hushed and deserted in the daytime. The children, clutching at the early morning, would pick up their broken
baskets and go out to collect whatever they could find to collect;
by nine o'clock the heat from the sun in its poisonous flowering
would crack open the skin that covered their bony backs, and
the only thing that would be left for them to do would be to
bring back home whatever they had been able to pick up, and
eat whatever food the grownups could give them. After the meal
the larger ones among them, if they could scrape together even
the world's smallest amount of capital, would go buy a few fragments of ice from the ice plant, scrounge a few more, and take
them out with all despatch to get them sold before they had
melted.

If they couldn't find the requisite capital, they would join
together in a crowd and go out to the River of the Protecting
Wall to bathe, stealing a few lumps of coal from the railway
station on their way or perhaps collecting a few live dragonflies
and spiders to sell to the children of rich men's homes.

The smaller youngsters, not daring to run off to such long
distances, would all go outside the compound gate to places
nearby where there were trees, and in the shade of them play
about, collecting locust bugs or digging gold mines.

With all the children outside, and all the menfolk gone too,
the women would be in their rooms, their backs bare to their
waists, no one of them daring to venture outdoors—not because

they were afraid of the way they looked but because the ground in the courtyard was already so hot it would scorch their bare feet.

Only when the sun was about to go down would the men-folk and the children begin, one after another, to drift back. By this time the courtyard would be shaded by the wall, there would be a breeze, faintly cool, while the rooms would still have closed inside them the whole day's heat, as a vessel for broiling food contains the steam; everybody would be sitting around the courtyard waiting for the women to finish cooking the food. At this moment the courtyard would be full of an extraordinary bustle and excitement, like a market place but without any of the merchandise. Everybody would be red-eyed with the heat they had borne through the day, and no one would be in a good humor; the hunger in their stomachs would have made every face among them even more lean and strained.

For a single sentence that was off the right track there were those who beat their children and others who beat their wives; if they couldn't beat them, they would curse them to complete satisfaction. This shouting and brawling would go on continuously until everyone had finished the evening meal. Then some of the children would lie down in the courtyard and go to sleep, others would go out to the streets to scatter about and play. The older people would be in much better temper after they had had their meal, and those who liked to talk would gather in little groups of three or four and tell each other of the hardships of the day.

There would be those others who had no food to eat. By that hour of the evening there would be no place that you could go to pawn or sell anything, even if you had anything to pawn or sell, because it had already grown dark. The man in such a family would either throw himself down on the brick bed, paying no heed to the heat of the room and without making a sound, or he would shriek and curse in his rage. Holding back the tears in her eyes, the woman would do her best to smooth things over, and then go out and, somehow or other, after bumping her head against the hard nails of no one knows how many refusals, finally manage to borrow a dirty little torn bit of paper, a twenty-copper note. Holding this precious scrap crumpled up in her hot moist hands, she would go buy a bit of mixed flour to fix up a pot of congee for the family to eat.

Neither Tiger Girl nor Little Lucky One was a part of this pattern of life. Tiger Girl was pregnant, and this time it was real. Happy Boy went out at dawn; it would be at least eight or nine o'clock before she got up. That it was not proper for pregnant women to move about much was a mistaken belief that had come down by tradition through countless generations, and Tiger Girl put great faith in it. Moreover, she wanted to use this as an excuse to make manifest her superior position: everybody else had to get up very early and be about their work, except only herself, who could in a leisurely and comfortable manner sleep until any hour she chose. In the evening she would take a little wooden bench out to the street beyond the gate in a place where there was a little breeze, and squat there, not coming back in until just about everyone in the courtyard was already asleep. She would not bemean herself to engage in idle conversation with the other tenants.

Little Lucky One got up late too, but for quite another reason. She was afraid the men in the compound would squint at her, so she waited until they had all gone off to work before she dared come out of the door of her room. In the daytime, if she didn't come over to look up Tiger Girl, she would go out to saunter on the streets, because she herself was her only advertisement of her stock-in-trade. In the evening, in order to avoid the gaze of people in the courtyard, she would not come stealing back in until she figured that everybody had already gone to bed.

Among the men it was Happy Boy and Second Vigorous who kept unusual hours. Happy Boy feared coming into this big compound, and even more going into his room. The poor-mouth talk of the mob in the courtyard shook his heart with vexation; what he wanted to do was to find a secluded spot where he could sit down by himself. As for the room, he had come more and more to feel that Tiger Girl was truly like an old she-bitch of a tigress; the little room was so hot and stifling, and when you added in the tiger-bitch too, it was almost as if the moment he stepped into that room he was no longer able to breathe. Some days before he had had no choice but to come home early so as to avoid having Tiger Girl brawling at him and picking a quarrel with him for being late. In the last little while, since she had had Little Lucky One as a companion, she did not keep so tight a control over him, and he was coming in later.

And Second Vigorous—well, it seemed that he hadn't been coming home much at all of late. He knew what kind of business it was that his daughter was engaged in, and he didn't have the face to come in the gate. But he had no way to stop her; he knew he didn't have the strength himself to provide for his sons and daughter; the best thing for him to do was not to come back again, but to make out instead that "what the eyes do not see will not vex the heart." Sometimes he hated his daughter: supposing Little Lucky One had been born a boy child, he would guarantee that there would have been no need to have made such a stench as this; since the unborn was to be a girl, why had she chosen his wife's womb to steal into? Sometimes he pitied her—was not his daughter selling her body to nourish her little brothers?

Hating her or feeling for her—neither supplied him the means to do anything about it. And when the time of his drunkenness came, and he had no money in his hands, he neither hated nor pitied her; he simply came back and demanded money of her. At such times he regarded his daughter as an object that could make money; he was the father, and it was fully appropriate to his position and in accord with the teachings of the ancients that he should ask her for money. In these periods he would also be mindful of his good name; did not everyone despise Little Lucky One? Well, her father didn't make any excuses for her either, and didn't forgive her. While he was pressing her for money he would at the same time be reviling her, as if to make it clearly known to everyone that it was no fault of Second Vigorous, it was simply that Little Lucky was just naturally worthless and had no self-respect.

While her father was shouting these things at her Little Lucky One would emit no sound, and not even so much as sigh. Tiger Girl on the other hand would meet him on his own ground, and, half urging him and half cursing him, manage to get him to leave. Naturally he had to have a few—even if it was very few—coppers put in his hand; however many these were, they would be just sufficient to permit him to go again to drink wine, because if he should sober up and see them, and remember where he got them, he might jump into the river or hang himself.

On the fifteenth day of the sixth moon the weather was so hot it drove you mad. The sun had hardly come out when the ground already felt as if it had been pushed down into a fire. A layer of dust-laden air that seemed like a cloud but wasn't a cloud, and seemed like a mist but wasn't a mist, floated low through the atmosphere, making people feel as if they were being smothered. There was not the slightest breath of wind. Happy Boy went out into the courtyard and looked up at that dust-red sky, calculating that he should pull the late shift, waiting until after four o'clock to go out. Supposing he couldn't make enough money, he could keep on pulling his rickshaw right through till dawn of the next day; the night would in any case be a little easier to bear than the daytime.

Tiger Girl pressed him to go out, for fear his being around the house would get in the way. Suppose by a remote chance Little Lucky One brought back a guest with her?

"Do you think it'll be any easier to bear at home than on the street? By noon even the walls of the room are roasting."

He said never a word, but drank a gourd of cold water and went out.

The willow trees on the street were as if they were sick; their leaves, covered by a layer of dust, were curling back on the stems; their branches could not find the energy to make even the slightest movement, and only hung listlessly down toward the earth. There was not a drop of water anywhere on the avenue; it was so dry it gave off a shimmer of white light, like heat become visible. In the by-ways the dust rose up very high, joining with the gray air of the heavens to form a floating carpet of the cruelest dust and sand, to scald the faces of people who walked the paths beneath it. Everywhere it was parched; everything you touched burned your hand; everywhere it was stifling; the whole city was like a burned-out brickkiln. People could not draw their breath, and dogs lay panting in the street, their red tongues stuck out. The nostrils of horses and mules were extraordinarily distended; the hawkers did not dare to cry their wares; the macadamized roads began to melt away; even the brass shop signs hanging now so still before the store fronts seemed about to melt.

The street was extraordinarily deserted and quiet; there was only the monotonous ting-tong of the hammers from the copper and iron stores, that made you even more uncomfortable. The rickshaw pullers, knowing full well that if they did not keep moving they would not have food to eat, yet were reluctant to try to find fares. Some of them found places that were relatively a little more cool and shady, parked their rickshaws there, put up the tops, and sat down in them to take a nap; others slipped into some teahouse and sat there sipping tea; there were still others that didn't take their rickshaws out at all, but simply walked down to the corner to see how things were, and discovered for themselves that there was no possibility of pulling a rickshaw in such weather. Those who actually picked up fares, even if they were the smartest-looking lads of the lot, had even at that to accept a loss of face: they did not dare run, but could only walk slowly along, their heads down. Each time they got close to a well platform, the thought of water would seem to them to be the star of their salvation, and, disregarding the fact that they might only have come a few steps on the way that they were to pull their fare along, they would head straight for the well. If they could not reach freshly drawn water, they would share the trough with the horses and mules, and gulp a big mouthful of the water used by the animals. There were still others who, because they were already sunstruck or were in the first stages of cholera, walked on and on, aimlessly, their heads hanging almost down to the ground, and never lifting them up.

Even Happy Boy was a little bit fearful. He had not pulled his rickshaw many steps when he could feel the hot air besieging him everywhere from his face to his feet; the very backs of his hands were pouring sweat. But, when he saw a passenger, he still wanted to take him, believing that if he could get started running he might on the contrary feel a little breeze and be more comfortable. It was only when he did find a fare and began running that he knew the weather had already reached a degree of severity that would not permit of any man's working in it. As soon as he would start running he would no longer be able to breathe, and his lips would become parched; although he knew he was not really thirsty, still every time he saw water he would rush to drink it. If he did not run, the poisonously flowering sunlight would bake the skin on his hands and back until it split. By the time he had somehow or other got his fare to the destination, his pants and vest would be plastered to his body with sweat. He would pick up a palm-leaf fan and fan himself, but that was no use—the breeze he made was hot too. He had already lost track of the number of gulps of cold water he had swallowed, and yet he rushed as fast for the next teashop as he

nifying glass, and any spot where you were was the point of focus, bringing down so intense a heat that everything about you seemed on the very point of breaking into flame. In this white light every color stabbed the eyes, every sound was a piercing shriek, and every breath in the nostrils stank with the rancid stench of the steaming earth.

Already the streets were empty of people, and it was as if the avenues had become much more broad, like boundless and deserted sheets of glare, without a single breath of cool air coming over their glistening surfaces.

It made a man's heart afraid. Happy Boy did not know what to do. His head down, he pulled his rickshaw along, moving forward as slowly as he could and still move at all, without any objective. His mind was lost in a haze of heat, and his body stank with sticky sweat. After he had been walking a while his feet got so wet and hot that his shoes and stockings seemed to become all one gummy mass that made him feel with every step he took as if he were sliding in slime. It was a terrible feeling. He had decided that he was not going to drink any more water, but every time he passed a well he would go over, through no volition of his own, and gulp down several more big draughts of it. It was not to quench his thirst but simply and solely to feel the coolness of the well and with the water to cool his throat and stomach, to get from that sudden douse of coldness and delicious quick shiver that its dank chill gave him. That was a wonderfully comfortable moment, but almost before he was through drinking he would start hiccupping, and the water would rush back up his gullet in a burning hurry, trying to get out again.

Walking a while, resting a while, he was from first to last without the energy to hunt for a fare. At high noon he still did not feel hungry enough to eat anything. He decided to eat anyway at his regular time; but the sight of food made him sick. His stomach was full of all kinds of water from a dozen different wells, and every once in a while he could hear it gurgling a little inside of him, in the way that you can sometimes hear the water slopping about inside a horse or a donkey that's just had its fill.

If you were comparing winter and summer, Happy Boy would have been sure to claim that winter was the more to be feared. It had never occurred to him that summer could be as hard to bear as this was. It had been many more than a single summer that he had passed within the city's walls, but he could not remember one as hot as this. Was it really that this summer was hotter than the ones that had gone before it, or was his body growing less able to resist it? The moment this thought came to him, the fog in his mind lifted, and his heart suddenly grew cold. That was it! It was his own body that was no good anymore! He was frightened, but there was nothing that he could do. Tiger Girl was avid for every last drop of strength she could wring from his loins, and night after night she was after him, draining away his substance even after he was too weary to move. There was no way he could drive her off. He would soon be turned into just another Second Vigorous, or would become like the tall fellow he had met that time: he would be the grandfather of Little Horse. Happy Boy was finished.

It was just a few minutes after high noon when he got another fare. This was the very hottest hour of the day, the very hottest day of the whole summer, but he had made up his mind to make another run. He didn't care how hot it was under the glaring sun. If when he'd finished this run it hadn't hurt him any, that would be proof enough that his body hadn't gone bad at all. If on the other hand he couldn't manage to carry this fare, what would there be left to say? If he couldn't pull a fare wouldn't he be better off if he slipped and dropped dead on this burning ground?

He had only taken a few steps with his fare when he felt the breath of a cool breeze on him, as you feel a draft of cold air coming into a terribly hot room through the crack of a momentarily opened door. He hardly dared believe his own senses, and looked at the branches of the willow trees. Sure enough, they were swaying ever so gently. Suddenly more people began to appear in the street: they were piling out of stores and houses, holding rush-leaf fans over their heads and hunting about in every direction, saying to each other, "There's a cool breeze! A cool breeze! The cool air has come down!" It was as if everyone were about to begin jumping up and down and shouting. The leaves on the willow trees had become messengers of Heaven, commissioned to transmit Heaven's tidings. "The willow branches are moving! May the venerable Old Gentleman of Heaven vouchsafe us more of this cool breeze!"

It was still hot, but one's heart was much more composed. The cool breeze, even though it was only a very very small one, brought everyone hope. After the first few wafts of cold wind the sun did not seem so strong. It would be bright for a moment and then be darkened, as if a blanket of floating sand had moved across it. Suddenly the wind became much stronger, and the willow branches, that had until a moment before been motionless all the day, acted as if they had learned abruptly some piece of very good news, and were dancing and swaggering from the joy and the pride of it. A heavy gust of wind blew over them, the heavens passed into the shadow, and all the gray dust from the desert rose up to float in the sky. When the dust and dirt had settled a little you could see on the northern side of the heavens the gathering clouds, deeply black. Happy Boy had no more sweat on his body. After a glance to the north he set his rickshaw down and put up the rain guard. He knew that in summer the rain comes the instant it tells you it is going to, and gives you no leisure to make ready for its coming.

He had hardly got the rain cloth up when there was another blast of wind, and the black clouds rolled over and over until they had covered half the heavens. The heat from the earth blended with the cold wind, and the rank smell of the dry dust was added to the mixture. It seemed cool and yet it still felt hot.

The southern half of the heavens were resplendent with the brightness of a clear summer day, while the northern half was clouded over as black as ink. It was as if some terrible natural catastrophe impended, and in the panic the whole world had lost its head. Rickshaw men hurriedly put up their rain guards, and shopkeepers rushed to take in their street signs, while with hasty hands and scurrying feet the street hawkers rolled up their sidewalk displays. Pedestrians quickened their steps, pressed to reach the places they wanted to go while there was yet time. Then there came another heavy blast of wind, rolling everything up in its passage, so that when it was gone everything else seemed to be gone too, save the willow branches dancing madly to the wind's music.

Even before the clouds had spread over the whole sky, the earth was already black. A bright, hot summer noon had suddenly become the darkest hour of night. The wind, carrying raindrops in its folds, tore about with reckless madness as if in search of something, rushing first in one direction and then in another. Far out in the northern sky a streak of red lightning ripped away the black cloud like a strip of burnt flesh, as if to show the crimson blood beneath it.

The wind was smaller now, but its sharp soughing made a man shudder. When it swept by it left everything in its trail confused and unsure. Even the willows seemed to wait in frightened uncertainty for they knew not what. Another flash of lightning, directly overhead, spread a white and silver light through the heavy rain that began at that instant to fall. The big drops struck hard at the dust, beating it into the ground. They fell too on Happy Boy, so coldly that they made him shiver. By the time this shower had let up a little, the black clouds had spread themselves evenly across the whole of heaven.

Again the wind moved in, even more terrible than before. Willow branches were torn from their trees, the dust swirled everywhere, the rain came down hard again, riding a road it knew. The wind, the dust, the rain were all stirred in together until they became one boundless howling force that sought to encompass the sky and swallow every living thing. You could not tell what was tree and what was earth or what was cloud and what was water; the four directions and the eight points of the compass were all now confused, and all echoing the same long moan. When the wind had died away once more there was nothing left but torrential rain, tearing the heavens and ripping the earth, a solid column of water. For long minutes there was no telling earth from sky but for the direction in which this vast river between them was hurrying its flood. Occasional flashes of lightning lit up the illimitable wastes of water.

Happy Boy's clothing had early been soaked through; there wasn't a dry spot on his whole body; his hair had been wet under his straw hat. Below him the rivulets pouring across his feet had made each step forward very difficult; above, the rain beat him on the head and back, sweeping sidewise across his face and wrapping itself around his loins. He could not lift his head, nor

285

force his eyes open, nor breathe, nor pick up his feet. The best thing he could think of was to stand still in the midst of the water; he did not know where the roadway was, or which was back and which was forward. The only sensation he had was of cold cold water, soaking through every inch of his body straight to the bone; he was aware of nothing else but of the constant drumming in his ears of the sound of falling rain, and the vague and fearsome fever that was beginning to burn in his heart. He wanted to put the shafts of his rickshaw down, but he did not know where it would be best to stop. When he thought of running forward at something like a more normal gait, the water caught his feet. So he just kept dragging himself and his rickshaw along, with his head down, taking one painful step after the other, and more dead than alive. The man riding in his rickshaw acted as if he had died in it; without saying a word, he allowed his puller to struggle desperately in the rushing water.

The rain slackened a little, and at last Happy Boy could straighten himself up and draw a full breath. "Master, let's take to shelter for a while and then go on."

"Get along, and be quick about it! What kind of business would you count that, leaving me in a spot like this?" The man seated in the rickshaw shouted and stamped his feet.

For a moment Happy Boy truly thought of putting his rickshaw down and going off anyway to find shelter. But looking down at the water running off him, he knew that as soon as he stood still anywhere he would get a chill all over his body. Clenching his teeth, he began running, heedless of how deep the water might be. Before he had got very far the sky grew black again, and once more his eyes were blurred with rain.

When finally he got his fare to the destination, the fellow stepped down truculently and handed him the price first agreed upon, without adding a single copper to it. Happy Boy said nothing; he was already having enough trouble just keeping himself alive.

There was a lull in the rain, and when it started up again it fell much less heavily than before. Happy Boy pulled his rickshaw back home, running all the way without stopping. Hugging the fire, he toasted himself for a while: he was shivering like a leaf in the wind and rain. Tiger Girl brewed him a cup of preserved ginger tea. He took it like an imbecile, grasping the cup in both hands and drinking the hot brew at one gulp. When he had finished it he wriggled down under the covers on the brick bed and lay there unconscious of anything around him, seeming to sleep without sleeping, with the "shwah shwah" of falling rain sounding ceaselessly in his ears.

By four o'clock the black clouds were beginning to show signs of weariness, and the red streaks of lightning that flashed through them had lost their strength. In a little while the edges of the breaking clouds showed gold and yellow, and the thunder sounded only weakly from the south. In the eastern skies a seven-colored rainbow appeared, its ends resting in clouds and its arc sweeping high into the clear blue sky. In a while it was gone, and with it the last trace of a dark cloud. The blue firmament emerged from its cleansing like the earth beneath it, born anew from its darkness into brightness and beauty.

Even to the mud holes in the compound enclosure a few gaily colored dragonflies came. But except for the barefooted children who chased them, trying to catch them, no one in the compound enclosure had time to take pleasure in the dragonflies or the rainbow or the beauty of the world when the storm had passed. The retaining wall of the compound, at the point where it formed the back wall of Little Lucky One's room, had collapsed, and she and her two little brothers were busy patching up the hole with the matting from their brick bed. The compound wall had fallen in many places around the yard, but no one paid any attention to that: they were all busy cleaning up the debris in their own rooms. In some of the rooms the floor was too nearly level with the ground outside, with the result that they were flooded with water; in them the whole family would be using seven hands and eight feet scooping out the water with broken rice bowls and old dustpans. In others the roof leaked like a sieve, soaking everything, and their occupants would be urgently moving everything out, to dry it by a stove in the yard or to lay it out in the sun. While the rain was falling they could only crowd into these rooms, the walls of which might at any time collapse and bury them alive, and commend their souls to the Venerable Old Gentleman in Heaven; when the storm was past they could count the cost of repairing the damage done. Although the coming of rain would bring down the price of rice by a few coppers a catty, their losses were not so slight as to be repaired with this scant saving. They paid rental regularly, but no one ever came to repair the place they rented, unless the walls and roof tumbled down so completely that no one could live there any more. Only then would a mason come, and with a little mud and a few broken bricks patch up the walls against the time when they would fall again. If the tenant couldn't pay the rent when it fell due, he and his whole family would be run out and his belongings seized in payment. But if the roof was broken or the walls likely to fall inward and crush you, nobody paid any heed. For the rent they paid, that was the most they could expect. Suppose there were holes in the walls and the lives of tenants were endangered? What of it? It was their damned fault.

But the greatest of all losses that storms could bring them was sickness. Grownups and children alike, they all scrabbled every minute of every day to get enough to keep alive, working with what strength there was in them. Their bodies covered with sweat, their pores open, they could not fend against the sudden storms that swept the north in the summertime with the cold rain. The best they could hope for was to be ill only a day or two with fever, but if in that time one of the children was also taken sick, there would be no money to buy medicine for it.

Such a rain pushed up the corn and kaoliang in the countryside, but it sprinkled death for many a child of the poor within the city. And if the grownups were sick it was even worse.

The well-fed makers of poetry may sibilantly sigh forth their soft hymns to the jewel-bright bud of the water lily when the rain has passed, or to the beauties of the double rainbow; for the poor, when the storm is over and the worker is ill, the whole family starves. Each storm adds to the number of girls turned prostitutes and boys turned thieves, and there are more men to fill the jails. The rain falls on the rich and the poor alike, and on the just and the unjust. But the bitter truth is that there is no equity even in the fall of rain, because the world on which it falls is so unjustly ruled.

Happy Boy was sick. Nor was he the only one.

19

ᖴOR two days and two nights Happy Boy slept a deep, heavy sleep. Tiger Girl was beside herself with fear. At the Temple to the Goddess of Mercy she besought from the spirits of the other world—by shaking the bamboo sticks in the little round box until one fell out before the others—a miraculous prescription. Following its requirements, she mixed a little of the ashes of incense sticks with two or three kinds of medicinal herbs into a liquid and poured it down Happy Boy's throat. It is a matter of actual fact that he opened his eyes and looked around, but in only a little while he went to sleep again, his lips continually making a gee-gee koo-koo gurgle from which it could not be known what he meant to say.

It was not until then that Tiger Girl called in a doctor. He punctured Happy Boy twice with a sharp needle and gave him a dose of medicine. The patient recovered consciousness, asking as soon as his eyes were open, "Is it still raining?"

The second dose of medicine was already concocted when he refused to take it. Because in his heart he was loath to part with money, and at the same time hated himself for being so far below standard that a rainstorm should lay him up sick, he was unwilling to swallow that cup of bitter juices. In order to prove that there was no need for him to be taking medicine, he thought to get up at once and get dressed. But hardly had he sat upright when his head felt as if it were being crushed under the weight of an immense rock. His neck went soft, his eyes saw golden stars before them. There was no further need of speech: he reached for the cup and swallowed the medicine.

He lay on his back for ten days, and the longer he was there the more worried he became. Sometimes he pressed the pillow in his arms and wept soundlessly. He knew he could not go out and earn money, and that therefore Tiger Girl had to advance it from the little money she had. When that was gone they would be completely dependent on his rickshaw. The way Tiger Girl loved to spend money and eat good things, he knew he couldn't support her, and, moreover, she was with child! The longer he lay ill, the more confused and extravagant his misgivings became: the more he upset himself with these anxieties, the harder it was for him to get well.

Hardly was he out of the danger of death when he asked Tiger Girl: "How about the rickshaw?"

"Don't worry. It's rented to Ding Four to pull."

"Ah!" His mind was not at rest about his rickshaw. The thing he feared was that Ding Four—or somebody else—would get it smashed up or wear it out with ill-usage. But since he could not pull it himself, naturally it had to be rented out. Could it be left idle? In his mind he cast up the account. If he were pulling the rickshaw, he could make in a full day at the very worst fifty or sixty cents. That was hardly enough—counting the rent, coal, rice, firewood, lamp oil, tea and water—for two people to live on, and that didn't allow for buying new clothes. Even then it would be necessary to scrape and weigh every penny, and Tiger Girl could not go on as she had been, just paying no attention to anything. Now their only income was the something over ten cents daily in rental for the rickshaw; it was necessary to make good, without any chance of recovering it again, the additional forty cents each day. And that didn't count the cost of the medicine.

Supposing he just never got well? Yes, you couldn't blame Second Vigorous for drinking; you couldn't blame your down-and-out friends for acting stupidly and without regard for propriety: the road of the rickshaw man was a dead-end road! No matter how hard you worked, or how ambitious you were, if you got married or got sick or went a little bit off the track, you were finished. Huh! He thought of his first rickshaw and of the money he had struggled so hard to save. He had hurt no one, offered no one offence, had been neither sick nor married, and yet with no shadow of justification in feeling or reason both rickshaw and money had been taken from him. Whatever you did, good or bad, ended the same: the road he was on could lead only to death, death that would meet him he knew not how soon or in what fashion. When his thoughts brought him to this, his worries would give way to the exhaustion of utter despair. Ha! His mother's! If he could not get up, he would go on lying there on his back. That was about all there was to it anyway. It would end the same way. So everything would go out of his mind and he would lie in perfect quietness. But in a little while this would again become unbearable, and he would want to get up right away to set about his bitter business. The road was a dead-end road, but the heart of man is living, and until it has been laid in the coffin there is no end to its hopes.

When he had tried once more to rise and couldn't, there would be nothing he could do but turn miserably, piteously to Tiger Girl, to speak to her.

"I tell you that rickshaw is bad luck!"

"Think more of getting well. Always talking about your rickshaw. You're rickshaw-crazy."

Then he would not say anything more. That was right: he was rickshaw-crazy. From the time he had first begun pulling a rickshaw, he had had utter faith that his rickshaw was everything, but the real truth was. . . .

As soon as his sickness got a little lighter he got up and looked at himself in the mirror. He did not recognize the person he saw there. His whole face seemed to be covered with grisly whiskers; his temples and cheeks were as sunken as the jaws of an old woman who has lost all her teeth; his eyes were two deep holes; even his facial scar was covered with wrinkles. The room was terribly hot and close, but he did not dare go out into the yard, first because his legs were as soft as if there were no bones in them, and, second, because he was afraid someone would see him. Not only in this one compound alone but at every rickshaw stand in all the West City he was known as an absolutely No. 1 cudgel among No. 1 hard-staffs. Happy Boy and this invalid could not possibly be the same person! He was unwilling to go out; inside their little room he was stifled with boredom. He hated himself because he could not gulp down in one great swallow enough food to bring his body back to strength so that he could go out and pull his rickshaw. But sickness comes to tear down its victim, and it cannot be got to leave him so easily.

When he had been recuperating for a month, he determined to disregard the fact that he was not yet recovered and started pulling his rickshaw in spite of everything. So that no one would recognize him and he could run as slowly as he pleased, he pulled his hat far down over his eyes. The name "Happy Boy" had become a synonym for "speed"; there was no way in which the two ideas could be separated, and he could not brazenly go about slowly dragging one foot after the other: everyone would despise him for it.

To begin with, his body had not got altogether well, and on top of that Happy Boy could not forego pulling two or three extra fares so as to make up more quickly for the loss that idleness had cost him. In a few days his illness came back, only this time dysentery was added to it. He was so aggravated that he wanted to strike himself across the mouth, but it was no use. The skin on his belly seemed almost to have touched his backbone, and still the flow did not stop. When finally it was checked his legs were so weak that even to squat over the stool exhausted him. There was no use even thinking of trying to pull a rickshaw. So he rested for another month, knowing the while that Tiger Girl's money would soon be finished.

On the fifteenth day of the eighth moon he made up his mind and took out his rickshaw. In his heart he swore an oath: if he got sick again, he would drown himself.

During his first illness, Little Lucky One had come over frequently to see him. Happy Boy's tongue had never been the equal of Tiger Girl's, and because of the terrible stifling feeling in his heart he would occasionally exchange a few sentences with Little Lucky One. This enraged Tiger Girl. When Happy Boy was not at home, Little Lucky One was a good friend, but with Happy Boy there she was—according to Tiger Girl—a disreputable woman who had no regard for face who came to flirt with another woman's husband.

She pressed Little Lucky One to pay her the money owing her, and told the poor girl, "From now on, I won't permit you to come in here."

Little Lucky One thus lost a place in which to receive her guests. Her own room was so ramshackle, with a gaping hole in the back wall only half stopped up with the matting off the brick bed, that there was nothing for her to do but to go down to the

"Transport Company" to register her name. But the company had no need of the kind of goods she had for sale. The standards of the organization were very high: they specialized in introductions to girl students and in the auction of virgins raised in the families of the great; their prices were high, and they did not want any ordinary article such as she brought them. She had no way out. If she thought of going down into a regular house of prostitution, the fact that she was without capital would make it impossible for her to do anything but mortgage her body. That would cost her her freedom. Who then would take care of her little brothers? It would be the simplest and easiest thing to die; life was already only mortal torture. She was not afraid to die nor did she want to die, because what she wanted to do was braver and finer than dying. She wanted to see her two little brothers old enough to earn their own livings; then she would die, and with an easy heart, but only when her death would save two lives.

She thought coming and she thought going: there was only one road to travel. She would sell herself much more cheaply. Nobody who was willing to come into that broken-down hovel of hers could be expected to pay a high price for his pleasure. All right, then, it didn't matter who came, just so they left her a little money. In this way there was at least a saving on clothes and rouge: the kind of people who patronized her now could not expect that she be decked out in the latest styles. They could take their fun according to the pittance they paid: they should feel lucky enough that she was so young.

Tiger Girl's body had already become not very convenient for her, so that even to go out to the street to buy something to eat was now a thing she sought to avoid. With Happy Boy away all day again, and Little Lucky One unwilling to come over to see her, she was as lonely as a dog chained in an empty house. The lonelier she got the deeper her hatred became: she felt that Little Lucky One's policy of making more sales at a cheaper price had been adopted on purpose to irritate her erstwhile friend. Tiger Girl was not going to take any loss of face like that, so she sat in the outer room, with the door open, and waited. Whenever anyone went into Little Lucky One's room, Tiger Girl would stretch her throat and make a lot of loud talk, to shame both the girl and her guest; when Little Lucky One's guests became fewer and fewer, Tiger Girl was in high spirits.

Little Lucky One knew that if this went on for long, soon everyone in the compound would be echoing Tiger Girl, and they would run her out. She was only afraid: she did not dare to be angry. When a person falls to as low an estate as she had, they learn to place realities before either anger or tears. She led her two little brothers across the yard and knelt down in supplication before Tiger Girl. Little Lucky One said nothing, but from her expression it was perfectly clear that if this was not a sufficient humiliation, then she had no fear at all of dying, but neither had the Tiger Girl any room to think of living.

The most fearful and awesome sacrifice is the acceptance of shame, and the deepest shame will give birth to the bitterest resistance.

This sudden reversal left Tiger Girl speechless. The thing had lost its flavor however you tasted of it, but with a stomach as swollen with pregnancy as hers was, she didn't dare risk a fight. Since she could not bring out a warlike answer, the next best thing was to provide herself with the stairway by which to leave the stage on which this anticlimax had caught her. Why, she was only jesting with Little Lucky One! Who could have thought that anyone could have taken this pretense for reality? Little Lucky One had too small an eye in her heart—she took things too seriously. With the whole thing explained away after this fashion, the two of them became good friends again, and once more Tiger Girl supported Little Lucky One in everything.

From the day in mid-August when Happy Boy brought his rickshaw out again, he had become more careful of each move.

His two bouts of illness had made him understand that he was not built of iron. He had not altogether forgotten his ambition to make more money, but the repeated shocks he had absorbed had left him with a clearer perception of how feeble a thing is the strength of one man alone. There comes a time when the real man must grit his teeth and show what he's made of, but for all the teeth-gritting he may soon enough be spitting blood. And even though Happy Boy's dysentery was cured, from time to time he would be almost bent double by terrible cramps in his stomach. Sometimes, just as he had started to stretch his legs and was thinking of getting up a little speed, a horrible knot would tie itself up in his stomach, and he would have to slow down, or sometimes stop altogether and, with his head lowered and his stomach drawn in, force himself to bear the pain as best he could. When he was alone with only his own fare to consider, the matter could be handled without too much difficulty, but when he was one of a group of rickshaw men whose fares were all in one party, and he suddenly came to an abrupt halt, it made everybody wonder what mysterious thing could be happening, and was almost unbearably chagrining for himself. Here he was still in his early twenties, and already becoming such a laughing-stock! What would he be like when he was thirty or forty? When he thought of it he would snort in disgust, and his body would come out in a cold sweat.

From the standpoint of his own well-being, he longed greatly to go back to hiring himself out by the month. That would in any case be lighter work. At the same time he knew for a certainty that Tiger Girl would absolutely refuse to let him out of her hand. When you're married your freedom is gone, and Tiger Girl was particularly fierce. He would just have to put up with it.

So it was that he passed the four or five months of fall and early winter, halfway making out, afraid on the one hand of being reckless in the amount of work he did, and on the other of being too lazy. His heart stifling from all the things that pressed down into his breast, he kept his head low and went about his bitter slavery in silence. His head was always down now: he no longer had the courage to dash about in reckless disregard of everything, as was once his wont. When it came to making money, he still earned somewhat more than most rickshaw men. Except when his stomach was paining him, he was never willing to pass up a fare; if he should haul a passenger, he hauled him. Nor had he from first to last picked up any of the evil practices of so many rickshaw men. He had never learned to deliberately demand an exhorbitant price from a passenger who might be ignorant of the proper fare, nor to stop halfway there and order his passenger to get out, nor even to sit waiting half the day for a really good paying passenger to come along. By his method he worked harder, but he earned a sure income every day. He was not looking for lucky breaks, and so was never in danger.

Still the money that came in was too little. There was never any left over. It came into his left hand and went out from his right, and at the end of each day he was clean again. As for putting any money aside, the very thought was one he no longer dared think. He knew how to save, but Tiger Girl knew how to spend. Her "month" was due to fall sometime early in the second moon of the new year, and from the beginning of winter the foetus had already begun to show its shape. More than that: Tiger Girl took a deliberate pleasure in sticking her stomach out even further to show off her own importance. Contemplating her own belly with such immense satisfaction, she was too indolent even to get down from her bed. The cooking of food and rice she turned over altogether to Little Lucky One. Naturally in return for this service she had to turn over to Little Lucky One and her small brothers the water in which vegetables had been cooked, and any left-over soup, for them to eat. This was a big waste.

Outside of her regular meals, Tiger Girl also had to have

special collations. The bigger her belly got the more necessary she felt it to be that she eat all kind of tidbits; she could not let her appetite go wanting. Not only did she buy these incidentals from time to time for herself, but she instructed Happy Boy to bring some home to her. However much he earned, she would spend it. Her demands rose and fell with his income. Happy Boy couldn't say anything. When he was sick he had spent her money, and now it was only right that in his turn he should requite her; he could not do other than let her spend whatever he had. If Happy Boy tightened his fingers even a little she would immediately get ill.

"Carrying a child," she would say, "is a nine months' sickness. What do you understand?" And the words she spoke were true.

By New Year's time she had thought up even more ways to spend money. She herself could not move from her nest, so it was necessary to send Little Lucky One out any number of times every day to buy things. Tiger Girl hated herself for not being able to go out, and at the same time she had such a tender love for herself that she was unwilling to go out. But not going was terribly boring, so that the only answer was to buy more things for her amusement and comfort. With every breath she made it clear that it was not for herself that she made these purchases: it was out of her feeling for Happy Boy. To him she would say:

"You have worked hard all year, and you don't dare eat a mouthful of sweets at New Year's? You've never got back all your strength since you were sick, and if you won't eat at festival time, what are you waiting for? Until you are so starved that you're like a shrivelled-up bedbug?"

It was not convenient for Happy Boy to enter into an altercation with her, nor was he able to do so. When the delicacy, whatever it happened to be, had been prepared, she would swallow two or three large bowls of it. Nor would she take any exercise at all, and when she got frightfully swollen from too much

298

food she would clasp her stomach in her hands and swear she was suffering from an affection of pregnancy.

After New Year's she would under no circumstances permit Happy Boy to be out at night. She did not know at what hour she might give birth, and she was afraid. It was only now that she gave thought to her real age, and although she had never clearly told Happy Boy how old she was, she no longer tried to conceal the years between them by saying, "I'm just a little older than you are."

The continual clamor that Tiger Girl raised about first one thing and then another had Happy Boy in a state of complete confusion. It is only by bringing forth sons and daughters that human life prolongs itself; although it was not in the least necessary for them to have a child, still Happy Boy could not help the stealthy feeling of pride and happiness that was growing in his heart at the thought that that simplest and yet most mystic of words, "father," would one day be applicable to his own person. It was enough to make any man, even if his heart were of iron, sit with closed eyes and think; the more he thought of that word, the more his heart would be moved by it. Happy Boy, with his heavy hands and heavy feet, could hardly think of anything about himself to be proud of; as soon as he thought of this rare and mystic word, he suddenly felt his own nobility and worth. It was as if the fact that he had nothing was no longer of importance. If only he had a child his life would not be empty. At the same time his only desire was to do his uttermost to serve Tiger Girl, to wait on her and make her comfortable. She no longer was just one person; granted that she was irritating and disagreeable, it still had to be admitted that in this particular matter she deserved one hundred per cent of the credit.

But however great her merit, her capacity for brawling around was becoming almost unbearable. Every minute she had some new idea, and was forever making a confused hubbub about seeing ghosts or devils. And through it all Happy Boy had to earn their living and he had to get rest. Accepting the fact that what money he could make would be spent foolishly, he still had to get a full night's sleep so as to be able to go out the next morning and begin another day of bitter labor. When she would neither let him go out to work after dark nor get a good night's sleep at home, he was at his wit's end. The whole day he would go about in a haze, with everything whirling around his eyes and not knowing what he should do next. Part of the time he was very pleased with himself; part of the time he was sick with anxiety; part of the time he was sad. Sometimes the feeling of pleasure would turn to shame, or from his sadness he would become unaccountably happy again; his emotions were so twisted in the tangled knot inside his heart that from the simplest and most direct person he had been worried into one who no longer knew the east from the west or the north from the south. It actually got so bad that once he carried a passenger past his destination, forgetting where the man had said he wanted to go!

At about the time of the festival of the lanterns Tiger Girl decided to have Happy Boy go call a midwife; she could stand her pregnancy no longer. The midwife told her that the time had not yet come and explained the signs by which she would know when the hour to get close to the tub had arrived. Tiger Girl bore it for another two or three days, and then set up such a commotion again that once more they called the midwife. It was still not time. Tiger Girl wept and screamed and said she was going to find some way to die; she could not go on under this horrible affliction. Happy Boy had not the slightest idea what he should do, but to show that he was trying his very hardest to help, he gave in to Tiger Girl's wishes and temporarily stopped pulling his rickshaw so that he could be at hand all the time.

This confusion continued right up to the end of the month,

when even Happy Boy could see that the time had now truly come. Tiger Girl no longer looked like a human being. The midwife came again, and hinted darkly to Happy Boy that she was afraid it was going to be a hard delivery. Because of Tiger Girl's age and the fact that this was her first child, that she had not taken any exercise, and that during her pregnancy she had loved to eat fatty things, the foetus had grown very large: these circumstances, all taken together, made it vain to hope that the birth would be a smooth and easy one. And, moreover, they had not once had a doctor and no effort had been made to correct the position of the child in the womb. She, the midwife, did not possess this skill, but there was this much she could say: it was to be feared that it would come out crosswise and be a fractious delivery.

In the compound in which they lived the deaths of mothers in childbirth had always been almost as much a commonplace of conversation as were the births themselves. But Tiger Girl was in even greater danger than the others. Other women continued right up to the day of their confinement to move about and do their work. Moreover, because they never had enough to eat, the child in their womb could never grow very large, so that it would be that much easier to deliver. The greatest danger to such a mother would come after the baby had been born. It was directly the opposite with Tiger Girl: her advantages were her misfortune.

Happy Boy, Little Lucky One, and the midwife stood watch over her for three days and three nights. Tiger Girl called on all the spirits that had achieved Buddhahood, and made countless vows in propitiation of them, but all in vain. Finally her voice grew so hoarse she could hardly speak, and all she could whisper were the agonized words, "Ma-ah! Ma-ah!" There was nothing that the midwife could do, nothing that any of them could do. Then Tiger Girl herself managed to suggest that Happy Boy go outside the Gate of Victorious Virtue and invite Second

Grandmother Ch'en to secure the intercession of the mystic genius of the Immortal Toad. Since without five dollars Second Grandmother Ch'en would not come, Tiger Girl brought out her last seven or eight dollars.

"Good Happy Boy, my Happy Boy, go as quickly as you can! Spending the money is of no importance. Wait till I'm well again, and every day I'll love you. Go quickly!"

Second Grandmother brought with her a "young lad"—required by the rites to be a child innocent of life's experiences—who was in fact a great robust yellow-faced son of Han a little less than forty years old. It was almost time for the lighting of lamps when they finally arrived. Second Grandmother herself was in her late forties. She wore a blue pongee jacket and a big red sandstone pomegranate flower in her hair, with a full outfit of gold-plated rings on her fingers and bracelets on her arms. Her eyes glittering like a magician's, she first washed her hands, set up a row of upright incense sticks on the table, lighted them, and knelt down, knocking her head on the floor before them. Then she sat down behind the table staring stupidly at the burning tips of the incense. Suddenly her whole body began to jerk and shiver as if in convulsion. She hung her head, closed her eyes, and gradually subsided, not moving at all for a long time. Even Tiger Girl gritted her teeth and made no sound: you could have heard the noise of a falling needle.

Slowly Second Grandmother Ch'en lifted up her head and nodded to the assembled company. The "young lad" tugged at Happy Boy's sleeve, telling him to kotow quickly. Happy Boy did not know whether he believed in spirits or not, but he felt fairly sure that knocking his head on the ground could do nobody any harm. In his befuddlement he bumped his head on the floor he didn't know how many times. When he stood up again and saw the glittering eyes of the sorceress, the bright of the still burning stubs of the incense sticks, and smelled the curious odor of their smoke, his heart filled with a vague hope that this whole act might bring some good result. He stood staring dully before him, the palms of his hands wet with perspiration.

With a full throat and booming sound, and not without condescension, the Immortal Toad began to speak. "No—no—no—no matter! Write out a charm—a charm—a charm for hastening childbirth!"

With the greatest agility the "young lad" brought forth a scroll of silken paper. The Immortal scratched about in the ashes of the incense sticks, and then, wetting one with her spittle, began to write on the scroll. When the charm was written, the Spirit spoke again through many a silly grin and grimace on the face of the medium. The general purport of these oracles was that in a previous existence Tiger Girl had incurred a debt to this child, and in payment she must suffer this affliction now. Happy Boy, at his wit's end, beating his own head, could understand little of it all, but was frightened by it.

Second Grandmother Ch'en yawned a big long yawn, and after sitting a while longer with her eyes closed, suddenly opened them, as though she were awakening from a vivid dream. The "young lad" hurriedly reported to her the sayings of the Immortal. She seemed to be delighted. "Today the Immortal is truly in fine spirits. He has taken to talking!" Afterwards she showed Happy Boy how to get Tiger Girl to swallow the charm, giving her a pill which she took at the same time.

Enthusiastically Grandmother Ch'en awaited the results of the charm, and she required that her dinner be prepared while she watched. These instructions Happy Boy transmitted to Little Lucky One, who went out and bought sesame sauce, meat cakes, and salt twists; Grandmother Ch'en complained, for all that, because there was no wine.

After Tiger Girl had eaten the charm, and Second Grandmother and the "young lad" had had their dinner, the patient still twisted and rolled in her pain. When it had continued un-

relieved for another hour, the pupils of Tiger Girl's eyes were already slowly turning upward. Grandmother Ch'en had another plan: without haste or excitement she asked Happy Boy to light another stick of incense and kneel down before it. Happy Boy had already lost the greater part of his faith in this woman, but since he had already spent the five dollars, he thought it best to try out all her schemes with the best good will he could muster. There was still one chance in ten thousand that they might have some effect.

With his back stiff and straight he knelt before the tall incense stick. He did not know what spirit it was whose help he was beseeching, but he knew his heart must be sincere and devout. Watching the dancing flame on the tip of the incense, he pretended that in its red embers he could see the form and shadow of some spiritual thing, and in his heart he prayed to it. The longer the incense burned the shorter the stick got, until it seemed that embers were turning to ash. His head dropped down to his chest, he put his hands on the floor, and, through the haze, sleep came to him. It was already two or three days since he had been to bed. Dozing, his head suddenly went forward, and he awoke with a start. Glancing at the incense, he saw that it was burned out. Without waiting to know if it was properly time to do so or not, he stood slowly up on his legs that had grown a little numb.

Second Grandmother Ch'en and her "young lad" had already stolen away.

Happy Boy did not have time to hate her. He went at once to Tiger Girl, knowing that things had reached the worst possible point. She had left to her now only that last mouthful of mortal breath that goes out when life goes out: she could no longer speak. The midwife told him that he must find some means to get her to a hospital, that her skill was of no avail.

Suddenly Happy Boy's heart split within him, and he opened his mouth and began to sob. Little Lucky One wept too, but because it was her duty to help she kept her mind clearer than his. "Elder brother! You must not cry. Shall I go to the hospital and ask?"

Without regarding whether Happy Boy had heard her, she wiped away her tears and ran out.

An hour passed before she came running back again, panting so hard that the words would not come out of her mouth. She held on to the table, her lips dry, until finally she could speak. To get the doctor to come one time, you had first to pay him ten dollars, and that was only to look at the patient, and did not cover receiving the newborn. That was twenty dollars more. If the birth was difficult, you had to go to the hospital, and that would be several more tens of dollars.

"Elder brother, what shall we do?"

There was nothing that Happy Boy could do. Where could he get all that money so late at night? The only thing left was to wait; they who were fated to die would just have to die.

Stupidity and the cruelest avarice in themselves and the order of their world had brought them here, and now left them no way to leave.

At midnight Tiger Girl bore a dead child and stopped breathing.

20

ℋAPPY BOY sold his rickshaw!

Nor could his hand close over the money as it slipped through his fingers. There was no getting around the fact that Tiger Girl's body had to be carted out, and it cost money even to get a death certificate to paste on the front end of the coffin.

Happy Boy watched dumbly while everyone scurried back and forth in front of him: all that he was good for was to shell out money. His eyes were so red they were frightful, with sticky yellow pus oozing from their corners; his ears heard nothing; in a numb, uncomprehending way he followed the milling confusion of the others, with no idea what they were doing or how he came to be there.

It was only when he had followed Tiger Girl's coffin out beyond the walls of the city that the outline of things became a little clearer to him, but he still could not bring himself to try to think about them. There was no one to accompany the body to the grave except Happy Boy and the two small brothers of Little Lucky One. Each of the boys carried in his hand a thin little packet of imitation paper money which they scattered by the wayside to bribe the devils who would otherwise block the road against the spirits of the dead.

With the same numbness Happy Boy watched the bearers lower the coffin into the grave: he did not cry. A fire of consuming fury smouldered in his breast, and its heat had dried up all tears; he could not have wept had he wanted to. Stupidly he watched, hardly knowing what it was they were doing. Only when the head bearer came over to look after him did he realize that everything was over and it was time for him to go home.

Little Lucky One had already put the room in order. When he got back he just flopped down on the brick bed, so tired he couldn't move. His eyes were too hot and dry for him to close them, and he lay there staring dully at the big stains that leaking rainwater had made in the paper on the ceiling. Because he couldn't sleep, he finally sat up, not knowing what to do with himself. Then he went out and bought a package of cigarettes, and sat on the edge of the bed smoking, afraid to look around him at the room. But he didn't want to smoke, and held the cigarette away, watching the blue smoke curl up from its tip.

Suddenly the tears came, first like beads on a string, and then in one long flood. It was not only of Tiger Girl and his dead child that he was thinking, but of all the rest besides. These years since he had come to the city—this, no more than this, was what all his hard work had brought him to! So deep was the pain that even his sobbing was soundless. His rickshaw—his rickshaw—it was his own rice bowl! And he had bought it, and lost it, and bought another, and sold it: three times he had reached upward and three times been thrown back to the earth. The thing he wanted was like an apparition of the dead: he could reach out and grasp it but his hand closed over nothing, and it was for that emptiness that he had suffered all his wrongs and all his bitter labor. He had nothing, nothing—not even his old woman. For all that Tiger Girl had been sharp and mean, still without her how could he have a home? If you looked at the things in the room—they were all hers, but she herself was buried in a grave outside the walls of the city.

And his son had been born dead.

The more he thought of it the more cruel and horrible it seemed. The flame of his rage dried the tears again, and in bitter anger he puffed at his cigarette. The more he disliked smoking, the harder he smoked. When the cigarettes were all gone he put his head in his hands, his mouth and his heart dry and puckered with bitterness. If he could only shriek in his madness, spitting out all the blood in his heart, he might then be for a while in peace.

He did not know when it was that Little Lucky One came into his quarters to stand before the kitchen table in the outer room watching him open-eyed.

When suddenly he lifted his head and saw her, the tears poured out in a torrent again. Just then he would have wept if it had only been a dog that he had seen. His whole heartful of wrong and misery spilled out at meeting another living being that knew suffering too. He wanted to tell her all about it and to have her sympathy, but the words were too many and he could not even open his mouth.

She stepped forward toward him.

"Elder Brother," she said, "I straightened everything up."

He nodded his head, but could not thank her: for those in grief, the conventional forms of politeness are meaningless.

"What do you figure on doing, Elder Brother?"

"Eh?" It was as if he had not understood, but when the words entered his consciousness he shook his head. He could not bring himself to make any plans.

She walked a couple of more steps forward, her face suddenly suffused with color and her white teeth showing, but she could not speak. The way she made her living had made it impossible for her not to forget any sense of shame, but when it came to a matter touching the deeper proprieties she was still a sincere and true-hearted woman. "I think . . ." She could get only that little bit out. The words in her heart were many indeed, but when her face flushed they all suddenly fled from her and she could not think of them again.

The truth which people have to communicate to one another is little enough to begin with, and the blush on a woman's face sometimes says more than a long speech: even Happy Boy understood the idea in her mind. In his eyes she was one of the most beautiful of women, with a beauty that was in her very bones. Even if her whole body had been covered with sores, and her flesh was rotten with them, in his heart she would still be very beautiful. She was beautiful, she was young, she was diligent and frugal. If he was thinking of marrying again, she was an ideal person. He had most definitely not thought of taking another wife right away, and he was loath to put his mind to any question like that. But since she was already willing, and the pressure of her situation had forced her to bring it up without delay, it seemed to him that he could not possibly reject her. She was such a fine person in her own self, and she had helped him so much, that he could only nod his assent. What he really wanted to do was to take her in his arms and put his head down on her breast and weep until all his wrongs had been washed clean by his tears. Afterwards they could go on together, working with all their energy and with a single heart, however bitter the road might be. It seemed to him that her person held all of that comfort and consolation that a woman should bring her man. His mouth was slow to speech, but when he saw her he felt like talking freely because, with her to listen, nothing that he said would be wasted; her nod or her smile would be the most beautifully sufficient of any reply that he could ever receive, and he would know then what it really meant to have a home.

Just at this moment Little Lucky One's second brother came running in. "Sister, sister, papa's coming!"

She frowned. Hardly had she opened the door when Second Vigorous appeared.

"What are you doing going into Happy Boy's room?" The old man teetered on his wobbling legs and glared at her. "Haven't you sold yourself enough times? Do you still have to give it away free to Happy Boy? You cheap, filthy thing!"

Hearing his own name, Happy Boy came quickly out and stood behind Little Lucky One.

"I say, Happy Boy." Second Vigorous wavered uncertainly, trying to throw his chest out in a gesture of great dignity, although he was hardly able even to keep his feet. "I say, Happy Boy, do you still pretend you're a man? Who do you think you're getting something for nothing from now? What kind of cheap play do you call this? Who else do you think you can take advantage of?"

Happy Boy was unwilling to mistreat the poor drunken devil, but his pent-up grief left him incapable of controlling his anger. He stepped forward, and eyes that were red and swollen from weeping glared into eyes that were red and swollen from drink. It was as if their stares would strike fire in crossing. Happy Boy gripped the old man by the shoulders, and as if they were playing a children's game gave him a quick shove, pushing him a long way off.

Second Vigorous tumbled backward, ending in a sitting posture in the middle of the courtyard, in a position which suggested none of the severe dignity that he had meant should attend his highly moral reproof of Happy Boy. His drunkenness had been at least in part put on, and his fall made him almost sober. He would have liked to counterattack, but he knew clearly that he was not Happy Boy's match. To just go quietly away now, like a whipped dog, would be ten parts of the wrong flavor. He was therefore unwilling to get to his feet, although at the same time he realized that he could not conveniently go on sitting there indefinitely. With his heart in such complete confusion, all he could do was to let his mouth run on unrestrained.

"What business is it of yours if I correct my own children? You strike me? Your mother's! You'll have to pay for it!"

Happy Boy had no desire to reply; he was quietly waiting for the fellow to get up and fight.

Little Lucky One tried to keep back her tears, hardly knowing what to do with herself. It would be useless to try to pacify her father, and yet she could not stand by tranquilly and watch Happy Boy beat him. Frantically she felt in all her pockets, finally managing to scrape together some ten copper pieces, and gave them to her brother. Ordinarily the little boy would never have dared to go near his papa, but today, seeing that the old man had been knocked down, his courage was a little greater.

"Take this and get out!"

His eyes still glaring, Second Vigorous took the money, and, struggling to his feet, muttered the while: "I offended the Lord of Heaven when I loosed you brats from the stomach of a slave girl. Your mother's! One of these days I'll get a knife and cut your throats like pigs." Making for the street door of the compound as fast as he could, he yelled over his shoulder, "Happy

Boy, we'll put this by for another time. We'll meet outside and settle it."

When Second Vigorous had gone, Little Lucky One and Happy Boy went back to the room together.

"There's nothing I can do!" The girl spoke as if to herself, expressing in that one sentence the whole burden of her despair and at the same time conveying something of the one hope that she now had: if Happy Boy would take her as his wife, there would be things that she could do.

But having gone through this scene, Happy Boy could now see many dark shadows behind the slender person of Little Lucky One. He was still fond of her, but he was unequal to the responsibility which the support of two little brothers and a drunken father involved. He did not dare to think that now, just because Tiger Girl was dead, he was free to do anything he pleased: Tiger Girl had Tiger Girl's good points; at the very least she had helped him a great deal when it came to money. Nor did he think for a moment that Little Lucky One would deliberately eat even a single mouthful of his food without making her full contribution in return, but it was still an absolutely certain fact that her whole household was incapable of earning even one red penny.

Love or no love, the poor have only one way of deciding any issue that confronts them, and that is on the basis of dollars and cents, on the possession or the lack of pitifully small amounts of the currency affording the means by which the rich exploit them and destroy their lives. Only in the homes of the very wealthy can the seeds of passion grow to their full flower.

He began collecting his things.

"Are you going to move?" Little Lucky One's lips were ashen-white.

"I'm moving!" He made his heart hard: in a world so cruel in its injustice, the poor can only maintain the terribly limited freedom that is still theirs by learning to be cruel themselves.

She looked at him just once, and then went out, her head down. She did not hate him, she was not angry, she did not nag. Only the hope in her heart was broken.

Tiger Girl's head ornaments and her better clothing she had worn with her to the grave. What was left was nothing more than a pile of old and worn-out garments, a few wooden utensils, and a collection of dishes, bowls, pots, ladles, and what not. Happy Boy selected a few of the dresses that were a little better than the others and put them to one side; the rest of the things he lumped together and sold. He called a "drum beater" in and turned it all over to him for the first offer that was made to him —something over ten dollars. He was in a hurry to move, in a hurry to be rid of all this junk, so he had no mind to call in one man after another and gradually force up the price. When the "drum beater" had carried the stuff away, there was nothing left in the place except his own bedding roll and the few frocks he had held back, lying on the brick bed now shorn of its cover of straw matting. With the room so completely empty he felt easier, as if he had freed himself from a whole tangle of ropes that had bound him down. Now he could take long strides and go great distances, or even take wings and fly high into the heavens if he chose.

In a little while he began to think of the things again. The table was gone, but around the spots on the floor where its square legs had rested there were collected tiny little four-walled embankments of fine dust, like the square towers at the corners of the bastions of a city. Looking at these traces in the dust of things that had been, he thought also of the person who had lived among them: like a dream she had gone. It did not matter whether the things were good or bad, or even whether the person was good or bad. Without them there was no place anywhere that his heart could be at rest. Sitting on the side of the brick bed, he pulled out another cigarette.

With it a ten-cent piece came out of his pocket, and without

313

thinking he began to search through his clothes to fish out whatever money he had on his person. In these last few days he hadn't got around to casting up his accounts. When it was all out—the silver dollars, the ten-cent notes, the copper notes, the copper pieces, some of every kind—he piled it all in one pile and counted it. There wasn't quite twenty dollars. Adding to that the ten dollars that he had got from selling the things, his entire financial resources came to only a little over thirty dollars.

He put the money on the edge of the brick bed and sat staring at it, not knowing wheither to cry or to laugh. The room was empty both of people and things, and all he had left of his life in it was this pile of dirty, filthy, poisonous money. How could you explain that?

Sighing, he took the only course open to him: he put the money in his vest, collected the dresses and his bedding roll, and went to find Little Lucky One.

"You keep these few dresses and wear them. I'll leave my bedding roll in your keeping for a while, until I've found a rickshaw shed, when I'll come back for it." He did not dare look at Little Lucky One, and blurted out these few words all in one breath.

She made some little sound that meant assent, but said nothing more.

When Happy Boy had located a rickshaw shed where he could stay, he came back for his bedding. Little Lucky One's eyes were swollen with crying. He was incapable of saying anything, but by exhausting every resource he had for articulate expression he managed to get out this one sentence:

"Wait—wait for me until I've got started again, and then I'll come for you—I'll certainly come!"

She nodded her head, saying nothing.

Happy Boy only rested for one day, and then began pulling a rickshaw as before. His heart did not burn as it had before

314

to get passengers, but still he never purposely loafed on the job. Thus without great enthusiasm and yet without distaste he passed one day after another, until soon another month was gone. His heart felt tranquil and at peace; his face filled out a little, although it did not regain its old full roundness. Nor was his complexion flushed and red as it had been; it had become a sallow yellow, not seeming healthy, but at the same time not revealing any signs of wasting away. His eyes now were always bright, without showing either emotion or sympathy: it was as if they were forever alight with energy but never saw anything. His whole spirit and expression was like that of a tree that has survived a violent tempest and now stands very quietly stretching its boughs in the sun, afraid to move again. In the past he had not enjoyed talking; now he liked even less to open his mouth. The days were turning very warm again, the willow trees covered once more with their leaves, and sometimes he would put down the shafts of his rickshaw in a place facing the sunlight and sit there with his head on his chest, his lips moving ever so slightly in the language he muttered to himself. Then perhaps he would throw his head back so the sun fell on his face, and doze for a while. Except when he was absolutely obliged to open his mouth, he simply never passed a word with anyone.

Cigarettes, though—that was a habit he had long since firmly accquired. Whenever he sat down between the shafts of his rickshaw, his hands would automatically begin feeling under the matting of the footrest where he kept his cigarettes. When he had lighted one, he would draw in the smoke and exhale it again ever so slowly, moodily watching each puff as it drifted tardily upward and away. Then he would nod his head, as if that eventual dissipation of the smoke in the air bore for him some special message, told him something of the inevitable course of life that he too had already learned, made a statement of truth that he could subscribe to.

When he picked up the rickshaw shafts, he was still a more

315

expert runner than most, but no longer would he put his whole life into running. In turning corners or going up and down inclines he was especially careful, perhaps even too careful. And suppose another puller wanted to race with him: no matter how much he was teased, or what the other did to arouse him, he would keep his head down and not emit a sound, keeping right on at the same pace that he had been running before, neither slower nor faster. It was as if he had seen through this whole business of pulling a rickshaw, and had no more illusions about it, and no more thought to wrest from it whatever small honor or praise it might bring.

In the shed, though, he undertook to make friends. For all he did not like to talk, the silent eagle was still happy to fly with the flock. If now he had not made a few friends, his loneliness would have been unbearable. Whenever his packet of cigarettes came out of his pocket, it made the circle of the group, was offered to each in turn. Sometimes when the others saw that perhaps he had only one left, and were embarrassed on that account to reach out their hands, he would say, very simply, "I'm going to buy more."

And on occasions when the crowd was gambling, he no longer—as was once his wont—held himself aloof, but came over to have a look and once in a while he would pick a number and place a bet of his own, not caring at all whether he won or lost, but just to show the crowd that he was one of them, whatever they did, and that he understood full well that after you had fagged yourself out with days of toil you owed it to yourself to be happy and carefree for once.

When they drank, he drank with them; not much, but he himself would put up the money to buy another round of drinks and some meat balls for the crowd. The things which earlier he had looked down on, he now felt were diverting. Since he had found his own road blocked against him, he could not but admit that the others had been right. Whenever among his friends there was one in whose family there was a wedding or a funeral, he—who had once not known what it meant to carry out one's social obligations—now put out his forty coppers or whatever his share might be. And not only did he give money, he went himself to sacrifice to the dead or to offer appropriate felicitations, because he understood that this was not a matter of wasting money but rather of fulfilling the obligations inherent in human relationships. On these occasions people were really weeping or honestly smiling: they were not just raising a hullabaloo for the sheer devilment of it.

The thirty dollars, though, he did not dare to touch. He got a piece of white cloth, and with his clumsy fingers and a big needle he sewed the money up inside it and hung the sack in a secret nearby place. He didn't want to spend it, nor did he think any more of adding to it until he could buy another rickshaw. He only wanted to keep it close by, as a kind of preparedness—who knew what calamities and misfortunes the future might bring! Sickness, some unexpected accident, anything—it all might come upon his own person at any time. Certainly he should have some preparation. Man was not made of iron: that much he now thoroughly understood.

It was close again to the Beginning of Autumn when once more he found himself a job by the month. This time it was an easier job than he had ever had before in a private household; if that had not been the case, he would not have accepted it. He knew now how to pick and choose among the places open to him; his heart was no longer on fire to work in private families; if the job wasn't suitable, there wasn't anything wrong with working for hire on the public highways. He understood that his own health was precious; a rickshaw puller who tried to work himself to death, as he had used to do, would only end by killing himself without getting any benefit whatever out of it. Experience taught a fellow that he should be a little sly and cunning about things—you only had one life!

This time the house where he worked was near the Palace of Harmony. The master was named Hsia; he was over fifty, a man who knew the books and understood the proprieties; at home he had a wife and twelve children. Very recently he had taken a second wife, and, not daring to let his family know about it, had especially selected a secluded spot in which to set up a small household. In it there was just himself and his new wife, with a maidservant and rickshaw man—the latter being Happy Boy.

Happy Boy liked this job very much. First there was the compound. There were only six rooms altogether. The Hsias occupied three, the kitchen one, and the other two were servants' quarters. The yard was very small, with a little date tree growing against the south wall. In its branches were some ten half-ripe fruits. When Happy Boy swept the yard, it seemed that it only took three swipes of the broom to get from one end of it to the other: it was wonderfully easy. There were no flowers or grasses to water, and although he was strongly tempted to lavish a little labor on straightening up the date tree, he bethought himself that it was of a species that just naturally grew crooked and resisted all correction, so he left it alone.

Of other work there was also very little. In the morning Mr. Hsia went to his office to carry on his official labors, and did not come back until five in the evening. All Happy Boy had to do was to take him there and bring him back; when he got back home, he would not go out again. It was almost as if he were a refugee hiding from the police. Mrs. Hsia, on the other hand, went out all the time, but around four o'clock in the afternoon she would be sure to come back so as to let Happy Boy go pick up Mr. Hsia. When he had brought the old man home, his day's work could be counted as done. Moreover, Mrs. Hsia seldom went anywhere but to the Market of Eastern Peace, or the Public Garden of Middle Mountain, and when he had got her there, he still had long periods of rest. A job like this was play for Happy Boy.

Mr. Hsia was very tightfisted; he would not lightly let go of a single copper. Coming to and from his work he would look to neither side of him, as if the streets were empty of both people and things.

The wife was just the opposite: her hand was lax. Every two or three days she had to go out to buy things; if it was food, the things that she didn't like she'd give to the servants; if it was some article or other, when she went out the next time to buy a new one, she'd give the old one to the servants, so that when she asked Mr. Hsia for the money for it she could say with truth that she didn't have one. It was as if Mr. Hsia's whole destiny were to wear himself out making official bows at the yamen and to spend the rest of his energy and all of his money in respectful offerings to his concubine. Beyond these two he had no livelihood and no enjoyment. According to reports, his original wife and the twelve children lived in Paoting, and would sometimes go for four or five months without receiving a single copper from him.

Happy Boy despised this Mr. Hsia: his back bent over and head drawn down so that you couldn't see his neck, going in and out like that the whole livelong day, for all the world like some petty thief, his eyes fixed on the toes of his shoes, never saying anything, never spending any money, never smiling, and looking, even when he sat in the rickshaw, like an emaciated monkey. If by some chance he should suddenly say two whole sentences together, it would be bound to be something nasty, something that would turn men's hearts against him. It seemed as if no matter who he was speaking of or to, the other fellow was a scoundrel and he himself was a truly superior man who knew the books and understood the proprieties. Happy Boy had no use for that kind of a man, but he viewed his job as a job; as long as he got paid every month, why should he bother about anything else? Besides, the mistress was very open and easy to get on with; he was always being given something extra to eat or to use; he'd just leave it at that, and consider that he was pulling a monkey who had no understanding of human feelings.

So far as the mistress went, Happy Boy simply regarded her as a woman who was capable of presenting him with occasional extra money: he was far from being ten parts fond of her. She was much more beautiful than Little Lucky One, and the way she steeped herself in fragrant perfumes, and wrapped her body in satins and silk gauze, put her even further beyond any comparison with Little Lucky One. But, in spite of the beauty of her features and the smartness of her appearance, for some reason which he could not name she made Happy Boy think of Tiger Girl. There was something about her body that was very much like Tiger Girl's. It was not her clothes and it was not her looks, but some similarity in the manner and spirit of her movements: Happy Boy could find no proper word to describe it. He was certain that she and Tiger Girl were—to use the only expression he had for it—the same line of goods. She was very young— twenty-two or twenty-three years old at the very most—but she had the air and bearing of an old hand at the game. Never in the world did she seem like a newly-married girl who has just left her own family, but rather she appeared, exactly as had Tiger Girl, to be a person who could not have known the time when she had been a modest and bashful maiden. She curled her hair, she wore high-heeled shoes, and her tight-fitting clothes helped bring out every outline of her body with each move she made.

Even Happy Boy could see that, for all the stylishness with which she decked herself out, hers was not the spirit which marks the ordinary wife. Still, she did not seem to have come from a singing-girl's background. Happy Boy could not figure out what she was all about; he only knew that you had to fear her, as of old he had had to fear Tiger Girl. But Tiger Girl had not had this girl's youth; nor had she had a tenth of her attractiveness; for these reasons Happy Boy was even more afraid. It was as if she bore in her own person all of the peril and the vicious poison that could be imagined in the body of a vicious woman. It was a simple fact that he did not dare to look straight at her.

After he had been on the job for a few weeks, his fear of the woman mounted even higher as a result of his observations of his new master's behavior. Pulling Mr. Hsia about, Happy Boy had never seen the old man spend much money, but there was one thing that he bought very regularly, and that was a special kind of medicine from the local drug shop. Happy Boy did not know what kind of medicine it was, but each time after he brought his master back from the drug shop he noticed that Mr. and Mrs. Hsia would seem to take great joy in each other for the next two or three days, and Mr. Hsia, who ordinarily couldn't draw as much as a big breath, would act as if he were especially full of energy. In another two or three days he would be breathless again and his back would be even more bent. It was like buying a big fish on the street: when first you put it in a pail of water, it flashes and flicks about with energy and joy, and then in a little while it grows quiet again. Whenever he saw Mr. Hsia sitting in his rickshaw as limp as a dead fish, he knew that it had come time again to visit the drug shop. He didn't care for old man Hsia, but each time they made the drug-shop trip he could not help feeling sorry for the shrivelled-up old monkey. And when they got back to the house with Mr. Hsia hugging his packet of drugs, Happy Boy would think of Tiger

Girl, his heart ill with a sickness that he could not describe. He had no wish to hate the spirit of the dead, but, looking at himself and at old man Hsia, he would be swept with a feeling of deep hatred in spite of himself: whatever you said, his own body was nowhere near as vigorous as it had been, and the greater part of the responsibility for that circumstance rested on the person of Tiger Girl.

He was strongly inclined to quit the job. But still, to quit for a thing like this, that did not adjoin the borderline of one's proper functions, did not sound right. Taking out a cigarette, he asked himself a muttered question:

"Why should I always be minding somebody else's business?"

21

BECAUSE, at the time when the chrysanthemum flowers came to market, Mrs. Hsia had bought four pots of them, and Yang Ma, the womanservant, had broken one of the pots, the mistress began abusing her. Yang Ma had come from the village, and began in the first instance with a conviction that grasses and flowers were not to be regarded as matters of importance; however, since she had broken something belonging to another person, even if it were a thing without value, that certainly showed that she had been awkward and careless, wherefore she did not dare to make a sound. When it developed that Mrs. Hsia intended to keep right on bawling at her without ever stopping, and was cursing her in the same breath as a country bumpkin and an uncouth savage, Yang Ma could no longer press down the fire within her, and she answered back. A villager who once gets excited can no longer speak in measured phrases; Yang Ma scraped the bottom and fished up the coarsest abuses. Mrs. Hsia hopped up and down in her vexation, handed the servant a new course in cursing and told her to roll up her bedding and wiggle her eggs out of there.

From beginning to end Happy Boy had made no move to come forward to urge them to compose their differences. His tongue was no good at settling quarrels, and it was particularly inadequate to a situation in which the protagonists were women. And when the thing got to the point that he heard Yang Ma curse out Mrs. Hsia as a vile vagina that a thousand men had mounted and ten thousand had fingered, he realized that it was pretty certain that she would have to resign her job. It was definitely beginning to look that way. At the same time he could see that if Yang Ma was fired, he would have to be fired too: it did not seem likely that Mrs. Hsia would want to keep a servant who knew so much about her personal history.

After Yang Ma had gone, he waited to be told that his services were no longer required; he calculated that when the new maidservant arrived the time would have come for him to roll up his bedding. But he did not fret himself with anxiety on this account: his experience had taught him to take a job or lose it with the same cool indifference; it was not worth while to let yourself be emotionally disturbed by it.

Contrary to his expectations, however, after Yang Ma walked out, Mrs. Hsia was extraordinarily affable to Happy Boy. Since she no longer had a maidservant, she had to go down herself to the kitchen to cook the meals. She gave Happy Boy money and asked him to go buy the vegetables. When he had brought them back, she instructed him as to what should be peeled and what should be washed. While he was peeling and washing the vegetables, she was chopping up the meat and boiling the rice, working away on the one hand and on the other hunting for words with which to engage him in conversation.

She wore a smock of pale-pink color, with light silken trousers under it, and on her feet were small white satin slippers embroidered in red, that made a quick little slap-slap noise as she walked back and forth. Happy Boy bent over his bench doing as best he could with his clumsy fingers the tasks that had been

assigned to him; he did not dare look up. And yet he wanted very much to look; the fragrance of her perfume was always in his nostrils, as if it meant to tell him that he had to look at her whether he wanted to or not, enticing him as the scent of a beautiful flower entices the honey bee.

Happy Boy knew how deadly a woman can be; he knew, too, what they have to give a man. A Tiger Girl would have been enough to teach any man how much women are to be feared, and at the same time to make it impossible for him to be without women. And how much more true these things were of a woman who was so far beyond comparison with Tiger Girl in every way. He stole a sidewise glance at her. Supposing it was true that she was as dangerous as Tiger Girl, she still was in several ways many more times as desirable to a man than Tiger Girl could ever have been.

If this had happened two years previously, Happy Boy would never have dared look at her as he had a moment ago. Now he paid very little heed to such conventions. In the first place, he had already once been the victim of a woman's seduction, and he no longer had any means of controlling himself. In the second place, he had come by very gradual stages to fit into the groove of the average rickshaw man: what the other rickshaw men recognized as right, he too now felt to be right; since his own hard work and self-denial had brought him only to failure, it must then be that the behavior of the others which he had once thought beneath him was in fact in accord with the true principles of conduct. He therefore was determined to be a "rickshaw man" like other "rickshaw men," whether he felt like doing the things they did or not: you travel with the crowd or the road is closed to you.

Now, as anybody who is poor and works hard can tell you, there's nothing wrong with getting something for nothing whenever you can get away with it, which is not often. Why should Happy Boy see something cheap and pass it up? All right, he had looked at this woman. What of it? She was just a woman like the rest, and if she was willing, he had no way to refuse her. He could hardly believe that she could lower herself as much as that, but suppose by some remote chance that she did? If she made no move, Happy Boy would make no move; if she should move first, finding some way to make known her desire, he would not know what to do next. Had she not already given him some hint of her feelings? If not, why had she not hired another maid as soon as she had fired Yang Ma? Why had she chosen instead to have Happy Boy help her in the kitchen? Why had she sprinkled herself with so much perfume just to do the cooking?

He did not dare to draw any conclusion from all this, nor to entertain any special hope, but the suspicion of a judgment had already formed in his mind, and in his heart the first glimmer of desire had early been aroused. It was as if he were asleep and dreaming a beautiful but unreal dream; knowing all the time it was a dream, he still wanted to keep right on dreaming it,

325

and hoped against hope that he wouldn't awake. There was a warm pressure in the life within him impelling him to confess to himself that he was worthless, and in this acceptance of worthlessness to find a wonderful pleasure—or maybe it would only turn out to be a terrible trouble, who cared which?

This faint whisper of desire aroused his courage a little, and a little courage set up a hot fire in his heart. How could it be cheapening at all for either of them? Neither of them would be lowering themselves: carnal passion was common to all mankind.

Then a moment of fear awakened wisdom, and a brief reflection dampened down the fire in his heart: he almost thought of skipping out of there as quickly as he could. Here there could only be trouble and suffering for him; if he followed this road he could only end by making a fool of himself.

At one moment hot with hope, at the next shivering with fear, Happy Boy felt as if he had suddenly been taken down with the intermittent chills and fever of malaria. This was harder to get through than was the pass to which Tiger Girl had brought him; then he did not know anything, and was like a little bee that has ventured out for the first time and falls straightway into a spider's web; now he understood how careful he ought to be, and at the same time he knew how to be bold. For some strange reason he wanted to keep slipping downward until he took the plunge, while in the very same instant he had the clearest and most vivid fear of falling in.

He did not look lightly upon this second wife of another man, this unregistered prostitute, this woman of great beauty: she was everything and she was nothing. And even admitting that he would have some explaining to do himself, he still felt that it was rather that old dried-up monkey of a Mr. Hsia who was to be despised—he ought to have some misfortune befall him! With a husband like him, nothing that she could do would be wrong. With a master like that, he, Happy Boy, could do anything without its making any difference. His gall was growing larger.

But she didn't show any sign of being aware whether he looked at her or not. She ate alone in the kitchen, and when she was through she called to him:

"Go ahead and eat. But when you're finished you must wash the dishes. In the afternoon when you go to get Mr. Hsia, buy the vegetables for tonight's dinner first, so as to save going out again. Tomorrow is Sunday, the master will be home all day, and I'll go out and hunt for an amah. Do you know anyone that you could recommend? Amahs are certainly hard to find. All right, first you go eat, don't let the food get cold."

She had spoken in a poised, dignified, and yet very natural way. Suddenly that pale-pink smock changed—in Happy Boy's eyes—to a hue more pallid and chaste. He felt a kind of disappointment, and then a mounting sense of chagrin. He saw clearly that he was not only a person who sought to better himself, but he was a rascal as well. In a kind of stupor he managed to pile two bowls of rice into his mouth, and to eat a little of the cooked vegetables. Never had he felt more dispirited. When he had finished the dishes, he went back to his own room to sit down, smoking he did not know how many cigarettes one right after the other.

In the afternoon when it came time to go get Mr. Hsia, he began—for some reason he couldn't have explained—to feel the greatest hatred for the old dried-up monkey. In all truth he thought of pulling the old man along right merrily, as fast as he could, and then just dropping the shafts and letting the aged tool roll out on the road and half kill himself. Only now did he understand a thing that had happened a long time before when he was the rickshaw man in the home of a wealthy family. The master's third concubine and his eldest son had some connection between them that was not very clear, and when the old master found out about it the young master came near to poisoning his father. At the time Happy Boy had figured that the young master just didn't realize what he was doing; not until now did Happy Boy perceive how much the old man had deserved to die.

But Happy Boy didn't have any desire at all to commit murder; he simply felt that old man Hsia was disgusting and hateful, but that he had no way of making him suffer for these qualities. When the emaciated monkey got into the rickshaw, Happy Boy purposely jerked the shafts up and down a couple of times just to give him a good shaking up. But the old monkey didn't say a word, and Happy Boy felt as if somehow he had got the worst of it. He had never before done anything like that, and now that suddenly he had found himself doing it he could not forgive himself, however good his reason might have been.

His regret gave him a feeling of indifference to the whole thing: why should he deliberately rob himself of his peace of mind? He was a rickshaw man—he would work hard and do his best for his master; what use was it thinking of other things?

His heart became more tranquil, and he put out of his memory that brief drama that had come to no climax; if occasionally it recurred to his thoughts it was as something to be laughed at.

The next day Mrs. Hsia went out to hunt for a womanservant. When she had been away a while she came back with a trial maid. Happy Boy's heart gave up all hope, but, however he thought of the matter, it left a bad taste in his mouth.

After the noon meal on Monday Mrs. Hsia dismissed the trial maid: she felt that the girl was too careless about keeping things clean. A little bit later she asked Happy Boy to go out and buy her a catty of chestnuts.

When he had brought the catty of hot chestnuts back, Happy Boy stood outside of her door and called in to tell her.

"Bring them in," she said from inside.

Happy Boy went in. She was just in the act of powdering her nose before the mirror, and had on again the delicate pink smock, but she had changed to pale green trousers under it. Seeing Happy Boy's entrance in her mirror, she turned about quickly and smiled at him. Suddenly in this smiling countenance he saw the face of Tiger Girl, a younger and much more beautiful Tiger Girl. He stood there like a piece of wood. His bravery, his hope, his fears, his carefulness, all were gone; the only thing that was left was a breath of steaming heat that was broiling his body, and that could swell up into a big thing or shrivel away into a very small one. When it wanted to go in he would go in, when it wanted to draw back he would draw back. He himself was already without any clear plan; all he could do was to go on almost out of habit, like a farmer who uncovers an old well and lowers the bucket down—down and up, up and down, with a motion as old as any ploughman knows. . . .

On the evening of the following day he rolled up his bedding and went back to the rickshaw shed.

A thing which formerly he had felt was the most to be feared and the most disgraceful he was presently divulging to the whole crowd, shamelessly, as if it were a joke: he could not urinate.

Everyone competed with everyone else to tell him what medicine to buy, what doctor to go to. No one felt that it was anything to be ashamed of, and out of their sympathy for him they all tried to offer him helpful suggestions. Moreover, they took pleasure in recounting to him—their faces a little red as they spoke—their individual experiences in the acquisition of this manly ailment. Many of the youngsters among them had used money to purchase it; many of the more mature had picked it up for nothing; others—pullers who were working by the month—had had experiences differing rather in degree than kind from that of Happy Boy with his master's concubine. The rest, who might not themselves have enjoyed such liberties, had all heard stories about their masters and mistresses that were well worth retelling. This little illness of Happy Boy's caused them all to open their hearts to him.

He himself forgot his shame, and although he didn't feel that he had covered himself with any special glory, he suffered the sickness to run its course in the same calm mood with which he would have accepted the inconvenience of having caught a cold. At times when he had to take a twinge of pain, he felt some slight remorse, but after he had again been comfortable for a while, the memory of the pleasure of the experience would recur to his mind. On no account was he going to excite himself about the matter: he had already lived enough to know how little life is worth. What use could there be in worrying about it?

A little bit of medicine here, a pet prescription there, and he had put out more than ten dollars, without really curing the root of his ailment. In this half-hearted, hazy way he finally counted himself well again, and stopped taking medicine. On dark rainy days, or at a turning of the seasons, the pain would come back to his joints and bones, and as a temporary expedient he would take some more medicine, or else grimly determine to face it out without doing anything about it. In neither case would he regard the matter as of any importance. Since life was already the ultimate in bitterness, what did his health count for? You had to see this thing clearly: even a fly in a cesspool takes his pleasure on occasion; why then should a fellow as big as he was feel sorry for doing the same thing?

But when the illness had largely passed, it seemed to leave behind it an entirely different person. He was still as tall as ever, but the uprightness of spirit and expression was gone; in his bearing as well, he seemed intentionally to let his shoulders hunch forward, and his lips drop loosely, with a cigarette always hanging down from one corner of his mouth. Sometimes he would stick a half-burnt butt behind his ear, not because that was a convenient place for it but for the particular purpose of putting on a tough act. He was still loath to talk very much; when he opened his mouth at all, though, he strained to use the hard smart slang of the street. Allowing that he couldn't get it off with any easy fluency, it was still, good or bad, an effort in the right direction. His heart had eased its grip, and his bearing and manner had exchanged their freshness for a dissolute look.

Yet, compared to the typical rickshaw man, he could still not be counted as too bad. At moments when he sat down alone and thought of himself as he used to be, he still wanted to improve himself; he was not content to slip on downward in the way he was going. Even though ambition was a useless thing, he could not see how ruining himself was to be regarded as anything very high or bright. In these moods his mind would turn once more to the purchase of a rickshaw. Of his thirty-odd dollars he had spent more than ten to cure the sickness—he had cheated himself there! But he still had over twenty dollars to use as a start, and when you came right down to it he had more hope of getting somewhere than most of the others, who had to fire their cannon with neither powder nor ball. When he got to thinking about it, he wanted very much to throw away the unsmoked half of his packet of cigarettes, swear off smoking and liquor from that moment forward, grit his teeth and begin saving money. From the thought of the money his mind turned to buying the rickshaw, and when he thought of that he remembered Little Lucky One. It was a little hard to face her even in his imagination. First to last, he had not been back to see her since the day he left the compound, and he had not only not tried to better himself, but had covered his body with a foul disease.

When his friends came along, he smoked with them as before, and drank a cup or two of wine whenever the opportunity afforded, forgetting Little Lucky One clear and clean. In their company, he never took the lead to suggest what they should do. There was this to be said, however: he could hardly

Whenever the thought occurred to him that he should not be squandering the hours of light and darkness in this way, his heart had forever ready a stock answer, a sentence cut deep in it by the slow chisel of experience:

"I started out with plenty of ambition, and what good did it do me?"

No person alive could refute the implications of that question, nor explain them away. Who was there, then, who could keep Happy Boy from going straight to hell?

22

WHEN he had first come to Peking, the one hope that Happy Boy had had in his heart was to pull a rickshaw, but now he was disgusted with rickshaw pulling. He was beginning to think that he'd have to find a better way to get money, some scheme that would be easier than wrestling with a two-wheeled cart. Of course he could not hope to break off all connection with his present profession suddenly, but whenever he could find some other means of making enough money to supply his three meals for that particular day, then for one day his hands would not touch the shafts of a rickshaw.

The lazier his body got, the sharper his ears became: every idle rumor brought him rushing forward. Whether it was a protest parade of the citizenry, or a picket line presenting a petition, or whatever it might be, just so long as he got paid for his pains, he would take part in it. Twenty cents was good enough; thirty was so much the better: for either one, more or less, he was perfectly content to tote a banner the whole day long, following the curious winding marches of the crowd.

Happy Boy would have no theories as to what might be inscribed on the banner he was carrying, or for precisely what purpose all these people might be parading back and forth, but he felt that in any case this was better than tugging a rickshaw. You didn't earn much money, but neither did you have to use much strength. He would follow along, holding aloft a light silken emblem, with his head down, a cigarette butt hanging from his lips, without uttering a sound, and with a smile on his face that was not a smile at all.

At those moments when it was absolutely required of him that he let out two or three loud cheers for something or other, he was perfectly capable of opening his mouth wide, as if he were yelling louder than anyone, but without making the slightest noise. He didn't want to take any chances on cheering himself hoarse.

In this, as in any other endeavor, he saw no reason to exhaust himself: he had tried his hand at working really hard, and he knew how little reward it brought you. Occasionally while he was busy carrying signs and pretending to raise his voice for some cause about which he knew nothing, it happened that the marchers met up with one kind of danger or another; when they did, Happy Boy was the first to take to his heels, and when he ran he ran fast. He could go on destroying his own life, but he wasn't going to make the smallest sacrifice for anybody else. Those who will labor only for themselves also know well the way to work their own destruction: this is the great paradox of individualism.

One morning in late autumn, on a day when he had found no parades to join, Happy Boy was trailing his hired rickshaw listlessly along behind him through a street in the West City. A fare hailed him, a girl not much over twenty who wanted him to take her to Ch'inghua University. He could see from her plain blue gown that she was a student, and probably not one who could afford to pay him more than the lowest rate. Since he no longer had any feeling that just because someone wanted to go to a particular place, he was obliged to take them there, and because the destination brought back to his mind that other trip so long ago when his first rickshaw was taken from him, he did not assent immediately but stood bargaining over the price. And in real truth he was too lazy to run all that distance.

The girl would not give up. Looking directly into his face, as if she recognized him, she said: "I know how far it is, and how much you need the money. I'll pay whatever you ask."

She spoke so simply and yet with so much sympathy that Happy Boy could not refuse her.

As the road passed under the towers that surmount the portals at the West Gate, the way became crowded with vehicles. There were rickshaws coming in with fares from the country— farmers coming to town—or piled high with cabbages for the market; there were heavy wooden-wheeled pushcarts, and sedan chairs supported on the shoulders of weary bearers. Just as Happy Boy was coming abreast of this throng, an automobile, wrapped in the cloud of dust that its own wheels raised, bore down toward them, sounding continually the contemptuous command of its horn. Happy Boy hated automobiles and he hated their horns, and he would not turn aside for any of them, no matter how much noise and dust they made or what dire threats the driver might scream at him.

The car lessened its speed a little, but with its horn making an even louder noise it kept coming on. His passenger yelled at him to watch out, but without the slightest regard for whatever she might be shouting he stopped dead, dropping the shafts of his rickshaw, and glared in hostile defiance at the frosted glass eyes of the vicious machine that was offering him his choice between running away or being run down. When he did not move at all the car swerved sharply, headed up the side of the dirt embankment along the road, and halted its course. Everybody else stopped too, and although nobody had been hurt there was as much confusion as if there had been a train wreck.

The chauffeur got out of the car white with anger. Not only was his professional prestige at stake, but his rich master's arrival at a family festival would now be unseasonably delayed. Thinking to recover some of this lost face by a full-throated cursing out of the stupid beggar who had caused it all, he walked over to Happy Boy, sputtering vile imprecations at him. But nowadays when the moment came for a fight, Happy Boy was surer than at any other time of his own strength and cleverness: he felt it to be a high and honorable thing to bring all the force in his body down crushingly on the flesh of an antagonist. It made even the light of the sun seem for a moment more vividly bright and clear.

This gathering of all his strength in preparation for a fight was something that earlier in his life he would never even have dreamed for an instant of doing, but now it was a regular practice, and moreover it was one way that he had of bringing clear joy to his heart; he loved to do it, so much so that sometimes he would break out laughing just at the thought.

The driver coming over with such officious haughtiness to remonstrate with him was dressed in a foreign-style suit that must have cost him fifty or sixty dollars. Cutting the fellow short in the midst of a sentence that was intended to be especially impressive, Happy Boy grabbed the man's sleeve, closing his hand over the skinny forearm of this servant of wealth. His grip was so tight that it hurt, and his great paw, covered with sweat and soot, would leave a mark on the fellow's precious coatsleeve that would never come out. Happy Boy knew how afraid these proud gentlemen who wore western dress were of getting their clothes dirty; he knew, too, how stingy they were be-

336

neath their domineering exterior. So he kept this trick in readiness and frequently used it with great effect on passengers who would not pay him the fare he demanded: they not only got their clothes soiled but they discovered how much strength he had, and in the end still had to pay him what he had asked in the first place. The dirt on their sleeves was his present to them, a gift that gave pleasure to the giver.

Another thing Happy Boy had learned was how to glare at people: the way he was staring down into this chauffeur's eyes was shrivelling the bastard to a cinder.

A policeman came over to intercede: it was his duty in life to keep the road clear for automobiles, especially if they were long and sleek and official-looking. But Happy Boy had no fear of him either. In such situations he had developed the practice of moving his lips but not his body, prolonging as long as possible the period in which he could curse out the whole police force. If the policeman was unwilling to abide this language, Happy Boy was more than ready to give the fellow a real beating as well. After that if he had to stay for two or three weeks in a dirty jail, he would still feel that the pleasure had been cheaply bought.

But this time, before either he or the policeman could open their mouths, the slender little girl student jumped down from the rickshaw.

"The driver was in the wrong! He was coming so fast that we were both sure he was going to hit us. It was not the rickshaw man's fault at all."

The policeman turned on her, but not with the same assurance that he had felt when he had started over just a few seconds earlier with the intent in his heart to administer a good kicking and clubbing to an obnoxious rickshaw boy. As between the latter and the owner of a big car he need not hesitate: his duty was clear. The rickshaw boy would be penniless and helpless; the car owner would be wealthy and have wealthy friends: the very government itself would bow and scrape to do his bidding.

Students were another matter. Some of them had money and some didn't, but at the very least somebody had to be sponsor for them: it cost money to go to school. And however much they were to be hated for it, the students were always parading and making speeches; they were dangerous. Your rice bowl might well depend on the whim of the man in the car, but if you got the students against you, you might lose it just the same.

The girl maintained her insistence: "It's true, it's the car's fault! Do you think a rickshaw is going to run into a car?" She would yield nothing to either the policeman or the chauffeur and, in his surprise at this unexpected assistance, Happy Boy dropped the driver's arm and stood silent. This girl student certainly had ability.

He had hardly got through thinking this thought when she addressed him.

"Come on! No one can prevent us from attending to our proper business. If they want to stand here wrangling all day, let them." She got into the rickshaw again, signalling Happy Boy to get back between his shafts and pull away. He did as he was bidden, maintaining the while a vigorous show of defiance to the other two. The chauffeur swore bitterly over his soiled garment, but the policeman was helpless, because, not having solved the problem as to whether the student or the car owner would be likely to have the more influence, he had no clue as to whom to declare right and who wrong. By the time an irate voice from the car recalled him from these reflections on justice, the rickshaw had disappeared into the traffic at the West Gate.

It could not be considered that Happy Boy's regular running gait was a slow one and in these latter days he had adopted the rule that he would not under any circumstances increase that pace without being paid extra for it. The moment a passenger urged him to run faster, he would bring his big feet down flat to the ground and ask: "Faster? How much will you add to the fare?" He was sweating his own blood, and there was no such thing as being polite about it: he no longer hoped that anybody would give him anything just out of the goodness of their hearts. He would not expend an ounce of extra strength until the extra coppers he was to receive for it had been agreed upon.

But toward this girl student he felt differently. It was almost as if he could respect her as much as he respected Little Lucky One; he wanted to show her how fleet he was on his feet and to say to her through his bearing toward her how ashamed he was now of the sharp bargain he had sought to drive when she had hailed him. It was with this thought in his heart that on the long road northwestward from the West Gate he ran harder than he had for many months.

The thing that she said next startled him almost as much as what she had said to the policeman. It seemed that she could look out through his eyes.

"You shouldn't run that fast for anybody, no matter what they pay you. You're not a pack animal." Almost grudgingly Happy Boy slackened his pace.

"There's something I want to ask you," she went on, "but first tell me one thing: what is your name?"

Happy Boy looked back over his shoulder, a little grin of pleasure on his face, and spoke his name.

"Didn't you carry a placard in the demonstration for the release of political prisoners? Or were you just selling your strength for the few tens of cents they presented you with?"

Even the back of his neck was red with his embarrassment. He did not know what gathering she was talking about, but he could not deny that it was he that she had seen, nor could he account to himself for how stupid and foolish he felt about it. Certainly this was the first time anybody had ever made him feel ashamed for having done something simply for the money to be got out of it. How could he know what the placards said when he could not recognize the characters in his own name?

"Even if I was too poor to learn to read, I still have to eat," he said at last, pronouncing every word with a distinctness that was almost fierce. By now he had slowed down to hardly more than a walk.

"I understand, I understand," the girl said quickly, her voice full of the same sympathy that had marked it when he had tried to argue with her about the fare. "You weren't doing anything wrong. You were helping too, whether you knew it or not. I only meant that if you hadn't heard why we were demonstrating, I'd like to tell you."

Then she recounted the story of the prisoners and why the students sought their release, which Happy Boy could understand easily enough. And if, in trying to go on to describe the broader objects which she and the paraders and the prisoners all held in common, she said many things that he could only comprehend very dimly, still she gave voice to grievances that he had long carried mute in his own stomach, believing that he suffered them alone, and at least for the time that she was speaking he felt that a new road had opened in his heart.

340

One thing was certain without any confusion: this girl student was clean and honest and unselfish. She sought him no harm. When they had reached the University she offered him more than he had asked. He tried to refuse, but she insisted, saying: "Because we are both poor I know you have more need for this money now than I have, so you must take it."

Back inside the wall, at a teahouse in the West City, Happy Boy thought painfully on the meaning of this whole affair. Finally he decided to dismiss it from his mind: if much that the girl had said still seemed very reasonable to him, the things that she hoped to do—whatever they might be—were sure to be unworkable. And, in any case, none of it could help him much. Where was there any money in it? It was not that some of her ideas did not make sense but that money—money that you could use to buy a little something good to eat or some wine to drink or a night in a "white house"—made much better sense.

For, although Happy Boy perhaps did not realize it, experience is the fertilizer of life: the experiences through which you have passed mold you into the person that you are. In the wastes of the Shamo Desert no camellia ever came to flower. Happy Boy had entered completely into the groove of life in which he found himself: he was now no better and no worse than the generality of his kind, but only a rickshaw man like other rickshaw men, even to the point of detesting his calling, as they did. Without perceiving why, he was yet more comfortable because of this fact. As he was now, the others found him more agreeable in their sight: all crows are black, and he didn't want to be the only one whose feathers were white.

If anything, he was even more of a tough than before, especially where the police were concerned. In their eyes, Happy Boy was a "thorn-head" of the very first rank, and yet they did not dare provoke him. It is when the bitterly poor see that hard work brings them only to emptiness that they become shiftless;

341

that such a one should turn into a "thorn-head" as well is perhaps only a fitting recompense to the social order for its pains.

Again winter came and the yellow, sand-laden winds that the desert blew over Peking froze many tens of homeless people to death in the streets of the city each night. When he heard the sound of the wind, Happy Boy would bury his head back under the covers and would not dare to get up. Not until that sound of wolves howling and devils wailing had altogether subsided would he finally arise, willy-nilly, having no further excuse to stay abed. Then he would be unable to decide whether it was best to go out or to rest for a day. He was loath to lift the ice-cold shafts of a rickshaw and afraid of that wind that sighed so deeply it made you sick in your insides.

The wildest wind itself fears the setting of the sun: on this day too the soughing became tranquil and then utterly silent sometime after sundown, when in the twilight the heavens bore a western glow of the faintest rose. Happy Boy forced himself to muster his energy and took his rickshaw out. With the shafts under his armpits, his arms folded over his stomach and his hands tucked into his sleeves, he propelled the rickshaw slowly forward by pushing his chest against the crossbar at the shaft ends. He wandered thus aimlessly about the streets, without spirit, making an empty show, the butt of an old cigarette hanging from his lips. The sky was by now almost black, and he bethought himself that he had better hurry up and haul a passenger or two, so that he could take his rickshaw back earlier to the shed. He was too lazy to light his lamps, and only after the policemen along the roadside had reminded him four or five times did he finally do so.

Beneath the lamp at the Drum Tower he managed at last to grab a fare. He didn't even take off his padded gown but went along just as he was, five parts running and five parts walking, in a piddling, half-hearted manner. He knew that this made a very poor impression, but if it did not have a proper appearance, well, it just didn't have a proper appearance. Would anybody be willing to give him an extra copper for a proper appearance? This wasn't pulling a rickshaw; it was merely dragging oneself along, getting by as best one might. There was a perspiration on his forehead and he still was unwilling to shed his long gown; he would make out as he was as long as he could.

He was turning into a narrow by-lane when a street dog started to bark at him, probably because it felt that a rickshaw boy pulling his rickshaw in a long gown was a sight not pleasing to the eyes. Happy Boy put down the shafts and, grabbing up his cloth duster, set out after the dog, beating him for dear life with the duster handle. When he had chased it so far away that there was no shadow of it left, he stood waiting a while to see if it dared come back. The dog did not return and Happy Boy felt no obstruction to his contentment with himself. "Its mother's! You thought I was afraid of you!"

In anything but a good spirit, the man in his rickshaw spoke up. "I must ask you, what kind of a rickshaw man do you think you are, acting like this?"

Happy Boy's heart jumped. The sound of this voice was very familiar in his ears. The by-lane was quite dark; although the lamps on his rickshaw were bright, the light they threw fell downward toward the ground. He could not see clearly who his passenger was, perceiving only that he wore a heavy fur headpiece against the wind, had his coat collar turned up, and had wrapped a thick wool scarf around his neck and the lower part of his face, covering his mouth and nose, so that the air he breathed would not be freezing cold when it reached his nostrils. From all this bundling his two eyes alone shone out, and his voice came through low and muffled.

Just as Happy Boy was busy guessing who it could be, the man in the rickshaw spoke again.

"Aren't you Happy Boy?"

Then the truth came clear and white in Happy's mind: the

man in the rickshaw was Fourth Master Liu! He grunted affirm-
atively in reply, his whole body hot and sour like the sourest
sauce.

"My daughter?"

"She's dead!" Happy Boy stood there dumbly, not knowing
whether it was he himself or some other person who had spoken
those two words.

"What? Dead?"

"Dead!"

"Falling into hands like yours, how could she do anything
but die."

Suddenly Happy Boy found himself.

"Get out! Get out! You're so old a good beating would kill
you! Get out!"

Fourth Master Liu's hands shook as he climbed uncertainly
down, supporting himself on the rickshaw shafts. He was trembling all over.

"Where is she buried, I ask you!"

"None of your business!" Happy Boy picked up the rickshaw shafts and started off.

When he had gone some distance down the lane, he turned
his head to look back. The old man was still standing where he
had left him, a miserable shadow dimly visible in the darkness.

23

$\mathcal{H}$APPY BOY forgot where he was going. His head thrown back, his hands clenched tightly over the shafts of his rickshaw and his eyes flashing with all the light that there was in the darkness, he strode forward, thinking only to keep on walking, without caring at all in what direction he moved or to what destination. His heart was full of joy; his body was light and free; all of the bad luck that had weighed him down since he had taken Tiger Girl to wife he had in one short moment spewed out on the person of Fourth Master Liu!

He forgot the cold and forgot to solicit passengers. All he could think of was to keep on marching, as though these firm strides could not but bring him in the end to the place where he would find once more the self that of old was his, the ambitious and always hard-working Happy Boy, unhampered and pure in heart.

When he thought of that black shadow standing back there in the middle of the lane, that old man, it seemed that there was no need of saying anything further. To have triumphed over Fourth Master Liu was to have triumphed over everything. Although he had not taken as much as one crack of his fist at the aged tool, and had not even kicked him, still the old bastard had lost the only relative he had, while Happy Boy on the other hand was completely at his ease and perfectly composed. Who was there to say that this was not retribution. If the old man did not actually die of his vexation, it would still bring him not far from death. Fourth Master Liu had everything;

Happy Boy had nothing at all; yet now Happy Boy could go on in the highest spirits pulling his rickshaw and old Fourth Master could not even find his only daughter's grave. All right, Old Man, you can have your piles of silver dollars and your temper so great that it fills the heavens. You've been beaten by a wandering beggar who has first to earn the money before he buys each meal and who is as poor as a polished egg.

The more he thought about it, the more delighted he was. In all truth, he yearned to sing out the loud chant of this hymn of his, so that all living people in the world might hear it: "Happy Boy is alive again! Happy Boy is alive again! Happy Boy has won the victory!" The cold air of the night cut his face, but he did not feel chilled; its sharpness made him glad. The frozen glare of the street lamps seemed to illumine his heart with warmth and cheer; there was light everywhere, making bright the path that would lead him to his future.

It was at least an hour now since he had smoked a cigarette, and he would not smoke again. From now on he would touch neither cigarettes nor wine. At the drum's beat he had opened a new account, working hard and trying to better himself as he had of old. Today he had triumphed over Fourth Master; from now on and forever against all the Fourth Masters of the world he would triumph. The curses of Fourth Master Liu were just what he needed to assure him of the fullest success: to have heard the old bastard tell him he was hopeless flooded him with hope.

Having spit out all that malevolence in one breath and divested himself of the spirit of evil that was the dark influence of the Lius—father and daughter—Happy Boy would always breathe the fresh air of a freer atmosphere. He looked at his own hands and feet: was he not still young? Happy Boy would be forever young! Let the Tiger Girl die. Let Fourth Master die. Happy Boy would still be Happy Boy, laughing, ambitious, and alive. Evil men would all meet with evil, and come in the end to die: the soldiers who stole his rickshaw; Madame Yang who starved her servants; Tiger Girl who had cheated and oppressed him; Fourth Master who despised him; Sun the detective who had swindled him of his money; the Second Wife Ch'en who had made a fool of him; and Madame Hsia who had seduced him—all were doomed, all must die. Only Happy Boy—the loyal, simple, honest Happy Boy—would go on living, would live forever!

"But, Happy Boy, from now on you must work hard," he admonished himself.

Himself it was who replied: "What excuse would I have for not working hard? I have the spirit, I have the strength, and I'm still young!"

"Once Happy Boy's heart is free and no longer obstructed," he spoke in defense of himself, "who will be able to stand in his way and stop him from establishing a family and building a business? What other person could have kept his spirits up under the load that he was bearing until today? Who is there who would not have gone down and down under it, as he did? Now all that has passed, and tomorrow you will see a new Happy Boy, with more ambition than ever—much more!"

While his lips were busy forming the sentences of this conversation with himself, his legs and feet gained a new accession of strength, as if in testimonial that these words were not falsely spoken: he had really found a new determination. For all the fact that he had been sick and had had a despicable disease as well, what difference did it make? Now that his heart had changed, his members would grow strong again; there was no question about that.

He had come out all over his body with sweat, and his mouth had gotten so dry that he thought of getting himself something to quench his thirst, before he realized that he had already reached the After Gate. He felt that he didn't have time to go to a teahouse, so he put his rickshaw down at the rickshaw stand to the west of the Gate and called over to him a small boy—toting a big teapot and a yellow clay bowl—who sold tea. He drank two bowls of the foul stuff: it tasted like water that had been used to wash a cooking pot and was terribly hard to swallow. But he told himself that from now on this was what he must drink: he could not spend all the money he earned buying good tea and expensive food.

Having reached this firm decision, he proceeded with brisk good spirits to eat a little snack of something that was hard to get down his gullet, and that served well as an introduction to this new life of long-enduring frugality upon which he had so lately entered. It was a kind of pastry roll, the insides being nothing but stewed cabbage butts and the outside being at once leathery and full of gritty sand. No matter how hard things like this were to eat, he would eat them.

When he had finished he wiped his mouth with the back of his hand. Where should he go?

In his heart there were only two people to whom he could go for refuge, on whom he could rely. If he planned to work hard and make something of himself, he must find these two: Little Lucky One and Mr. Ts'ao. Mr. Ts'ao was a sage and would certainly forgive him, help him, and find a way out for him. If he followed whatever plan Mr. Ts'ao thought through for him, and afterwards had Little Lucky One to help him as well—he would meet the world outside, and she would mind the hearth within—they could not fail, they could not fail; there could be no doubt of that.

Who knew whether Mr. Ts'ao had come back or not? No matter—tomorrow he would go to Long North Street to inquire. If he could not find out there, he could go to Mr. Tso's house to ask. If only he could go to Mr. Tso's house to ask. If only he could find Mr. Ts'ao, everything else would be easy to arrange. All right, this evening he would work his rickshaw all evening and tomorrow he would go hunt for Mr. Ts'ao. After he had found him, he would go to see Little Lucky One and tell her the good news: Happy Boy hasn't done well at all, but he's determined to do better from now on, and the two of us must put our hearts together and work hard and go forward as one.

Having laid his plans in this wise, he flew to the first prospective passenger he saw, peeling off his padded gown before he had even got the amount of the fare settled. His eyes were as bright as an old eagle's and darted in every direction. And though his legs were in all truth not what they once had been, a hot spirit seemed now to buoy up his whole body; he was putting his life into it. In spite of all that had transpired, Happy Boy was in the end still Happy Boy, and when he cared to run for all his life was worth there was no one in the whole city who could equal him. Every time he saw a rickshaw in front of him he would race past it, however fast its puller cared to move. A madness had seized hold of him. Sweat poured down his limbs and, when he had finished one trip, his body felt much lighter; his legs had regained their elasticity; he was ready for another run. Like a famed race horse that, when its course is completed, paws the ground with its hoofs in its impatience to be off again, Happy Boy could not bear to be idle. He kept going continuously until eleven o'clock, when he put his rickshaw up.

He slept straight through to daybreak, turned over and did not open his eyes again until the sun was already high in the heavens. No sensation is so sweet as sleep after exhaustion; he stretched himself languidly, listening to the light crisp sound of his cracking joints. His stomach felt completely empty; he wanted very much to eat a little something.

When he had finished dressing and had had a bite of food and a cup of tea, he smilingly told the manager of the shed, "I'm resting for a day—I've got some business to attend to." In his heart he had made clear calculations: he would take this one day off and arrange all of his affairs; tomorrow he would begin his new life.

He headed directly for Long North Street on the chance that Mr. Ts'ao might already have returned and be living in the same house as before. While he was walking he prayed: "Mr. Ts'ao must have returned, by a thousand times ten thousand entreaties! Don't let me grasp at emptiness! If this first affair does not come out fortunately, nothing will be fortunate for me. Happy Boy has changed entirely: can you, Venerable Master in the Heavens, then withhold Your protection?"

When he had arrived before the gate of the Ts'ao household his hand shook as he rang the bell. While he stood waiting for someone to answer, his heart seemed to be trying to jump out of his body. Standing in front of this very familiar door, he yet had no time to ponder over the past: he only hoped that the door would open and he would see a face he knew. He waited for what seemed a long time before he began to suspect that there was no one in the compound. If it were not empty, why would it be so quiet, so fearfully tranquil?

Suddenly there was a little sound within the door, startling him so that he jumped. He was like a man who, watching through the night beside the body of a dead friend, all at once hears a whisper from within the coffin. The door opened; over the clatter of the dropping crossbar and the screech of the hinges, there came in a precious and intimate voice the single ejaculation: "Oh!" It was Kao Ma!

"Happy Boy? We've seen little of you, in truth! How did you get so thin?" Kao Ma, on the other hand, had put on weight.

"Is the master in?" Happy Boy had no time for anything else.

"He's at home. You are a good one, though! All you know is the master, as if the two of us were strangers. You don't even ask if I'm well! Come in! Have you made out all right?" While she was speaking she led him toward the house.

"Huh! No good!" Happy Boy smiled as he answered her.

"How's that? . . . Master!" . . . Kao Ma called from outside a room. "Happy Boy has come!"

Mr. Ts'ao was in his study, engaged at that moment in moving the narcissus flowers from one place to another with the shifting sunlight.

"Come in!"

"Ai, you go on in. In a little while we'll have a chance to talk. I'll go tell the mistress; we have all of us thought of you often! A simple-minded person is attractive in a simple-minded way, so you needn't look askance at me." Kao Ma kept up her chattering as she went back toward Mrs. Ts'ao's room.

Happy Boy entered the study.

"Master, I've come!" He thought to ask after his master's health, but the words did not come out.

"Ah, Happy Boy!" Mr. Ts'ao was standing in the center of the room, wearing a short jacket, a slight smile of the deepest serenity on his face. "Sit down! Well!—" He thought a while. "We've been back a long time. Old Ch'eng told us that you—that's right, that you were working at the Human Harmony Rickshaw Shed. We even sent Kao Ma over there once to look for you, but she couldn't find you. Sit down. How are you? Have your affairs gone well?"

Happy Boy wanted to cry. He was unable to tell anyone what was in his heart, because his words were fashioned of blood and buried in the deepest recesses of his soul. For a long time he was silent, trying to regain his composure. He wanted very much to let that flow of bitter and simple language pour out from him. It was all there in his memory, as vivid as a crimson flag, and every time he thought of any corner of it the whole thing unfurled before him.

He must think slowly of everything, to be sure that each fact was in its proper sequence, and that they were all marshalled rank on rank in his mind. For it was a living history that he sought to relate: although he did not know its inner meaning, still the long record of the wrongs he had suffered was clear and true and unconfused.

Mr. Ts'ao could see that his visitor was in the midst of his thoughts, and sat down quietly, waiting for him to speak.

Happy Boy sat dumb and awkward for a long time. Suddenly he lifted his head and looked at Mr. Ts'ao, as if to say that if there was no one who cared to listen to him, he would not speak at all; that would be all right with him, too.

"Tell me about it," Mr. Ts'ao said, nodding his head.

Then Happy Boy began to recount the things that had happened, beginning with the story of how he had come from the village to the city. Originally he had not intended to speak of all these useless matters, but yet if he left even them unsaid, his heart would be unable to be happy because the tale would not have been completely told. His memory was cut deep through bloody sweat by the knife of his suffering; he could not make a joke of his recital, nor could he chop off the head nor leave off the back end of it. Every drop of sweat, every drop of blood, was wrung from his very life, so that every incident that had occurred was worth the time it took to tell of it.

It was all there in the words that were pouring from his mouth: how, after he had come to the city, he had worked as a laborer; how he had saved money and finally bought a rickshaw; how he had lost it; how he had come to his present circumstances. Even he himself felt it to be an extraordinary thing that he was able to speak at such length and in so natural a flow. The incidents seemed to leap, one after another and alive, from his lips and to be able themselves to find the words appropriate to their description: sentence followed sentence, each true to reality, and each according to its content worthy of love or the soft falling of tears for its sadness. His heart had no way to halt this parade of the past, nor had he any means to stop his own speech. He wanted with one breath and without hesitation to take out his whole heart. The more he talked the more relieved and happy he became. He had forgotten himself because he had put himself into the things he was saying: in every phrase there

352

was part of him, of that ambitious, grievously wronged, bitterly suffering, far-fallen self that was he.

When he had finished, you could see the perspiration on his forehead. His heart was empty of everything, empty and comfortable, like that of a man who has just regained consciousness after having fainted.

"Now you want me to advise you what to do?" Mr. Ts'ao asked him.

Happy Boy grunted in assent: he had said what he wanted to say, and now it seemed as if he was unwilling to open his mouth again.

"All right. But first you must let me tell you about that affair of the detective that you couldn't explain to yourself. You know, the time I went away—"

"Ah!"

"Well, it came about like this. You know that I was teaching two or three classes in the Northern University. There was a student in the school named Yuang Ming who was from the first very friendly to me, and who would frequently come around to talk to me. I'm supposed to be what people call a socialist—that is, I think that land and factories and things like that should be owned by the people and used for everybody's benefit, instead of being controlled by a few persons and used to support them in great wealth, with big cars and dozens of houses and more food than they can eat, while other people starve. Do you understand?"

Happy Boy nodded his head a little vaguely. It reminded him of the girl student that he had taken months before to Ch'inghua, but it still didn't sound very practical.

"Now this Yuan Ming claimed to be even more radical than I, so that we found a lot to say to one another that was mutually interesting. However, the difference in our ages and the fact that I was the professor and he the pupil made for a slight conflict between us. I viewed our relationship from the standpoint of my position as a teacher, and believed that I should put my whole heart into teaching the texts and lessons that comprised the courses I gave, that my students should try their best to learn those lessons, and that none of them should take advantage of his personal friendship with me to be careless about his grades."

Happy Boy's perplexity showed on his face. It was clear that, although he wished to preserve a perfectly respectful demeanor, he couldn't see what this had to do with Detective Sun.

Mr. Ts'ao answered the thought in his mind. "You'll see the connection in a moment." Then he resumed his narrative.

"Afterwards I realized that Yuan Ming's point of view had been a little different. He felt that it showed a sophisticated superiority to the confusion of the world to talk about laboring somewhat for the coming of the revolution, and to disregard as of no moment the question of whether he was doing well or poorly in his class work. He cultivated an association with me because, first, we had found a common ground of conversation and, second, because he hoped that I would give him, by reason of our friendship, a passing mark in the course no matter how far gone in rottenness his examination papers might be.

"I suppose," Mr. Ts'ao continued, his mind lost for this little while in the forest of his own speculations, "he saw that there is always an aura of worthlessness around the leaders who arise in periods of disorder; probably he felt that if I knew enough history I would find many precedents for treating him leniently on those grounds. For instance, which of our great men was not stupid in school?

"At any rate, when the examinations came, I didn't give him a passing grade. His marks in his other courses were so bad that, even if I had passed him, he would have been sure to flunk out of school. Nevertheless, his hatred for me was a special hatred because he felt that I had shown no regard for his face. Face is equally as important as the revolution!" Mr. Ts'ao paused to laugh.

"My failure to give him a passing grade only proved to him that I didn't understand a youth of strength and determination. The circumstance that, when our day-to-day relationship was so cordial, I could still place him in such an insupportable position at examination time, convinced him—according to what he said to other students—that I was a secretive and treacherous man.

"In all truth, if it would have saved his being expelled, I would have given him another examination and passed him. But he wouldn't bemean himself so much as to study. He claimed to be in such a great haste to change the social order that he didn't have time for learning. Because he despised learning, he had gradually made a habit of laziness, and he wanted the respect, the assistance, and the protection of those around him, without any pain or labor on his part whatever. He was certainly an advanced thinker.

355

"Well, when he discovered that there was no way of resisting his expulsion from the University, he evidently decided to vent his anger on me. He was like a person being kidnapped for ransom who hopes for a partner in his predicament; he thought it only proper that I should be put out of school along with himself. So he took everything that he could remember my having said—in my lectures or in casual conversation—on the subject of government or the social order, and edited them, putting them in the form of an information which he turned in to the local party headquarters in support of a formal charge that he made against me of propagating radical thought among the youth.

"I learned these details later. At the time all I heard was a bare rumor of what had happened, and I thought of it only as a joke. It was laughable to think that I should presume to the title of a prophet of the revolution. Too laughable to be taken seriously, although both my students and my teaching colleagues all warned me that I should be a little more careful."

What Mr. Ts'ao did not tell Happy Boy was that he knew well enough just how limited and superficial his own "socialism" was, and how deeply his traditional aestheticism would have hindered his effectiveness as a social revolutionary. But this experience which he was relating had had to teach him how irrelevant to the issue is the knowledge of one's innocence when such charges have been brought: he had thought that, even in a confused world, a clear heart and a calm demeanor were some guarantee of security. He was wrong.

He went on with his explanation to Happy Boy: "The winter holidays offered the secret police a good opportunity 'to tranquilize the academic world'; they set in in a great hurry to make investigations and arrests. I had already many times been aware that I was being followed, and the shadow that seemed always to be in back of me gradually caused me to change my attitude from one of ridicule to grave seriousness.

"I was obliged to give thought to the matter. If I wanted to

356

achieve fame, this was an excellent chance. To go to jail for a few days would be easier than throwing a bomb and more reliable." Mr. Ts'ao seemed about to laugh again. "Being put in jail is an absolute prerequisite to becoming a person of importance," he explained.

Happy Boy grinned broadly. This was something he could understand. He had gone to jail not a few times himself since he had last seen his master and, although it had not made him important, he could see where it might be definitely worth while.

"But I couldn't bring myself to do it," Mr. Ts'ao continued. "I couldn't play the same cheap game that the government played. It would have been easy enough to meet their strategy with a similar strategy of my own—and thereby create for myself a reputation that would have been false—but I couldn't do it." Behind his words was a deeper thought: he hated himself for not being a true warrior, but by the same token he was unwilling to become an imitation warrior.

"So I looked up my friend Mr. Tso. He had a plan. 'When it becomes necessary, you move into my house with me. They're not very likely to search my place.' Mr. Tso had friends, and friends are everywhere more powerful than the law. 'You come here and live a few days,' he told me, 'to get out of their way. That will be evidence enough that we're afraid of them. After that we can go to them and try to bring about an understanding. It'll probably be necessary to spend some money as well. When they have been given ample face by our show of fear of them, and they have the money in their hands, you can go back to your own house and that will be the end of the matter.'

"This Detective Sun that the secret police assigned to follow me must have known that I went frequently to Mr. Tso's house, and he could guess that as soon as the chase became close I would be bound to move to Mr. Tso's. But they didn't dare offend Mr. Tso, and they probably only wanted to throw a fright into me. However that may have been, not until they had chased me from my own house to Tso's would they have real hope of getting any money out of me. Besides that, the fact that I had fled my home would give them plenty of face.

"That is how it worked out. It cost quite a bit of money and alarmed me so that I went to Shanghai for a while, but as a matter of fact that wasn't necessary."

Happy Boy's face was red with his hatred for Detective Sun. "Why then did they rob me?" he asked.

Mr. Ts'ao sighed. "I don't think 'chipping' you was any part of the original plans of the secret service, but I guess that, since they saw you, they probably just regarded you as an incidental catch to be bagged by the way. You know how they reason: why shouldn't they pick up a few tens of dollars when the money is practically put down before them?"

"Ai—ya—a!" Happy Boy groaned in the agony of his memories. He could hardly keep from sobbing even now.

"Yes, that's correct—you just happened to be 'on the spot,' as the Americans say, and you had to take what you got. It wasn't your fault. You remember I asked you to go back, so the responsibility is mine." Mr. Ts'ao did not want Happy Boy to stay longer in the recollection of things that could not be changed. "It's sufficient that you know how it came about; we've already thought enough of the past. Let's speak of what you want to do now. Must you still pull a rickshaw?"

Happy Boy nodded his head. It was still the only thing he could really do.

"Since you want to go on pulling a rickshaw," Mr. Ts'ao said slowly, "then there are only two roads open to you. One is to collect enough money together to buy a rickshaw, and the other is to rent one temporarily. Isn't that so? Not having any savings in your hands, you would have to borrow the money, and wouldn't paying interest on it be almost the same as paying the rental? Wouldn't it be better first just to rent one? And working by the month is better than serving as a public conveyance. The work is more regular and you get your food and a place to live, along with your wages. According to the way I look at it, the best thing for you to do would be to come back to work for me. I sold my rickshaw to Mr. Tso, so if you do come back we'll have to rent one. What do you think about that?"

"That would be fine!" Happy Boy stood up.

"There's something I must warn you about." Mr. Ts'ao spoke as though he were thinking aloud. "I don't teach at the University any more, of course, but Yuan Ming has since become a powerful official. Although just now I'm on quite good terms with him, it's always possible—"

Happy Boy made a quick gesture with his hands. "If Master is not afraid, I am not," he said simply.

"All right." Mr. Ts'ao smiled and their contract was made. "Just now you told me about Little Lucky One. What are you going to do about her?"

"I don't have any clear plan."

"Let me think it over a little for you and we'll see what can be done. If you take her in marriage and rent a room outside, that still wouldn't be a very sound proposition. The rent, coal, light and charcoal would all take money. Your wages would hardly cover it. And where would you find a job for the two of you together? You couldn't depend on being so lucky as to be the rickshaw boy in the same household in which your wife worked as an amah." Mr. Ts'ao shook his head in perplexity. "You mustn't take this the wrong way, now: tell me, when you come right down to it, is that girl really to be depended upon?"

Happy Boy's face colored with his embarrassment and he swallowed for a minute before he could answer. "She only took up that trade when there was no other way out for her. I would dare to risk my head, she's a very good girl! She—" In his heart confusion opened; many different emotions had hardened into a ball inside him; now they were about to crack open and run

359

in all directions. He could not say the next word in the sentence he had started to speak.

"If that's the case," Mr. Ts'ao went on with some hesitation, as if the matter were a hard one to decide, "the only thing would be if I could put you both up here. Alone you would take one room; the two of you together would still take up just the one room, so there's no problem about a place to live. I don't know whether she's able to wash and do odd jobs or not, but if she is we'll have her help Kao Ma. Before long the mistress is going to have another baby, and Kao Ma, being alone here, is a little too rushed. Little Lucky One could eat here for nothing; on the other hand, she wouldn't get any wages. How does that look to you?"

"That would be wonderful." Happy Boy smiled with all the naturalness of a little child.

"And I'll give you a few dollars extra each month until I've made good the savings that were stolen from you." The look of inarticulate gratitude on Happy Boy's face was so poignant that Mr. Ts'ao hurried forward into the next thought in his mind. "There's just one other thing: about the girl—that's a matter that I can't decide altogether alone. I'll have to talk it over with the mistress—"

"There can't be any mistake!" Happy Boy, too, had turned to speak of Little Lucky One. "If the mistress is not easy in her heart, I will bring the girl here so that the mistress can see her!"

"That, too, would be good." Mr. Ts'ao smiled. "We'll do this, then: I'll first mention the matter to the mistress, and in a day or so you arrange to bring her here. If the mistress nods her head, we can count that we've been completely successful."

"Then may I go right away, Master?" Happy Boy was in a great hurry to hunt out Little Lucky One and report to her these marvelous tidings, better than he had even dared hope for.

When he left the Ts'ao household it was just before noon, that time in a late winter's day that is most to be loved. Today it was especially clear and crisp; in the whole of the bright blue heavens there was not a single cloud; the sun's rays bent down through the dry cold atmosphere, bringing to those they touched a warmth that was joyously happy. The sounds of the roosters crowing, of dogs barking, and of the street hawkers crying their wares, all carried to great distances; the noises of one street came loud and clear in the next, like the cries of wild geese coming down from the skies. The rickshaws all had their tops lowered, and their brassware shone with a yellow light. Along the roadsides the camels moved with a slow and stable gait; streetcars and automobiles took their urgent way up or down the center of the avenue; the people, the four-footed animals, the vehicles, the birds in the air, every aspect of the life and movement of the city, all were possessed by the serene tranquillity of the morning. In the midst of the hurry and bustle there was happiness, and happiness, too, wherever there was quiet. Lining the long roads, the trees stood tall in their silent assurance.

Happy Boy's heart wanted to leap out of his body and take wings and sail about in space with the pigeons. Everything he wanted was his: work, wages, and Little Lucky One! From a few sentences this wonderful solution had come—a thing that he would never have thought possible.

When some great good fortune falls to your lot, even the weather turns fine; Happy Boy could not remember a fairer day in any of his winters than this one was. To make even more real the expression of his joy, he bought himself a frozen persimmon and bit right into it. It turned his whole mouth as cold as ice, and then this cold that struck at the roots of his teeth moved down his throat until it reached his stomach, making him shiver all over. In two or three swallows he had finished the fruit. His tongue was numb, but he felt beautifully comfortable inside.

He stretched his legs on great strides to go find Little Lucky One. In his mind he could already see the common yard, the little room, and the person whom his heart loved. All he lacked was a pair of wings to carry him there in one swift flight. When once he saw her, all the past would be cancelled out by a single stroke; from that moment forward they would live in another world. His urgency now was even greater than when he had been on his way to see Mr. Ts'ao. Mr. Ts'ao was his friend and master and in their relationship a good deed requited a good deed.

She was not only a friend: she would soon give over her whole life to him. They were two souls only now freed from inferno, who would wipe away each other's tears and walk forward hand in hand. Mr. Ts'ao's words had moved him deeply; Little Lucky One had no need of words to move him deeply. He had spoken the truth to Mr. Ts'ao; to Little Lucky One he would say the things that were even closer to his heart; he would speak to her in words that could be spoken only to her. She was in this present moment his very life. Without her, nothing would count for anything. He could not eat and drink and work hard just for himself alone: it was absolutely necessary that he rescue her from that dirty cell in which she was caught, so that she could live with him thereafter in a clean warm room. They would live together as joyously as a pair of little birds, with the same simple propriety and the same warm intimacy.

She could give up trying to take care of her father and brothers and come to take care of Happy Boy. Second Vigorous was perfectly capable of earning his own living from the very start, and work could certainly be found for the two boys. Perhaps they could together manage a rickshaw. They could make out without her, but Happy Boy absolutely had to have her. To his physical well-being, his spirits, and his work—she was essential to each and all of these and to every other part of his life. On her side too, she needed just the kind of man that he was.

The more he thought the more he hurried and the more elated he became. Under the heavens there were unnumbered women and yet not a single other as good as Little Lucky One or as fit for him. He had already taken one woman in marriage and another by stealth; he had had intercourse with old women and young ones, women who were beautiful and women who were ugly; of them all there had been none who had stamped herself in his heart. They were only women, not the unique woman who would be his mate his whole life long.

It was true that Little Lucky One was not the pure virgin whom his heart had sought when he first came to the city, but precisely because of that fact she engaged his pity more completely and would be the more able to help him. That dumbly innocent maiden from the village would without doubt be altogether virginal, but she would never have Little Lucky One's ability or so many paths in her thought. Moreover, how about himself? There were a great many black spots in his heart. Well, then, he and she were just right to be matched with one another: as to innocence, or lack of it, neither was any taller or shorter than the other. They were like two pitchers of which both had been cracked but both were still able to hold any fluid put in them: it was proper that they should be placed side by side.

Thus, from whatever point of view the matter was considered, their union was a very appropriate one. Having thought over all this, he turned his mind to more practical things. First he would get a month's pay in advance—or else part of the money that was to be made good to him—from Mr. Ts'ao; then he would buy Little Lucky One a new cotton-padded gown and fresh shoes and stockings; after she had bathed herself all over and got dressed up in a completely new outfit of clothes, he would take her to see Mrs. Ts'ao. Clean from the top of her head to the soles of her feet, and attired in a spotless long gown simple and pure in color, she could rely upon the mold of her features, a certain style and spirit in her face that was her own, and her youth. With these things she would surely succeed in pleasing Mrs. Ts'ao! And no mistake about it!

When he reached the place he was covered with perspiration. Seeing that dilapidated old compound door, he felt as if he were returning after an absence of many years to his old home. The ruined door, the collapsing wall, the two or three lonely sprays of dry yellow weeds that grew out of the dirt piled up over the top of the doorway—he was suddenly very fond of them all. He went in the gate, and headed directly for Little Lucky One's room. He could not be bothered with knocking on the door or with calling out that he was coming.

The instant he opened the door, he instinctively drew back. There was a middle-aged woman sitting cross-legged in the middle of the brick bed, her feet drawn up under her. Because there was no fire in the room, she had wrapped her hunched, shivering shoulders in the tattered remains of a quilt, which the claw-like grip of her dirty bony hands kept tight around her. Happy Boy stood stupidly on the threshold.

From the figure on the bed came a harsh voice:

"What is this? Are you a bearer of ill tidings? Has somebody died? What are you doing, walking without a word into strangers' rooms? Who are you looking for?"

Happy Boy had no thought of speaking. The sweat on his body had all turned cold now, and he held to the rickety swinging door to steady himself. Still he did not dare throw all his hope away.

"I'm looking for Little Lucky One."

"I don't know who you're talking about. The next time you go looking for anybody, call out first before you go pulling people's doors open. None of this Little Lucky One, Big Lucky One business."

Mute and dull, he sat on his hands outside the compound gates for what seemed half a day, his heart an empty space, without remembering what it was that he was doing.

Slowly a part of it came back to him, and in his heart Little Lucky One began to pass back and forth, like a paper figure in

364

a jack-o'-lantern show, so that he could see just how tall she was and how she was to be described. But there was no use at all in her walking up and down like that forever, and he seemed for a time to have forgotten that there was a special connection between this figure and himself.

After a while the shadow of Little Lucky One grew smaller, and his heart became more awake. Only then it was that he knew how horribly it ached.

When the fortunate or unfortunate issue of an event is still not clear, man will always cling to his hope for the best outcome no matter how unlikely it may be. Happy Boy guessed that perhaps Little Lucky One had simply moved to some other place, and that there probably had been no other great change in her circumstances. It was he who was remiss. Why had he not come regularly to see her? Remorse whips one on to action, to make good the loss that the mistake has caused. The best thing to do would be to inquire around. He went back into the compound again and found an old neighbor and asked him. The news he got was vague and uncertain.

He still did not dare lose his hope. It was already late in the afternoon, but he had no wish to eat anything. He must find Second Vigorous, or if he could locate either of the two young brothers that would be all right, too. These three people would be sure to be somewhere on the streets, and it should not be difficult to find one of them.

Whomever he saw he asked. At the mouths of the little lanes, at the rickshaw parking stands, in the teahouses and the tenements, he asked everywhere. All that evening and the next day he walked until the strength of his legs was spent, without hearing any word of news.

When he returned at the end of the second day to the rickshaw shed his body was exhausted. He could not forget, but he no longer dared to hope. The bitterly poor die easily, and are as easily forgotten. Who could call it unlikely that Little Lucky

One was already dead? Or, drawing one step back in his thoughts, even supposing she were not dead, might it not be that Second Vigorous had sold her again, this time to some distant place? That would be more terrible than if she were dead.

The last thing that he wanted to do was to go to the Ts'aos' house. How could he face his master? How could he explain that, needing her as much as he did, he yet had not gone near Little Lucky One for so many months that he had lost all track of her? There was no use even in sending them word that he was not coming. Happy Boy's destiny was smashed now beyond any aid that even Mr. Ts'ao could give him in repairing it.

But finally, after ten days of futile searching, he went back to the Ts'ao household and moved into the room that in his heart was Little Lucky One's as well. He would say nothing, nor was even Kao Ma so tactless as to ask.

And no one scolded when wine and cigarettes became once more almost his only friends. If he did not smoke, how could he think? And if he did not drink, how could he stop thinking?

24

*T*HE year had come again to the festival of the Imperial Sacrifices, and again the weather had become very warm. Mr. Ts'ao had given him the day in which to do as he pleased, but Happy Boy had long been a stranger to any spirit of pleasure; in his utter discouragement he could think of nothing more to do than wander up one street and down another, like a ghost that had lost its way back to the burial ground.

But the city around him paid little heed to how Happy Boy

felt. The hawkers of paper fans seemed to have crawled out from wherever they had been hiding through the winter and to be swarming all over, their trays suspended from straps around their necks, with the bells hanging from the corners sounding "wa-lang, wa-lang" to draw the attention of the passers-by. At the sides of the road green apricots were already being sold by the pile; the bright red of the ripened cherries glistened in one's eyes; vast multitudes of yellow bees flew back and forth, to and from the bowls of red fragrant roses and the dishes of dates; the glassware on display in big porcelain platters reflected the sun in a milky light; the baskets swaying from both ends of the hucksters' shoulder-poles bore piles of cookies or cubes of seaweed jelly arranged with extraordinary neatness; on the street-stands there was set forth every kind and color of material for every conceivable purpose.

The people themselves had changed, where they could, from drab clothing to light garments of more delicate hues or of gayer markings, so that the streets seemed suddenly to have acquired a richer and much more variegated color and to curve like so many bright rainbows among the habitations of man.

The street-sweepers worked with even more than their usual diligence, ceaselessly sprinkling the roadways with water, but the fine dust rose regardless, filling the air and harassing pedestrians. Yet even at its worst this irritating haze still revealed the long branches of the willow hanging down through it and the quick-darting swallows that were unaware of it, so that one's spirits were high in spite of oneself. It was weather that left it hard to know how best to dispose of the hours: it made almost everyone feel relaxed and a little fatigued, so that one continually wanted to yawn.

Processions of every kind—those of the singers of the magical songs while the rice is transplanted; those in honor of the "Five Tigers," the great generals of ancient time; those in which long lines of men supporting the trailing forms of paper lions, of

367

which any unwary devil might well be afraid; and many others—
all, one after another, wended their way through the city and
out of it to the hills beyond. Beating gongs and drums, bearing
boxes of polished wood, or toting banners of apricot yellow, they
filed past, one group close upon the heels of the one before it,
lending the aged Peking an abnormal stimulation, giving the
people who lived within its walls a vague but very intimate
thrill, and leaving after them in the atmosphere the echoes of
their music and a floating film of the dust that to every true
Buddhist symbolizes the defilement of the world.

Those who participated in the processions and those who
watched them were alike swept with this warmth of feeling, and
touched with a sense at once of excitement and of devout belief. All the bustle and activity of a confused world are born of
superstition; the stupid find their only solace in self-deceit. The
blending of colors, the medley of sounds, the dusty streets, gave
everyone fresh energy and something to occupy their attention:
those who were headed for the hillsides went out to the hills;
those who were on a tour of the temples went to the temples;
those who were out to see the flowers went about looking at

fresh blossoms; the multitudes who could spend little time doing any of these things could at least stand by the side of the
road and watch the excitement for a while, repeating to themselves the blessed name of Buddha.

There was amusement everywhere, excitement everywhere,
and everywhere there was sound and color. On the still ponds
called the Southern and Northern Seas, young couples guided
their boats in under the shadows of the overhanging willows, or
lay side by side on the banks, humming the melodies of the love
songs they remembered. In this soft languor they kissed each
other with long glances: their eyes knew what their hearts meant
to do, and for their bodies it was almost as if it were already
happening.

At the Bridge of Heaven a huge matshed had been erected as
an open-air teahouse, where the whiteness of the cloths on the
crowded tables and the beautiful grace of the singing girls pre-

sented themselves across the distance to the old pine trees that grew from the walls of the Temple of Heaven.

Persons of elegance, scholars of refinement and culture were drawn by the peonies and the camellias to the public gardens, where they walked slowly back and forth with irresolute steps, agitating their valuable fans to cool themselves, and stealing sidewise glimpses at the virgins from the great families and the famous courtesans from the South who might be passing by. The weather simplified the problem of dressing both for the virgin and the courtesan: they need only wear a single simple gown of sheer texture to be beautifully arrayed, a circumstance which incidentally allowed them to display every curve in their bodies.

This first wave of heat in the opening of summer had acted like a divine charm, bringing out everywhere the fascination of the ancient city of Peking; in due season, regardless of suffering, calamity, or death, she had chosen to display her powers, hypnotizing the hearts of a million people and leaving them in a dream-like trance, able only to sing poems in her praise. She was filthy; she was beautiful; she was senile and decadent; she was lively and smiling; she was disparate and confused; she was at peace and in leisure; she was Peking, immense, inimitable, and much to be loved.

Happy Boy could still not have borne the thought of leaving this city, but for him the spell was broken. Once such a time of festival would have found him as lighthearted and eager as a child, but now he was hot and weary and indifferent.

It was still fairly early in the morning when his listless progress brought him upon a familiar face: it was the grandfather of Little Horse. The old man had given up pulling a rickshaw and in his clothing and general appearance he looked even more tattered and run-down than before. Across his shoulder he carried a pole of willow wood from the front end of which there hung a big teapot, while in back there was suspended a worn-out sycee basket with a few cakes and fritters in it, together with a large brick. He still remembered Happy Boy.

They started to talk, and Happy Boy learned for the first time that Little Horse had been dead for over half a year and that the old man had sold the broken-down rickshaw, depending now solely on what he could make from selling a few fried roll-cakes and a little fruit at the rickshaw stands. He was still as friendly and lovable as ever, though his back was much more bent, and his eyes ran tears whenever he faced the wind, his eye-lids being always red and swollen as if from weeping.

Happy Boy drank a cup of his tea, and told him in two or three sentences a little about his own troubles.

"So you thought you could come to some good just by relying on your own efforts?" The old man gave his judgment on Happy Boy's words. "Have we not all thought the same thing? But which one among us has come to good? When I started out, my own body was straight and firm and my heart was well disposed. I have worked and worried and struggled incessantly up to this very moment, and you see before you the total of all I have achieved. You are physically strong? A man who was made of iron could not escape this trap set by Heaven and sprung by Hell in which we are caught. Your heart is good? What use is that?

" 'Those who do good are rewarded with good; those who do evil are rewarded with evil'—there is in fact no such principle or law, either of God or man. When I was in the years of my youth, mine was truly a heart overflowing with sympathy. The other man's sufferings were as real to me as my own, and the work he wanted done I did as faithfully as if it were for myself. Was that of any use? It was not.

"I have even saved people's lives. I have rescued men who jumped into rivers, and cut down women who sought to hang themselves. Have I received any recompense? I want to tell you: there is no way for me to know when I will starve to death, or on what winter's night I will die by freezing. You can count me as one person who thoroughly understands that those of us who labor in poverty and hope to come to some good might as well try to reach Heaven by leaping up to it.

"How much spring is there in one lone man? Have you ever watched a grasshopper? When he is by himself, the fact that he can jump surprisingly far only makes it more likely that some small boy will catch him and tie him with a thread, so that he won't even be able to get up off the ground.

"But let him join with a swarm of other grasshoppers and go forth in battle array. Heng! In one sweep they will destroy an entire crop, and who can stop them? Where is the small boy with his thread? Tell me yourself, am I right or not?

"Because, in spite of everything, my heart is good, I cannot even keep one little grandson. He got sick; I had no money to buy him medicine; I watched him die in my arms. There's no use talking about it! . . . Get your tea here! Who will drink a cup of tea?"

Happy Boy truly understood: his victory over Fourth Master Liu was after all without any meaning. Fourth Master, Mistress Yang, Detective Sun—they would none of them by his curses come to the evil which was their just retribution; nor could he himself expect that, because he wanted to work hard and better himself, he would get any benefit. Alone, depending only on himself, he was in truth, as the old man had said, like a grasshopper tied by a thread: of what use were the strongest wings?

As he was hunting for the words in which to express how closely his own experience followed the old man's observations, a newsboy came running through the street, opening his small throat wide and shrieking shrilly: "Yuan Ming arrests dangerous radicals! News of the execution of the radicals! Condemned to be paraded at ten this morning!"

For those who were out finding what pleasure they could on a forenoon of festival, the added excitement of a diverting piece of news, a story that would be worthy of being read two or three times without getting boresome, was precisely the one thing that this gay bright day had lacked. And now just such news had come! A copper, a copper, and yet more coppers passed into the sooty black hand of the newsboy as pedestrians pressed to be first to buy his "Execution Special."

Close to where Happy Boy and the old man were standing a shopkeeper was deftly pasting his copy up on the outer wall of the compound next to his wine shop. The old man moved over to look at it and a small crowd shortly collected around him. Someone spoke: "Venerable Elder Brother, many of us do not recognize characters. Please read it to us."

Smiling in deprecation of the compliment that the assumption that he was educated implied, the old man began to read aloud the important parts of the story. It was largely the account of an interview with Yuan Ming, of the feats which the latter had performed in the service of the government of which he was now so important a member, and of the manner in which, through the aid of the secret police and a certain One Pock Li, this group of low criminals who had been plotting against the stability of the state had been apprehended. From all this it was clear that Yuan Ming was a great man and had acted with true courage. As if to afford visual evidence of these facts, a large likeness of the official himself was displayed in the center of the sheet, and the condemned were being brought on a tour of the city, the list of the avenues which they were to traverse showing that they would come down the very one on which this group was congregated.

If Happy Boy and the old man's auditors heard this news without enthusiasm, the generality of the holidayers appeared to welcome it much more warmly. Before another ten minutes had passed, the street was crowded with expectant, clamorous, pushing people, waiting the coming of the living villains in this exciting drama. The women had abandoned their cooking or

373

their promenading, as the case might be, the rickshaw men had stopped looking for fares, the clerks in the stores were disregarding their customers, the hawkers had stopped crying their wares, all in honor of the exploits of Yuan Ming and the hope of seeing his victims.

In history there had already been the Yellow Turbans, a powerful secret society of outlaws at the close of the dynasty of the Eastern Han; Chang Hsien-chung, who had helped to overthrow the Ming Dynasty, opening the way for the Manchus; and the people of the Dynasty of Heavenly Peace: they all had loved to watch a good slaughter and were all capable, as well, of getting themselves slaughtered. This morning their descendants were most of a mind that execution by rifle fire was a little too simple. They would have preferred decapitation, or the death of a thousand slices, in which the appendages are all slowly cut away before the condemned is finally dispatched, or the more delicate operation of peeling off all his skin while he is still alive. Just to hear the words was like eating ice cream: it made you shiver with pleasure.

This time, however, in addition to the executions, there was the tour of the city, and people felt a real gratitude to Yuan Ming for thinking up this excellent plan, making it possible for them to see the half-dead criminals bound in a cart for the titillation of their eyes. Granted that one could not oneself be the executioner, still this was almost the same thing.

Suddenly everyone grew quiet. In the distance there appeared a troop of mounted police, fully armed. "They're coming!" someone shouted. At the same time, like a vast engine, the whole crowd surged forward an inch, and then another inch: they were coming, they were coming! The murmur of voices grew loud again, and the stench of sweat seemed stronger, as these citizens of a state whose religion is the law of propriety pressed forward to gape at prisoners about to die.

In the back of the open truck that was being driven slowly

374

by there were kneeling three small, bedraggled figures, their arms bound behind them, their heads down, their faces tense and drawn, each with a big cloth placard on his back and shoulders denouncing the crime for which its bearer was to be executed. One was a woman, evidently still quite young. The three of them, huddled together in silence, looked like frightened street dogs who had got drenched in the rain. The spectators pursed their lips in disappointment. Was this all the show was going to amount to? Was it to be as flavorless and pointless as all this? Would they not even make a sound?

A fellow in front of the crowd had an idea: he wanted to have a little fun at the expense of these terrified monkeys. Turning to the rest of the audience, he proposed:

"Let's give them a cheer."

Everyone saw the point of this at once: in the theatre, when the villain—"the Great White Face"—turns in a really striking performance, he is met by a storm of applause, every throat in the house roaring out, "Excellent, excellent!"

So now nearly everyone joined in crying "Excellent! Excellent!" in an expression of the refinement of their contempt for the three figures in the slowly moving truck.

Neither of the men in the truck moved or showed in any way that he had heard, but the girl, evidently misunderstanding the purpose of her tormentors, lifted to the crowd a face of terrible intentness and began to recite the slogans for which she knew she soon must give her life. Her first words were inaudible; then she said:

"Freedom of publication!"

"P'ei! P'ei!" answered an old woman at the edge of the road, spitting toward the car. "What good is that, when only one in twenty can read? The fool deserves to be shot."

"Probably she's the agent of some rich publisher who wants to make himself richer cheating both those who can write and those who can read!" suggested a thin youth sneeringly.

The little girl who was condemned perhaps did not hear these taunts; she seemed oblivious now to everything but the tenets of her own pure unrealistic faith:

"Overthrow the secret police! Oppose crooked politicians and the sale of justice! Drive out corruption from the government!"

By this time one of the mounted police had ridden back opposite her and was beating her with a truncheon, cursing her the while for a filthy whore. In a final expression of perverse defiance to the order in which she lived, she screamed:

"Freedom of speech!"

And that was all. The cavalcade passed on, out of sight and hearing, except of those few who chased along after it to stay with it till it should come to the Bridge of Heaven, and the execution be in actuality carried out before their eyes. The others had had their show; the flavor of it was strange indeed, and very tart. The festival had somehow been spoiled a little.

The while the open truck and its escort were progressing through this stretch of their journey, the old man and Happy Boy had stood on an ancient refuse pile at the base of the wall close to the place where the newspaper was posted. They could see clearly over the heads of the crowd, but they had not shared its interest in the prisoners until the girl raised her head to speak.

Then Happy Boy knew: the girl was the Ch'inghua student who months before had been his passenger and who had sided with him against the policeman. The girl who reminded him of Little Lucky One. His whole body suddenly drew in together like a crouching animal's and his face turned a color that was not good to look upon.

The old man, who had slipped his teapot and basket to the ground and had been watching too, felt the hand that his younger companion had placed on his shoulder tighten with a sharp, convulsive, almost crushing force.

"She's only a girl!" The breath issued from Happy Boy's lips without any relaxation of his jaws.

376

The old man turned to face him, standing between Happy Boy and the scene on the road. There was no wind stirring to account for the tears in his aging eyes. "But they would simply kill you too," he implored, answering the impulse sweeping the heart of Happy Boy. "You can do nothing."

"I know." Happy Boy swayed back against the wall and slumped down to a squatting posture, his head buried in his hands for his shame. The old man sat down beside him.

Neither of them moved or spoke at all until a long time after the crowd had dispersed. Then slowly and with long hesitations Happy Boy managed to recount the story of Yuan Ming and Mr. Ts'ao, and also how the Ch'inghua girl had defended him in his argument with the policeman and the chauffeur, how she had talked to him of things which he still did not understand, although he could remember some of the words, and how at the end she had overpaid him.

"Because I needed the money more!" Happy Boy recalled.

"It is for those thoughts that she has been accused of all the crimes listed against her, and is being shot," the old man explained softly. "Whether it is true, as it is written in the canons, that 'all men are born good, but in living depart from it,' it is certain that in all the children of Han there is both darkness and light, and that it was in the hour of the ascendancy of the evil in them that they set up this doctrine called the source of wealth that she was probably trying to tell you about. It is the reason for money. And because it is dark and evil it draws out the darkness and evil in each of us, and stops up the good. The more we are willing to cheat and steal and watch others starve, the more money we will have; and the less able we are to match others in those things, the nearer we shall be to starving ourselves. And because nobody wants to starve or to have to beg for their food, and nobody wants their children to starve or to have to beg, maybe we can't speak too ill of those who have money and want to keep it—or perhaps even get more and more. The more

377

money they have, the more people they can have working for them, the safer they are, and the more power they have. But then they have to kill or imprison anyone who questions the roots of the principle, as the student did."

Happy Boy wanted to cry. Clearly he could recollect now how loath he had been to give up the little bit of money that Fourth Master had held for him, and how it was partly for money that he had stumbled into the course of his life with Tiger Girl. And now he could see that in this he had been as selfish as Mistress Yang; that he had been following in the footsteps of the Fourth Master and everyone else whom he hated.

"You spoke of Yuan Ming," the old man went on. "He's only a puppet, no worse than those whom he serves. The man who is truly to be despised is One Pock Li. The paper said he was the informer who reported the girl and the other two to the secret police, as Yuan Ming reported your master. But, instead of a job in the government, he got a reward of sixty dollars for the three: a market rate for human lives of twenty dollars each."

"Is he the same as the One Pock who used to pull a rickshaw in the West City?"

"Yes, that's the fellow. He was not much more fortunate than the rest of us. Then he got the habit of opium smoking, and for two years there hasn't been anything he would not do to get money into his hands. He's no better than a dog. And yet it's hard to say that the fault is really his. Men have through countless ages gradually pulled themselves up from among the animals, and even at the present time they still persist in driving their fellow men back down to the level of wild beasts. In this city of great culture many of us must become animals again."

"It is only by very little that I've missed being one of them!" Happy Boy said aloud. To himself he was thinking again of all the things that he himself had done for the sake of money, and the things that the lack of it had forced him to do. If he had had only a little money he would never have left Little Lucky One.

378

Were they, too, all condemned? Was there no road out? Then, because he had already told him so much, Happy Boy took the old man as a true friend and laid before him the affair of Little Lucky One.

"According to my guess," the old man responded, turning his mind to this problem, "there are two ways that might have been followed: if she was not sold by Second Vigorous to be some man's concubine, the only other thing that could have happened is that he put her body in pawn to a 'white house.' In all probability she went down to a 'white house.' Why do I say that? Since Little Lucky One has already, according to what you have just been telling me, been married, it would not be easy to get anyone else to accept her. Men buying concubines want the original goods in unbroken packages. So it's probable that there are eight chances out of ten that she's gone down into a 'white house.' I'm almost sixty and I've seen many things. When one of these robust young rickshaw men doesn't come for two or three days to the street corners where he's usually seen, and you go looking for him, if he hasn't got a job by the month somewhere, he's sure to be crawling about in some 'white house.' And if the wives or daughters of any of us who are bitterly poor suddenly disappear, there are seven or eight chances out of ten that they have gone to one of the same places. We sell our sweat and our women sell their flesh. You go look for her in some of those places. We can't say we hope she's in one of them, but—"

"I've asked everywhere inside the walls." Happy Boy shook his head in despair.

"You've probably heard men speak of 'White Flour Sacks'?" the old man asked.

"Yes, I've heard of her."

"Well, she's the head of a house outside the Western Gate of Forthrightness. She has many connections among the lowest-class 'white houses' and she might have some information about Little Lucky One."

379

"Your heart is truly good. I must leave now, but I will come by this corner another day to see you." Happy Boy could not go quickly enough; in one breath he ran all the way to the Western Gate of Forthrightness.

As soon as he was outside the portals he felt the empty quiet of the unending countryside. In the distance he could soon see the cool, remote Western Hills. To the north of the railway tracks there was a wooded stretch, and as he traversed that he saw, beyond, a cluster of low-ceilinged structures. He calculated that these in all probability made up the "white house" he was looking for. The leaves in the trees around him were without movement. Far off to the north was the marshy ground outside the Garden of Ten Thousand Living Things.

There was no movement, either, around the little houses; everything—far and near—was so tranquil that he began to doubt whether this after all was the "white house" he was seeking. Plucking up his courage, he walked toward the center room. On its door was a new door-screen of grass matting, freshly hung and of a glossy yellow color. He remembered now having heard that in houses like these—catering to the poorest of wayfarers— the women sat outside their doors in the summertime, bare to the waist, hailing passers-by. And men coming to patronize them were supposed to begin singing the "Song of the Potter's Shop" —a whorehouse tune—as soon as they came within earshot, to show forth the fact that they were "insiders," long members of the guild. Why was it so quiet now? Could it possibly be that they had all gone to the temples to celebrate the festival?

Just as he was hesitating, the grass screen on the door of the room to the side of the middle one moved a little, and a woman's head came out. Happy Boy started: that head, when you first looked at it, was extraordinarily like Tiger Girl's. He said to himself in his heart: "I've come looking for Little Lucky One; if I should find Tiger Girl, I'd be seeing ghosts in all truth."

"Come in, you stupid booby!" It was the head speaking; the

380

tone of the voice was not Tiger Girl's, but throaty and hoarse, very much like the rasping urgency of the hawkers of medicinal herbs at the Bridge of Heaven.

There was nothing at all in the room except the woman and a couple of wooden planks laid across two mules to serve as a bed. The stench was so heavy it was hard to breathe. There was a dirty strip of bedding over the boards, shiny with grease and age. The woman's hair was dirty and dishevelled and she had not washed her face. On the lower part of her body she wore light cotton trousers, while above she had on a single dark cloth jacket that she had left unbuttoned.

Happy Boy had to bring his head away down to get in through the doorway. The moment he had entered the room she embraced him, the jacket opening wide to display a pair of the longest and biggest breasts he had ever seen.

Because he could not lift his head or stretch his neck as long as he stood up, he sat down on the bed. This woman was without any doubt "White Flour Sacks" herself, and in his heart he was elated that he had found her. It was clear to see from what her familiar name had come.

The story was that with one flip she could toss those breasts of hers over her shoulders. Travellers who came to her as patrons frequently asked her, as a supplement to her regular labors, to perform that trick for them. But her fame did not come alone from these extraordinarily large udders. She was the only known case of an inmate of a "white house" who retained her freedom; she had entered of her own free will. It was the legend that she had had five husbands; that each one had dried up like fat pork that is fried too long and then died, whereafter she had given up getting married and entered a brothel to enjoy what in her single case was literally a kind of happiness.

Since she was independent, she was not afraid to talk; if you wanted to spy out anything of the affairs of the "white houses" you had to come to her: the other women were all afraid to disclose anything. As a result everyone knew of her, and there was no end to the people coming to ask her questions. Naturally, if you wanted to know something, you still had to give her tea money, so that her business was not only better than that of the others but a little lighter as well.

Happy Boy knew of this custom, and first paid the tea money. "White Flour Sacks" understood his intentions, and did not press herself any further upon him. With the directness of a man who when he wants to see a mountain opens his front door and looks out, he asked her if she had seen anyone called Little Lucky One.

She didn't know and hadn't heard of any such person.

When Happy Boy had described to her in detail what Little Lucky One looked like, it came to her.

"Yes, Yes! There's just such a person right here. She's young, and given to showing those white teeth of hers. That's right. We all call her 'Little Tender Flesh'!"

"What room is she in?" Suddenly Happy Boy's eyes had opened wide and become bright with a killing brightness.

The color of the woman's face changed. "You can't see her."

"I've got to see her!"

"She's dying."

Happy Boy leapt from the bed, his face white with rage.

"You take me to her or I'll kill you!" he shrieked in her face.

"I thought—I only meant—I'll take you." She understood that the moment might have a desperate issue, and the blood pounded in her head as she hastened to lead the way.

It was in the corner cabin, in what light the late afternoon shed through the half-open door lattice, that he saw her lying. In truth it was she!

He knelt beside the bed, calling her by name: "Little Lucky One!"

Her face was thin and sallow, and under the dirty sheet her body seemed now as small as a child's. Slowly her eyes opened, her lips parted, showing her white teeth, and she smiled in recognition.

"Happy Boy?" There was no breath behind her voice, so that, although it was quite distinct, it sounded like a distant whisper. After a moment she spoke again. "Elder Brother, why have you come so late?"

Happy Boy's heart was frantic. "I couldn't find you!"

"Ah! I came here last winter. Little Brother died of sickness. Then papa fell down drunk in the street and froze to death, and when that happened the other brother ran away. After I had paid the burial expenses there was no money left for rent. There was nothing I could do and no place I could go. This was the only house that would take me."

"What sickness has she?" Happy Boy asked, looking up over his shoulder at "White Flour Sacks."

"Who knows? She hasn't eaten for three days. She couldn't stand the life."

"I want to take her out. Aren't you the manager?"

"What? Nobody leaves this place alive who isn't bought out of it. Don't despise the establishment because the rooms are small. The place and the women in it are owned by Second Brother Chu, the great philanthropist and one of the most influential men in five provinces. You won't live long if you try to take any cheap advantage of him."

"All right. At least you can give her some food to eat."

"She won't eat."

"Yes, I will!" whispered Little Lucky One.

Happy Boy got up, his body cramped in the little room. He glared down at "White Flour Sacks." "Get some food!"

The woman went out.

This girl, this quiet figure lying there without complaint, was his life. She must not die. He could not let her die. Nor could he leave her here, in all the stench and rottenness of this vile hole. He had to have her: without her he would go on stumbling

383

blindly down the road of One Pock Li and so many others; with her at his side, they would both have a chance.

There was even in his heart the wordless hope that together they might work some harm on the things that meant to destroy them, that they might find a way to serve in the forces fighting the principle of evil that ruled under heaven.

But what should he do? In spite of the fact that Little Lucky One was of no use to them now, yet when they discovered how much he wanted her, Second Brother Chu and "White Flour Sacks" would ask him a price that he might never be able to pay.

The agony of these feelings made his head wet and the palms of his hands moist. It would be better for both Little Lucky One and himself to die now than that he should go out of this hut without her.

Suddenly he knew what he meant to do: no one could stop him!

With quick movements he lifted the frail body up, folding the sheet about it, and, crouching to get through the door, he sped as fast as he could across the clearing into the woods.

In the mild coolness of summer evening the burden in his arms stirred slightly, nestling closer to his body as he ran. She was alive. He was alive. They were free.